VIKING FUND PUBLICATIONS IN ANTHROPOLOGY
edited by Sol Tax

Number Thirty-One

SOCIAL LIFE OF EARLY MAN

SOCIAL LIFE OF EARLY MAN

Edited by
SHERWOOD L. WASHBURN

ALDINE PUBLISHING COMPANY · CHICAGO

This volume comprises one of a series of publications on research in general anthropology published by the Wenner-Gren Foundation for Anthropological Research, Incorporated, a foundation created and endowed at the instance of Axel L. Wenner-Gren for scientific, educational, and charitable purposes. The reports, numbered consecutively as independent contributions, appear at irregular intervals.

Fourth printing, 1970

Library of Congress Catalog Card Number 62-10630

First Published 1961 by

ALDINE PUBLISHING COMPANY

529 South Wabash Avenue

Chicago, Illinois 60605

Printed in the United States of America

INTRODUCTION

A T A meeting at Burg Wartenstein in the summer of 1958 the idea of a conference on the Social Life of Early Man took shape, as a result of conversations between the late A. C. Blanc, Raymond Firth, Adolph H. Schultz, and Paul Fejos. These four concluded that it might be possible to reconstruct a part of the social life of early man. Preliminary plans were made for a conference to be held in 1959, and several invitations were issued. During the winter Dr. Fejos asked me to continue with the organization, and it was decided to broaden the range of subject matter to be discussed by including genetics and psychology.

The conference was held June 22–30, 1959. Unfortunately, Dr. Firth was not able to attend. The deadline for papers was placed some months after the conference so that there would be ample time for revision. This policy led to both unexpected delays and the replacement of the discussion held at the conference by the expanded and revised papers. At first it was planned to publish an edited version of the discussion, but, since more than half of the papers were written or greatly modified after the conference, the detailed transcript was found to be no longer relevant. The main points of the discussions are included in the revised papers.

Thanks are due Mary Walpole for help at the time of the conference and for translating the papers by Vallois, Bourlière, Piveteau, and Debetz.

Anne Brower and Nancy Tanner helped in the editing and preparation of the manuscripts.

All those who took part in the conference are grateful to Dr. Paul Fejos for making the conference and this volume possible.

S. L. WASHBURN

TABLE OF CONTENTS

Types of Hominid	Chronology		Cultural Stages	Industries
		End of last Glaciation ± 8,000 B.C.		
Homo sapiens	UPPER PLEISTOCENE	Second Part of LAST INTERGLACIAL INTERSTADIAL	UPPER PALEOLITHIC Beginning of Upper Paleolithic ±40,000 B.C.	Composite and specialized tools: blades, burins, bone needles Marked regional specialization
Neanderthaloid types of man		LAST GLACIATION LAST INTERGLACIAL	(Mousterian) MIDDLE PALEOLITHIC	Flake tools: points, side-scrapers Levallois technique Specialized core tools Incipient blade tools
Archaic types of man	MIDDLE PLEISTOCENE	GLACIAL MAIN INTERGLACIAL GLACIAL	Beginning of Middle Paleolithic ? 200,000 B.C. LOWER PALEOLITHIC Beginning of Lower Paleolithic c. 500,000 B.C.	Simple core and flake tools
	LOWER PLEISTOCENE	INTERGLACIAL		
Australo- pithecines*		EARLIEST GLACIALS		Pebble tools
		Beginning of Ice Age		

* The interrelations of the last australopithecines and of the earliest men, and of the last of

Hunting	Extension and Control of Environment	Arts and Beliefs		
Many hunting and some fishing techniques	Reliable means of making fire Clothes Elaborate artificial shelters Means of crossing large bodies of water	Rock painting and engravings, sculpture, personal adornment Evidence of dancing (Tuc d'Audoubert and Addaura)	Elaborate burial customs	Elaborate hunting ritual Animal sacrifice (Addaura) Ceremonial use of parts of skull (Placard skull-cap)
Pitfalls (Stoke Newington?), spears (Lehringen) and missile stones	Increasing use of fire and fire-making Increasing use of improved shelters	Increased choice of material and aesthetic craftsmanship	First known deliberate burials	Ritual cannibalism? (Ngandong and Monte Circeo) Hunting ritual and initiation? (Basua Cave)
Missile stones and spears (Clacton)	First use of fire (Choukoutien) Use of natural shelter with little modification	Increasing choice of material Some symmetrical artifacts and some aesthetic craftsmanship		First indication of head-hunting (Choukoutien); intentional mutilation of skull base?
Scavenging? (Hunting at Olduvai)	Some use of natural shelter Caves avoided at night prior to use of fire			

c. 1,000,000 B.C.

the pebble tools and the earliest Chellian, are in doubt.

SOCIAL LIFE OF EARLY MAN

PATTERNS OF SOCIAL GROUPING
AMONG WILD PRIMATES

F. BOURLIERE

UNTIL now, very few species of primates have been studied so as to make possible a good comparison of their social grouping in natural conditions. No representative of such important groups as the marmosets and tamarins (Hapalidae) or the sakis, uakaris, capuchins, woolly monkeys (Cebidae) of the New World, or the African guenons (Cercopithecidae) and guerezas (Colobinae) of the Old World has yet been the object of a real ethological or ecological study in the field. As for the Pongidae, the social life in the wild of a species as well known as the chimpanzee still remains almost a complete mystery. In the face of the number and importance of the gaps in our knowledge, it would be completely useless to attempt a synthesis of the whole.

Moreover, the available papers and monographs are neither so complete nor so perfect as certain armchair naturalists or zoo psychologists might wish. To observe wild monkeys in their natural surroundings is certainly not so simple as it might seem at first sight. Merely to count the members of a troop may require hours or days of work, for rarely are all the individuals visible at the same time—especially among the arboreal species, which are by far the most numerous. Recognizing the individual members of a troop often presents insoluble problems. No system of individual marking has yet produced results that are applicable on a large scale. Although the use of alpha-chloralose made it possible to anesthetize and mark the rhesus monkeys, the attempts made with the same products on certain lemurs have been negative. Moreover, it remains to be proved that the use of anesthetics does not ultimately modify the behavior and the life expectancy of the marked animal.

To these difficulties in observation are added difficulties in interpretation. The human mind is quick to generalize, and one is only too ready to construct a whole system on the basis of a few observations—all the more if they have been made under difficult conditions. Thus it is common to see in the mammalogical or primatological literature mention of a certain species as polygamous, the male gathering around him a harem of females. But most of the time this interpretation is based on the mere discovery of groups formed of a male and several females, without proof that the same male was interested in the various mature females

1

of his band successively at their periods of oestrus. The use of terms with precise human sociological significance, then, should be systematically avoided by the field primatologist, and he should confine himself to a strictly descriptive vocabulary that does not imply a priori the existence of any preconceived social structure.

To have real value, observations of the social grouping of wild primate groups should be prolonged. To count the number of members of a group once or twice, to establish at this time its sex ratio, and to determine its age ratio does not suffice. Experience has shown that the structure of groups of a given species may vary not only from one place to another but also with time in a single locality. In fact, variability in the social behavior of primates appears to be as great as morphological variability.

We have a good example of this state of things in the howler monkeys (*Alouatta palliata*) of the Laboratory Group of Barro Colorado Island (Panama Canal Zone), studied successively by Carpenter in 1932–1935, Collias and Southwick in 1951, and S. A. Altmann in 1955.

In the twenty-three-year period from January, 1932, to November, 1955, the composition of the group occupying the same territory of the island varied as shown in Table 1. Although from 1932 to 1933 the number of adult males in a "clan" varied from three to five, we have no more than a "harem" with a single adult male in 1951 and 1955! And yet, as Altmann emphasizes (1959), "it seems a reasonable assumption that these howlers are probably all part of the same lineage."

The *Lemur macaco* of Nossi Komba Island, studied in the period 1956–57 by J. J. Petter, are another example of this variability through time in the composition of primate social groups. Table 2 shows the structure, at successive periods, of three groups that were followed from May, 1956, to April, 1957.

In the Japanese macaque (*Macaca fuscata*) the social structure of a group also changes with time. The group studied several years ago by the Japan Monkey

TABLE 1

VARIATIONS IN GROUP COMPOSITION AMONG THE MONKEYS
OF THE LABORATORY GROUP OF BARRO COLORADO ISLAND

Time of Census	Total of Individuals	Adult Males	Females with Infants	Other Adult Females	Juveniles	Infants	Reference
January, 1932 .	26	3	4	7	8	4	Carpenter, 1934
May, 1932 . .	27	4	1	10	11	1	" "
January, 1933 .	29	4	5	5	10	5	" "
May, 1933 . .	30	5	3	9	10	3	" "
March, 1951 .	17	1	3	6	4	3	Collias and Southwick, 1952
November, 1955	14	1	3	1	6	3	Altmann, 1959

Center at Takasakiyama (Itani, 1954; Frisch, 1959) demonstrates this well. The population of this isolate has grown from 160 in 1952 to nearly 600 in 1958. Yet the number of dominant males has decreased from 6 to 4, all of them being more than twenty years old, and the number of subdominant males is still 10.

GROUPING AMONG PRIMATE FAMILIES

These general remarks having been made, let us see what we do actually know of the social grouping pattern among different families of wild primates.

LEMUROIDEA

Until the last few years, almost nothing specific was known of the social life of prosimians. The research in Madagascar in 1956–57 of J. J. Petter, whose work has been referred to above, has recently filled in a certain number of gaps in our knowledge, and we thank him for having allowed us to look over his results, which are not yet published.

LEMURIDAE

At the present time the species that has been studied most is *Lemur macaco*. This black lemur, whose sexes are easily distinguishable in the field, generally lives in small groups of from 4 to 15 animals of different ages, which always include more males than females. All year, during the day, each group occupies a territory defended against the incursions of other groups of the same species. Ten groups studied by J. J. Petter had the following composition: One group of 4–6 animals, one group of 6 animals, five groups of 8–10 animals, two groups of 10–13 animals, and one group of 13–15 animals. Two isolated individuals (1 male and 1 female, both adults) were also observed.

The sex ratio of these ten groups taken together was 50 males and 35 females. It is an interesting fact that these groups, which jealously preserve their identity during the day, assemble for the night and form nocturnal groups that disperse again at sunrise. Thus, in April, 1957, a group of 5 males and 4 females moved to join with another group of 8 males and 7 females to spend the night.

TABLE 2

VARIATIONS IN GROUP COMPOSITION AMONG *L. macaco* OF NOSSI KOMBA ISLAND

Date of Census	Group I			Group II			Group III		
	M	F	J	M	F	J	M	F	J
May, 1956	7	3	—	7	3	—	2	2	—
November, 1956 . . .	5	3	2	6	4	3	4	2	—
April, 1957	6	4	—	6	7	—	4	2	—

Source: J. J. Petter, unpublished field notes, 1956–57.

Among the *Lemur mongoz*, the size of the groups seems to be comparable: one group comprised 3 males and 3 females, and the other 4 males and 4 females. Among the *Lemur variegatus*, the groups appear to be smaller. The four groups that were adequately observed numbered 4, 3, 3, and 2 individuals, respectively. *Lemur fulvus*, on the other hand, forms larger groups, encompassing as many as 30 individuals.

Although they belong to the same family, the *Lepilemur* are active at night and differ in social behavior from the *Lemur*. *Lepilemur ruficaudatus* is always seen isolated, only the female being sometimes accompanied by her young.

The mouse lemurs (*Cheirogaleus*) and dwarf lemurs (*Microcebus*), also nocturnal, likewise live apart from one another, the male apparently living with the female only during a short period of rut.

INDRIDAE

In the Indridae family of diurnal lemurs, on the other hand, the pair-bond seems to be much more lasting.

The sifakas (*Propithecus*) generally live in family groups composed of an adult male, an adult female, and one or two young.

The composition of twenty-eight groups of *Propithecus verreauxi coquereli* observed in Madagascar by J. J. Petter was three groups of 3 animals, twelve groups of 3–4 animals, six groups of 4 animals, one group of 4–5 animals, three groups of 5 animals, one group of 6 animals, one group of 7 animals, and one group of 8 animals (formed by the frequent union of two groups of 4 animals). Three solitary individuals have also been observed.

Among *Propithecus verreauxi verreauxi*, the three groups counted by Petter were also made up of 4 animals.

Among *Propithecus diadema*, J. J. Petter has observed a group of 3 and a group of 4 animals.

The social grouping of the woolly lemurs (*Avahi*) seems to be the same. In *Avahi laniger laniger*, J. J. Petter observed 2 couples (male and female) with a large juvenile, 1 couple (male and female) with a large juvenile and a small juvenile, and 1 female with her young.

Each group appears to be faithful to a defined territory; the meeting of two groups provokes an aggressive attitude on both sides.

For *Avahi laniger occidentalis*, Petter counted two groups of 4 animals (each of which includes 1 male and 1 adult female) and three groups of 2 animals (mother and juvenile).

Among the indri (*Indri indri*), small groups are also observed at all seasons of the year; a fact that suggests the existence of lasting couples among this species. As an example, the composition of eight groups observed by J. J. Petter was two groups of 2 animals (1 male and 1 juvenile), four groups of 3 animals (1 couple and 1 juvenile), one group of 4 animals (1 couple and 2 juveniles), and 1 isolated animal.

DAUBENTONIIDAE

The singuar aye-aye (*Daubentonia madagascariensis*), on the contrary, is solitary and nocturnal.

Thus the social grouping of the lemuriformes is extremely varied. Some species, it seems, are as little inclined to be sociable as are many insectivores or rodents, whereas others live in lasting (monogamous?) family groups, and still others form large bisexual groups in which the relations between the sexes at different age levels remain to be determined. Two types of widely differing social organization may even be found within one subfamily (in the *Lemur* and the *Lepilemur*, among the Lemurinae).

LORISOIDEA

In contrast to many Lemuroidea, none of the Lorisoidea are gregarious. The slender loris (*Loris*) and the Asiatic slow loris (*Nycticebus*)—like the potto (*Perodicticus potto*), the angwantibo (*Arctocebus calabarensis*), and the African galagos (*Galago* and *Euoticus*)—are solitary animals; at most, they are found in couples (with or without young) during periods of reproduction.

TARSIOIDEA

In nature, tarsiers are said to be monogamous, a pair nearly always being found together. Sometimes a pair have their youngest offspring accompanying them.

CEBOIDEA

Among the New World monkeys social organization appears to be variable, but to date the species studied in detail have been too few to make it possible to get an accurate idea of the range of this variation.

AOTINAE

The douroucoulis (*Aotes*) are the only American monkeys with nocturnal habits; they are solitary animals, at times met with in pairs (couples or female with young).

PITHECINAE

Uakaris (*Cacajao*) and sakis (*Pithecia* and *Chiropotes*) are gregarious, but we know absolutely nothing of the social structure of their groups.

ALOUATTINAE

Thanks to the work of Carpenter (1934), Collias and Southwick (1952), and Altmann (1959), we are better informed on the social life of the wild howlers living at large than on that of any other primate. In Barro Colorado, *Alouatta palliata* live in bands made up of 1–6 adult males, 1–4 adult females, 0–11 juveniles, and 0–9 children. Each of these groups occupies a defined territory, whose limits are apparently maintained solely by means of "vocal battles" between members of adjacent groups. According to Carpenter, the pair-bond is temporary and is not exclusive—one female in oestrus may be covered by several males of her group successively. Isolated individuals are rare, and each group constitutes a closed society.

CEBINAE

The capuchin monkeys (*Cebus*) have a highly developed social behavior, but the structure of their troops has never been studied in detail.

The squirrel monkeys (*Saimiri*) are also very gregarious. Sanderson (1957) says that he has observed a group of more than 550 individuals.

ATELINAE

The spider monkeys (*Ateles*) have been studied in Panama by Carpenter (1935). *Ateles geoffroyi* live in loose bisexual groups that may include as many as 40 animals and that are subdivided during the day into temporary subgroups. These small groups may consist of (*a*) a female and one or more young, (*b*) a number of females with their respective young, (*c*) one or more males and many more females with their young ones, or (*d*) males only. These male subgroupings constitute a distinguishing characteristic of the organization of spider-monkey society; they range in size from 3 to 10 individuals.

We know nothing about the structure of the group of woolly spider monkeys (*Brachyteles*) and of woolly monkeys (*Lagothrix*).

CALLIMICONIDAE

The goeldi marmoset (*Callimico goeldii*) has not yet, to my knowledge, been studied in its natural surroundings.

HAPALIDAE

The marmosets (*Tamarin, Tamarinus, Merikina, Oedipomidas, Leontocebus, Mico, Hapale, Cebuella*) live, in the wild, in small groups or family parties. The negro tamarin (*Tamarin tamarin*), for example, is found in small bands of 3 or 4 individuals, the crested bare-faced tamarin (*Oedepomidas*) in groups of 2 or 3 to a dozen, and the black-tailed marmoset (*Mico argentatus*) in bands of 8–12 individuals and more. *Tamarin inustus* is said to live in mixed colonies with capuchins.

CERCOPITHECOIDEA

Of the Old World monkeys, only a few species have been thoroughly observed, and conclusions like those of Sahlins (1959), who asserts that they "develop more permanent sex partnership" than do the New World monkeys, seem to be premature.

CERCOPITHECINAE

With the exception of the rhesus monkey (*Macaca mulata*), which remains to be studied in the wild, we now have numerous observations, especially of the semiwild Japanese monkey (*Macaca fuscata*), thanks to the work of the Japan Monkey Center (Itani, 1954; Imanishi, 1957; Frisch, 1959).

Macaca fuscata live in bisexual groups, which may number up to several hundred individuals. According to Itani (1954), the Takasakiyama group, which comprised at this time about 218 animals, was made up of 6 dominant adult males, about 10 subdominant adult males, about 20 subadult males, about 30 juvenile males, about 60 adult females, about 30 subadult females about to bear their first infants, about 30 juvenile females, about 30 infants, and, in addition, 2 adult solitary males.

To cite Frisch, this group was not only organized according to

a single rank order where each member of the group occupied its degree, but it rested on a system of classes, each one giving to the animal a definite status recognized by all other members and including functions and privileges.

The dominant males insured the peace and the good order among the females and their young feeding in the central area [of the temple precincts]. They prevented any subdominant male from entering this area, thus preserving the distinction between center and periphery. The subdominant males cooperated with the dominant males in policing the group, punishing the offenders by chasing and biting them; they also cooperated with the subadults in defending the group against outside enemies. The subadult males, placed around the group, were often seen perched in trees, watching for oncoming danger. They still spent much time playing, but their play was a rough kind and seemed to have an important role in determining the future rank order [Frisch, 1959].

Unfortunately, we have only fragmentary observations of the other species of macaques. In Thailand, Carpenter (1958) observed two groups of *Macaca assamensis* whose composition was 2–4 adult males, 6–10 adult females, 2–8 juveniles, and 2–4 infants. Moreover, the two bands of *Macaca radiata* studied by Nolte (1955*a* and *b*) in southern India were made up of 3–5 adult males, 7–13 adult females, 12–17 juveniles, and 7–8 infants. Thus, much smaller groups are evident than among the large and semiwild bands of Japanese monkeys.

The African baboons (*Papio*) have been the object of intensive studies during the past few years, in particular those of Bolwig, I. DeVore, and S. L. Washburn. Washburn's report here will free us of the necessity of stressing their results. Let us simply emphasize the extreme variability in the size of the groups, from a minimum of 4 individuals (1 male and 3 females) for the chacma baboon (*Papio ursinus*) of Kruger Park to more than 100 for the *Papio doguera* of Kenya. According to Bolwig, each troop is

built up of a number of adult males, a considerably greater number of females, and juveniles of all ages. . . . All troops observed had a typical patriarchal hierarchy. . . . The extent to which a male would allow the presence of other baboons when eating

or allow other weaker males to cover a female, depended on the individual's temper.
. . . On one occasion, an amiable old superior male allowed the other five mature
males of the troop to cover the same female in turn, after he had satisfied himself and
subsequently turned to food [Bolwig, 1959].

And so, once again, variability in behavior and social structure of a species in
natural conditions is evident.

The hamadryas baboon (*Comopithecus hamadryas*) is also extremely gregarious. Starck and Frick (1958) have observed bands of 200 individuals in Abyssinia
that appear to consist of subgroups of 8–12 animals, each one comprising 1 adult
male, 4–6 females, and several young.

The gelada (*Theropithecus gelada*) appears to have a similar social behavior.
The groups observed by Starck and Frick (1958) numbered from 12–20 to 50–70
individuals.

The various species of African monkeys belonging to the genera *Cercopithecus*
and *Cercocebus* have not yet been systematically studied from our point of view.
The observations of Buxton (1952) and of Haddow (1952) on *Cercopithecus
ascanius schmidti*, however, suggest important variations in the size and composition of a single group during a single day. Further, several "family groups" may
join temporarily during the day to eat, before separating again for the night.
Solitary males and females are not rare.

The social behavior of the patas guenon (*Erythrocebus patas*), with terrestrial
habits resembling the baboon's, has not yet been studied. Nor is anything known
of the social grouping of the African mandrill and drill (*Mandrillus*) groups,
of the *Alenopithecus*, or of the black ape groups of the Celebes (*Cynopithecus*).

COLOBINAE

This subfamily has perhaps been studied least of all from the point of view of
what concerns us here, although the langurs (*Presbytis*) are among the most
common and most easily observable of the monkeys of India and Southeast Asia.
The bisexual groups of the common langur *Presbytis* (*Semnopithecus*) *entellus*
observed by Nolte (1955b) had a membership varying from 17 to more than 50.
There were also small groups of isolated males.

Nothing is known about the social structure of douc langurs (*Pygarthrix*),
of the snub-nosed langurs (*Rhinopithecus*), or of the Asiatic *Simias* and *Nasalis*.

The way of life of the African guerezas (*Colobus*) also remains completely
unknown. As to *Colobus* (*Procolobus*) *verus* of Ghana, Booth (1957) tells us
that the bisexual bands number from 6 to 20 individuals, of which at least half
are immature. That this is not a case of simple "harems" is shown by the fact
that Booth has collected two adult males in a single group.

HOMINOIDEA

Two types of social organization appear to exist among the Pongidae.

The Asiatic gibbons (*Hylobates, Symphalangus*) appear to live in monogamous family groups, whose permanence from one year to the next, however, remains to be shown. The twenty-one groups of *Hylobates lar* studied by Carpenter (1940) in Thailand were all made up of 1 adult male, 1 adult female, 0–4 juveniles, and 0–1 infant. Isolated males were also observed.

Chimpanzees, gorillas, and orangs, on the other hand, live in larger, bisexual groups, whose sex ratio and age ratio are yet to be determined. For the chimpanzee of Guinea, Nissen (1932) found 35 per cent males and 65 per cent females in the groups he studied, which numbered from 4 to 14 individuals, the majority of which were not adult.

A group of orangs, observed by Carpenter on Sumatra, was made up of 2 adult females, each accompanied by a young offspring; an adult male was living nearby.

The mountain gorillas studied by Donisthorpe (1958) in the Virunga volcanoes at the border between Uganda and the Belgian Congo, always formed groups of 3–12 animals. On the average, their composition seemed to be the following: 1 old male, 2 adult females, and 1–2 juveniles. Nevertheless, there probably is more than one adult male per troop; solitary animals appear to be rare, and Donisthorpe has seen none. G. B. Schaller's present field work in Albert National Park will certainly reveal many new facts of the social life of the largest living anthropoid.

CONCLUSIONS

Insofar as we can draw any conclusions from this heterogeneous collection of observations, the following seem to be established.

1. The structure of primate societies is far from being uniform within a given family or subfamily. Conversely, the same types of social organization may be found in very different groups. Monogamous family groups, for example, seem to exist among the lemurs (Indriidae) as well as among the anthropoids (Hylobatinae).

2. Within a single species, there seems to be a great variability in the size and structure of social groups that have been observed. These, in many cases, seem to form true closed societies. The regulation of group size and its eventual adaptive nature is certainly one of the most promising chapters in the study of social behavior among wild primates.

BIBLIOGRAPHY

ALTMANN, S. A.
   1959. "Field Observations on a Howling Monkey Society," *J. Mammal.*, 40:317–30.
BOLWIG, N.
   1959. "A Study of the Behaviour of the Chacma Baboon, *Papio ursinus*," *Behaviour*, 14:136–63.

BOOTH, A. H.
1957. "Observations on the Natural History of the Olive Colobus Monkey, *Procolobus verus*," *Proc. Zool. Soc. London*, 129:421–30.

BUXTON, A. P.
1952. "Observations on the Diurnal Behaviour of the Redtail Monkey, *Cercopithecus ascanius schmidti*," *J. Anim. Ecol.*, 21:25–28.

CARPENTER, C. R.
1934. *A Field Study of the Behaviour and Social Relations of Howling Monkeys (Alouatta palliata)*. ("Comp. Psychol. Monogr.," Vol. 10, No. 2.)

1935. "Behaviour of Red Spider Monkeys in Panama," *J. Mammal.*, 16:171–80.

1940. *A Field Study in Siam of the Behaviour and Social Relations of the Gibbon (Hylobates lar)*. ("Comp. Psychol. Monogr.," Vol. 16, No. 5.)

1958. "Soziologie und Verhalten freilebender nichtmenschlicher Primaten," *Handbuch der Zoologie*, Bd. 8, Lief. 18.

COLLIAS, N. E., and C. SOUTHWICK
1952. "A Field Study of Population Density and Social Organization in Howling Monkeys," *Proc. Amer. Phil. Soc.*, 96:143–56.

DONISTHORPE, J.
1958. "A Pilot Study of the Mountain Gorilla (*Gorilla gorilla beringei*) in South West Uganda, February to September, 1957," *S. Afr. J. Sci.*, 54:195–217

FRISCH, J. E.
1959. "Research on Primate Behaviour in Japan," *Amer. Anthrop.*, 61:584–96.

HADDOW, A. J.
1952. "Field and Laboratory Studies on an African Monkey, *Cercopithecus ascanius schmidti* Matschie," *Proc. Zool. Soc. London*, 122:297–394.

IMANISHI, F.
1957. "Social Behaviour in Japanese Monkeys, *Macaca fuscata*," *Psychologia*, 1:47–54.

ITANI, J.
1954. *Japanese Monkeys in Takasaki-Yama* (in Japanese). Tokyo: Kokunsha.

NISSEN, H. W.
1932. *A Field Study of the Chimpanzee: Observations of Chimpanzee Behavior and Environment in Western French Guinea*. ("Comp. Psychol. Monogr.," Vol. 8, No.1.)

NOLTE, A.
1955*a*. "Freilandbeobachtungen über das Verhalten von *Macaca radiata* in Südindien," *Zs. f. Tierpsychol.*, 12:77–87.

1955*b*. "Field Observations on the Daily Routine and Social Behaviour of Common Indian Monkeys," *J. Bombay Nat. Hist. Soc.*, 53:177–84.

PETTER, J. J.
1956–57. Unpublished field notes on Madagascar lemurs.

SAHLINS, M. D.
1959. "The Social Life of Monkeys, Apes and Primitive Man," *Human Biol.*, 31:54–73.

SANDERSON, I. T.
1957. *The Monkey Kingdom: An Introduction to Primates*. Garden City, N.Y.: Hanover.

STARCK, D., and H. FRICK
1958. "Beobachtungen an äthiopischen Primaten," *Zool. Jahrb.*, *Abt. f. Syst. Okol. Geogr. Tiere*, 86:41–70.

BEHAVIOR AND WAYS OF LIFE
OF THE FOSSIL PRIMATES

JEAN PIVETEAU

W E CLEARLY can have only summary and conjectural information on the behavior of the fossil primates. Probably as a result of their ways of life, these mammals most frequently escaped fossilization. They are generally found in a disunited, fragmented condition, and, even where the skeleton remains are abundant, the excavations have often been poorly conducted (especially if ancient investigations are concerned).

In some cases I shall attempt to reconstruct the behavior of primate fossils; in exceptional cases the study of endocranial casts will permit, through analogy with recent forms, at least the expression of hypotheses concerning their degree of mentality; and examination of teeth will supply suggestions as to their diet. Therefore, let us consider several prosimians, a cercopithecoid (Old World monkey), and some pongids. I shall leave aside here *Oreopithecus*, which would merit a long survey, as well as the australopithecines, which perhaps passed over the threshold of hominization.

PROSIMIANS

Throughout the whole Eocene period, the prosimians developed abundantly in the Northern Hemisphere. In France the famous Quarcy phosphorite beds, formed in a tropical climate, have produced wonderfully preserved specimens, enabling most extensive anatomical study. But it is only skulls and teeth that are involved; so far, no one has been able, or has known how, to identify the corresponding parts of the limb skeleton. Thus for the genus *Adapis*, represented in the collection by a large number of skulls, only a fragment of a humerus, an astragalus, and a calcaneous bone are known, and these are known very little and as yet only in a conjectural way. The humerus, in the form of its head, greater trochanter, lesser trochanter, and bicipital groove, recalls that of the lemurs. The astragalus is likewise striking in its lemuroid characteristics: large peroneal facet; narrow tibial facet; well-marked groove, against which the calcaneus bone rests, as in the climbing animals. The anterior part of the calcaneus is weakly developed; the paleontologist Filhol has inferred from this that *Adapis* must have moved slowly, in the manner of the lorisiformes today. This conclusion can be accepted only with positive reservations.

In North America a complete skeleton of *Notharctus,* a genus of prosimian visibly at the same structural stage as *Adapis,* has been collected in the Middle Eocene of Wyoming. W. K. Gregory (1920) has made an especially careful study of it and has attempted to reconstruct its behavior. The hand (incompletely preserved) appears to have enabled a firm hooking onto the branches of trees but remained incapable of exercising the function of prehension. The structure of the vertebral column suggests a quadrupedal gait; in particular, the details of structure of the lumbar vertebrae—elongated centers, which are not very much raised, with strong parophyses and neurapophyses pointed toward the front, implying a clear development of the psoas, of the flat loins (*quadratus lomborum*), etc.—are similar to what is observed in the quadrupedal mammals.

The morphology of the sacral, coccygeal, and caudal vertebrae indicate that the elevator and depressor muscles of the tail, as well as those enabling lateral movements, were entirely similar to those of present-day lemurs; in other words, the tail of *Notharctus* was not prehensile. Finally, the form of the pelvis indicates that *Notharctus* was an arboreal quadruped, still incapable of sitting, that is, of putting its trunk in a vertical position, and that he moved about in the trees, from branch to branch, in a quadrupedal manner. Assuredly more primitive, that is, less agile, than the lemurs of today, *Notharctus* exhibited, in its general deportment, the same behavior as do the lemurs. This is an example of an extraordinary functional stability, a representation of morphological stability.

The similarities in the skulls of *Notharctus* and *Adapis* permit the conjecture that the brain of the first of these genera was at the same structural stage as that of the second. But the brain of *Adapis* is of the generalized Eutherian type: its very simple longitudinal fissuring corresponds to that of the primitive placental mammals.

THE SUBFOSSIL LEMURS OF MADAGASCAR

After a long eclipse, the group of lemuriformes finds its way again into the recent formations of Madagascar.

What is striking, first of all, among all the extinct lemur fauna of the large island, is their great diversity. Time and again emphasis has been laid on the bestial traits exhibited by some, in which the face attains dimensions that are enormous in comparison with the skulls, while others show a tendency toward acquisition of a larger brain, an essential feature in the evolution of the higher primates.

The Madagascar beds have produced, in addition to a number of skulls, parts of the limb skeleton, whose connection with the skulls could be made in only a conjectural manner. It is therefore very difficult to recover with certainty the general behavior of these ancient lemurs. It may, nevertheless, be considered that *Archaeondris* and *Paleopropithecus* were arboreal forms and that the Megaladapidae, the giants of the group, must have had a way of life very similar to that of the gorilla.

Without wanting to draw definite conclusions on the degree of their mentality, I shall emphasize the structural complication of the brain of some of the Madagascan lemurs. The genus *Archaeolemur* has a brain showing, in its frontal lobe, traits of an advanced evolution, which testifies to a complex fissuring, probably correlative with cortical transformations, and a marked enlargement of the region situated in front of the *sulous arcuatus*. In a sense, this brain may be considered as having reached an evolutionary stage comparable to that of the cercopithecoids. Another form, *Hadropithecus*, attains, with a few differences of detail, a structural intricacy like that of the *Archaeolemur*.

It is not yet at all possible to draw up a table of the activities of the subfossil lemurs of Madagascar, but there is every reason to consider, from the variety of morphological types, that there was at that time a greater diversity in their ways of living than there is among the present-day lemurs.

CERCOPITHECOIDEA

We know only the last phase of the paleontological history of the Cercopithecoidea, the one in which the group reached its present structural stage.

The earliest representative of the group is at the same time the best known. The one in point is *Mesopithecus* (*Mesopithecus pentilici Wagner*), of which Albert Gaudre has produced a reconstruction of the skeleton and a sketch of its way of life.

The large number of individuals collected in the Pikermi bed allows one to think that *Mesopithecus* lived in troops. Considerable differences in size are observed among these forms. Some have very large canines and lower jaws, whose ascending branches are large; in others, the canines are scarcely longer than the incisors, and the ascending branches of the lower jaw are narrow. Probably a sexual difference is involved, but the conditions in which the fossil material was collected do not allow one to attempt an evaluation of the make-up of the population according to sex.

It has been possible to reconstruct the general behavior of *Mesopithecus*. Their speed going forward must have been almost as high as their backward speed. The reports of the length of the limbs suggests that they walked on the rocks more often than they climbed in the trees. The length of the fingers, on the hind limb, must have been an inconvenience for walking, so that, like a number of present-day Old World monkeys, *Mesopithecus* was probably confined to limited areas.

The teeth appear to have been adapted, like those of the Semnopithecinae, to grinding ligneous sections and herbaceous parts of plants. The lower teeth are worn on the labial side, the upper teeth on the lingual side, which seems to indicate that in order to chew, *Mesopithecus* let the mandible slide within the upper jaw.

It is pertinent to point out that none of the monkeys found at Pikermi had teeth that were very worn. Gaudry concluded from this that they did not die of old age. But no clear pathological mark has been found on the skeletons.

The osteological and odontological study of *Mesopithecus* shows us that the structural evolution of the cynomorphs was completed at the end of Miocene times. There is thus reason to infer the identity, in way of life, of the fossil and recent forms. This inference is reinforced by the study of a natural endocranial cast of *Mesopithecus*, which revealed that the fissuring of the neopallium exhibits the same pattern as in the recent *Semnopithecus;* in particular the first "pli de passage" (*arcus parieto-occipitalis*) has come back to the surface, exactly as in *Semnopithecus*.

There is thus every reason to believe that the social life of the cercopithecoid monkeys has been marked, since the Pontien, by an extreme stability.

PONGIDAE

If, in the case of the pongids, paleontology presents more evidence than in that of the Cercopithecoidea, our knowledge of the anatomy of extinct forms remains fragmentary, and it is very hard to render a picture of their social life. Let us examine several Miocene genera: *Pliopithecus* and *Dryopithecus* of Europe, *Proconsul* and *Limnopithecus* of Kenya.

THE GENUS *Pliopithecus*

Pliopithecus, found in 1836 in the bed of Vindobonian age of Sansan (Gers), was the first fossil monkey brought to light. Known for a long time by the dentition alone and by a fragment of mandible, the recent discovery at Neudorf (Austria) presents us with a specimen (for which the subgenus *Epipliopithecus* has been created) in which the dentition is associated with important parts of the skeleton. The preliminary study that was made by Zapfe (1952) shows that the hand exhibits a structure different from that of the gibbon; it is a pongid with which *Pliopithecus* seems to have the most affinities.

THE GENUS *Dryopithecus*

Dryopithecus has played a large role in speculations on human phylogenesis. A humerus, lacking its two extremities, has been found associated with the type specimen, a mandible with its teeth, coming from the Vindobodien of Saint Gaudens (Haute Garonne). The diaphysis shows a slight curvature; the supinator crest, which is the insertion point of the brachioradialis muscle—always powerful in the primates that brachiate—is well developed here. But the humerus in question, from all evidence, is one of a young form.

It is relevant to say here a word about a femur found in 1895 in the Miocene of Eppelsheim for which Pohlig proposed the name "Paidopithex." Dubois estimated that this bone must have belonged to a giant gibbon and proposed that it be called "Pliohylobates"; Schlosser related it to *Dryopithecus*.

The femur of Eppelsheim is remarkable for the rectilineal character of its diaphysis. The angle of the neck, formed by the axis of the diaphysis and the axis of the neck, is close to what may be calculated for the gibbon; the neck is short. The lesser trochanter forms a rounded eminence; the intercondyloid surface is not very deep. With its dimensions it is not impossible that such a bone could have belonged to *Dryopithecus;* it would be going too far to deduce from this the behavior of the form to which it belonged.

THE PONGIDS OF KENYA: *Limnopithecus* AND *Proconsul*

The forms of the lower Miocene of Kenya must have lived in multifarious populations. They fall essentially into two genera: *Limnopithecus* and *Proconsul.* *Limnopithecus* has been put in the ancestral line of the gibbon, *Proconsul* in that of the chimpanzee. In a recent work, D. Ferembach (1958) showed that there are direct similarities between them and that, as a result, both are situated in the ascending line of the chimpanzee.

W. E. Le Gros Clark and D. P. Thomas (1951), observing in the proportions of the limbs of *Limnopithecus* great differences from the gibbon, have concluded that this primate, while leading an arboreal life, did not brachiate at all, so that in his way of life and his various activities he was essentially like the Cercopithecoidea. D. Ferembach (1958) thinks, on the contrary, that *Limnopithecus* may have moved about by suspending itself by its hands, but in the manner of chimpanzees not of gibbons. In support of this she points to the development of the epitrochlea, comparable to that of the chimpanzees; the straightness of the diaphysis of the humerus; the form of the bicipital tuberosity; the straightening of the head of the cubitus; the morphology and the position of the small sigmoid cavity, etc. She admits, on the other hand, that *Limnopithecus* may have adopted a quadrupedal gait in the trees. As to *Proconsul,* it likewise corresponds to an initial stage of brachiation and preserves many traits of quadrupeds.

But the calcaneus bone exhibits, in addition, odd peculiarities, described in the following terms by W. E. Le Gros Clark and L. S. B. Leakey for *Proconsul:*

> The posterior position of the basal tubercle of the calcaneum and the backward extension of the main facet for the talus appear to indicate that if *Proconsul* occasionally raised itself on its hinder extremities like the modern Pongidae, it was able to throw its weight back more towards the heel, and thus to balance itself in the erect posture more effectively [Clark and Leakey, 1951].

D. Ferembach believes that the same disposition is found again on the calcaneum of *Limnopithecus,* which therefore would also have been able to take up an erect standing position that was more assured than that of the modern Pongidae.

In conclusion, the discoveries of Kenya allow us to picture a mass of primitive Pongidae similar, in a number of their activities, to the Cercopithecoidea. They would show us, at the same time, brachiation in the nascent state and also a great facility for adopting bipedal posture. One may then wonder whether the accentuated brachiation of the present-day Pongidae (with the exception of the gorilla—but here a secondary regression is undoubtedly involved) and the perfect bipedalism that will bring with it the individualization of the Hominidae would by no means be attained directly from a quadrupedal form but from a form that is at the same time brachiator and quadruped and capable of adopting, at least temporarily, an erect position.

It is unnecessary to expand on the phylogenetic implications of such observations, which, in any case, remain conjectural. They make us catch sight of the possibility of reconstructing a history of the locomotion of primates, and it may be considered that to its various phases there must correspond a particular social state.

There is here an order of problem that has almost completely escaped the paleontologist up to now. It may be hoped that future excavations will come to clarify these points, enlarging the field of paleontology, which will then become capable of contributing to the history of the social life of the primates.

BIBLIOGRAPHY

FEREMBACH, D.
   1958. "Les Limnopitheques du Kenya," *Annal. de Paleontol.*, Vol. 44.
GREGORY, W. K.
   1920. *On the Structure and Relations of Notharctus, an American Eocene Primate.* ("Mem. Amer. Mus. Nat. Hist.," n.s., Vol. 3, Part II.)
LE GROS CLARK, W. E., and L. S. B. LEAKEY
   1951. *The Miocene Hominoidea of East Africa.* ("Fossil Mammals of Africa," No. 1). London: British Museum (Natural History).
LE GROS CLARK, W. E., and D. P. THOMAS
   1951. *Associated Jaws and Limb Bones of Limnopithecus Macinnesi.* ("Fossil Mammals of Africa," No. 3.) London: British Museum (Natural History).
ZAPFE, H.
   1952. "Die *Pliopithecus* Funde aus der Spaltenfullung von Neudrof an der March (C. S. R.)," *Sonder aus der Geol. Bundesanstalt*, Sonderheft C.

THE NATURE AND SPECIAL FEATURES OF THE
INSTINCTIVE SOCIAL BOND OF PRIMATES

M. R. A. CHANCE

MAN now forms social organizations that are larger than any previously developed by mammal. The forms of the societies that are still in existence are also very varied. We know that much of their size and variability is due to new features, to tool-making and -using, agriculture, new methods of movement and communication, etc.; and we can see that in the later and larger societies, more and more of the structure is dependent upon these new features and less is concerned with regulating the personal relations of people who meet one another in daily affairs.

Yet further back in the history of the primates there was a time when the ancestors of the present macaques and baboons were evolving the social bond that enables them to aggregate into social groups at the present day. These groups can comprise a hundred or more individuals.

This form of social life, shown by present-day baboons and macaques, may well have played a crucial part in setting us on the course that we have now taken. Our lack of information about comparative primate sociology is one of the greatest defects in our knowledge of our own behavior at the present time and means that we are totally unaware of the instinctive elements of behavior governing much of our social relations. My own view is that this defect goes a long way toward explaining why man's modern knowledge of himself leaves him so largely incompetent in the control of his own destiny.

If these instinctive social propensities, whose elements have only recently been seen in outline, play a part today, they must have played a very much more determining role in the social life of early man. I propose, therefore, to devote myself to outlining the properties of instinctive sociability in the primates, which the study of the existing social monkeys can reveal, and to bring forward certain features that seem likely to have special significance for man's evolution.

Unfortunately, the primates anatomically closest to us, the apes (Hominoidea), live in tropical and subtropical wooded country, so that it is difficult to observe their behavior. Few detailed observations have been made on apes, with the exception of the gibbon, but it seems clear that they do not form large groups.

17

TABLE 1

HABITAT AND GROUP STRUCTURE IN DIFFERENT SPECIES OF PRIMATE

Species	Habit	Country	No. in Group	Males	Females	Socionomic Index*	Heterosexual Groups		Authority
							Lone Males	Bachelor Bands	
Gibbon (*Hylobates agalis*)	Brachiating: structurally adapted for life in trees	Siam	Less than 6	1	1	100	(+)	—	Carpenter, C. R.
Spider monkey (*Ateles geoffroyi*)	Walks along branches; lives mostly in the trees	Central and South America	5–30	8	15	160	(+)	—	"
Howler monkey (*Alouatta palliata*)				3	8	230	+	—	"
Hamadryas baboon (*Papio hamadryas*)	Lives almost exclusively in open country	Central Africa	25–100	1	12	?			Kummer, H. Zuckerman, S.
Rhesus (*Macaca mulatta*)	Forages in open country and in the forests	India	Up to 150	6	22	500	+	+	Carpenter, C. R.
Japanese monkey (*Macaca fuscata*)	Inhabits partly wooded and open mountainous country	Japan	25–440	2	4	Small group 2 males 4 females	+	+ (Separate from but associated with the heterosexual group)	Itani, J. Imanishi, K.

*Number of females for every 100 males.

+ = present; — = absent; (+) = inferred.

We must therefore be content at this stage with observations on monkeys (Anthropoidea). Some types of monkeys spend much time in groups, and the average size of the groups can be used as a rough measure of their sociability.

ORIGIN OF THE SOCIAL BOND

As it happens, sociability measured in this way seems to be closely related to the animals' habits; those monkeys that spend a great deal of time in open country seem to form large social groups, whereas those that live in forests tend to have small and loosely co-ordinated groups. This can be seen from Table 1.

The theory of evolution has provided biology with a most powerful heuristic method of thought. It helps biologists fix their attention on the central issues of the problem by demanding that all biological phenomena should be related eventually to the selective advantages of adaptation and competitive existence. So here we simply start by asking What advantage do monkeys foraging in open territory derive from living in large groups? What is the origin of this "social bond"?

The simplest answer is that when feline predators are about, monkeys are safer in numbers (Chance, 1955, p. 162). Observations on baboons in Africa, which form closely marked social groups, point to this conclusion. It is confirmed by the observations of C. R. Carpenter (1934), who saw a young howler—a South American monkey—which was isolated from its group, attacked and bitten by an ocelot. The young monkey cried out and received protection from three males of the group.

The fact that gibbons do not appear to form social groups, but live in families, can be explained by the same argument. Gibbons live in treetops, where they are relatively free from predators, although they can be attacked by leopards, which climb trees easily. But gibbons have a unique method of escape by swinging (brachiating) from the slender branch of one tree to that of another. Leopards and other tree-climbing cats would have difficulty in following them over such arboreal pathways.

The spider monkey, a long-limbed monkey native in tropical America, seems to occupy an intermediate position between the howler and the gibbon. Spider monkeys are relatively large animals and usually move on all fours. But they are able, like the gibbon, to escape from danger by brachiating from tree to tree. They have a looser form of social group than does the howler, which cannot brachiate.

Although the adaptive features of living in groups are not exhausted by the protection afforded against predators, particularly in open country, it seems probable that this was the adaptive feature of their behavior that led many species to develop the faculty for forming large groups.

FORM OF THE SOCIAL BOND

These groups show a definite structure, with a predominance of females and young. As an adolescent male matures, he either takes his place in the main group, or he is himself expelled.

These excluded males represent an interesting feature of the social organization of monkeys. It is difficult to follow their fate while they remain solitary, and some presumably fall victim to predators. But observations of excluded howlers show that some of them quite soon become associated with another group. They gradually become acquainted with one member of it and are ultimately incorporated into the new group. This may mean that some other male is finally thrown out of it (Carpenter, 1934).

The Indian macaque shows a more exaggerated form of this behavior. Its heterosexual groups are large and contain a high proportion of females, so that a large number of males are expelled as the adolescents mature. Some of these excluded males join together to form bachelor bands, which exist separately from heterosexual groups. They contain young excluded males and old males that have retired from dominant positions in the breeding hierarchy.

The same social structure exists among the Japanese macaques, which have been closely observed on a peninsula set aside as a reserve for the monkeys. The stability of the bachelor bands is remarkable; they continue to exist even though bachelor and heterosexual groups have to come close together in order to visit the feeding site. The most likely explanation is that the males of the bachelor band have an attraction for one another.

When most kinds of animals are brought into close proximity in this way, by having to visit feeding or breeding grounds, the resulting encounters stimulate both aggressive impulses and the tendency to flee. Aggressive encounters are especially intense between mammalian males during the breeding season, when the conflict is frequently resolved by fights—as, for example, among deer. These fights merely serve to establish a rank order among the males, which then, in turn—the dominant stag starting—run with the herd of hinds.

A rank order among the males of a social group has been found to exist for all species of social monkeys that have been studied: for example, the Japanese and Indian macaque, the Hamadryas baboon, South American howler and spider monkeys. Their order determines the priority of access to food and mates, to sites for sleeping, etc., and imparts freedom of movement within the society as a whole. More significant, however, is the fact that there are never fights between male members of the monkey groups except on the rare occasions when the dominant male or overlord is displaced by another monkey. This sometimes occurs by the simple retirement of the overlord or after a period of assertive behavior on the part of the monkey that will ultimately displace him. Only during such episodes is the stability of the rank order disturbed. Monkeys of lower order seem to be well aware of their place in the community.

Around this constant core of males the breeding relations are organized in different ways, according to the species of monkey and probably to some extent dependent upon the past history and present circumstances in which the particular band of monkeys is living. For example, male baboons possess harems, the size of which is proportional to the rank of the male. A group of Japanese monkeys was studied over a period of several years, during which time the group varied from 160 to 440. During the whole of this period, six adult males formed the core of the society. These males followed strict rules, which led them to mate with females of their own harem, or with any other female, provided she was not attached to the harem of other males of the core. A female belonging to a harem does not permit herself to mate with a male other than her overlord, for, if another male is permitted to transgress, the retaliation of the overlord is directed at her and not at the transgressing male. This indicates the extent to which the male rank order has suppressed hostility among its members. Its effectiveness is all the more remarkable since the male monkeys are faced persistently with intense sexual provocation.

INTENSITY OF SOCIAL CONFLICT

Female macaques and baboons are sexually receptive for approximately nine out of the twenty-eight days of their reproductive cycle, so that in a group of monkeys where two or more adult females are present, the males will be in the presence of a sexually active female for more than half the time. And in larger groups there will be continual sexual provocation—a situation found nowhere else in the animal kingdom, except for a two-month interval during the mating season of the Pribilof seal. The extent to which this preoccupies the male seal can be judged from the fact that he does not feed at all during these two months but lives on his fat, spending his time defending his territory and his harem. A detailed examination of the factors producing conflict in primates is presented by Chance and Mead (1953).

The only explanation of the monkeys' ability to stick together in spite of this provocation seems to be the specific social attraction between members of the male sex, which also accounts for the formation of bachelor bands. Sociability is, therefore, more than an aggregation of a number of individuals in the face of external threats.

NATURE OF THE SOCIAL BOND

During the observation of a colony of Indian macaque monkeys at the London zoo in 1953 (Chance, 1956), I was startled to see a female being aggressive toward her prospective consort. As I watched her, I saw him counterthreaten her several times until she was attacked and bitten, after which she paid him no further attention.

Subsequently, I found that other females courted in the same way, but with important differences. The threat exerted by a courting female toward her prospective male consort was usually combined with submissive gestures, and in this case it did not lead to counterattack but served to arouse his interest in her.

Here was a clue to the social bond uniting the males. It has always been clear that the subordinate males are aware of the potential threat from those higher in rank. This threat has presumably acquired an ambivalent quality for monkeys—it attracts as well as repels them, just as the female's display of modified aggressiveness can attract a male. Any evaluation of their social behavior must take into account this strange ambivalence.

The next step in my observations of the Indian macaques was to study the evidence of attraction between males under varying conditions—when they were grouped without consort females; when only the overlord had a consort; and when the two leading males had a consort each. From these studies it appeared that potential threats—as conveyed by the awareness of the higher status of another adult male—act primarily as an attraction to subordinate males. The presence of consort females, however, brings about mild overt threats down the rank order; these engender a repellent influence between ░░░░░░░░░ breeding hierarchy, which is shown by an increase in the distance between them.

Very recently Hans Kummer of the Basle zoo completed a detailed analysis of the behavior of a family of Hamadryas baboons living in an open enclosure. His observations confirm the conclusions just outlined concerning the ambivalent response to threat. Concerning young monkeys that have left the mother but are not yet mature, he wrote:

During expressions of fear, the frightened individual does not remain where it was threatened. Either it flees from the cause of its fear or it seeks out an animal of the highest possible rank. When fear is intense the latter invariably happens. But in most cases the highest ranking animal within range of the dispute is itself the cause of the fear. This does not significantly change the behaviour of the frightened animal. It seeks out the highest ranking of the animals present though this individual has himself been the cause of its fear [Kummer, 1957].

After a subordinate monkey has run to the high ranking monkey, his behavior shows unmistakable signs of conflict. Ambivalent postures, screeches, etc., show his tendency to run away, yet he continues to sit nearby.

The young monkey, from a very early age, habitually seeks out its mother, and for much of the time she clutches it to her and suckles it (Itani and Hazama, 1953). Contrary to what one might expect, however, Harry Harlow (1958) has shown by the aid of model mothers that the mother is regarded primarily as a refuge rather than as a source of food.

Hans Kummer (1957)—if I may quote him again—gives us a glimpse of the final link in the succession of events that forge the social bond between the growing monkey and the other members of the colony when he writes: "It seems that with advancing age the elements of behaviour of the young in the relationship with their mother do not vanish but project themselves upon ever higher ranking individuals."

THE CONTEXT OF BOND-FORMING BEHAVIOR

The switching of attention by subordinate monkeys toward a dominant monkey, and their tendency to run to it under threat from whatever quarter, becomes bond-forming, whether the threat comes from within or outside the social group. (The protection from predators that monkeys get by this bond is mainly the result of the frequent threats or awareness of potential threat from dominant monkeys. It arises within the group and is a more persistent element than the sporadic attacks from predators. It is thus more efficient at keeping monkeys together, and they are, therefore, less liable to attack.) When the switching of attention to dominant monkeys arises from threats within the group, it is part of an ambivalent response, as shown by the tendency to alternate between flight from and approach to more dominant monkeys and by ambivalent postures, such as that which combines submission with elements of counterthreat.

This ambivalent behavior, which I have termed elsewhere "equilibration" is an essential prerequisite for maintaining social status within the group. It, in turn, is essential during immaturity for the eventual achievement of dominance, from which position alone fertile mating (the mating with fully receptive females) is possible. It will, therefore, have selective advantages. The evolutionary implications of this behavior have been exhaustively treated by Chance and Mead (1953).

Equilibration involves one of two possible modes of response to the constantly changing circumstances of the social environment. Either the movement of another monkey or its own behavior brings a particular monkey close to another. This encounter may develop into an "episode," in which each is aware of and becomes involved with the other. If this happens, the monkey must give a suitable gesture; on the other hand, especially if it is the subordinate of the two, it may anticipate this by altering its course of movement or its position and so avoid an episode. This gives rise to a spacing-out of monkeys during the active life of the group and was first noted by Carpenter (1942b). It is called "spatial equilibration" and is recognized often by the constant distance that any two monkeys, especially the males of the breeding hierarchy, maintain between one another. In either event, the monkey must be acutely aware of the exact social setup, and one can see that this kind of problem-solving is a current preoccupation of the truly social monkey.

I have seen individual monkeys involved in this type of behavior continuously for an hour or more at a stretch; the average for the colony of macaques at the

London zoo was one episode every two minutes. On theoretical grounds (Chance and Mead, 1953), and in the appropriate circumstances, this type of behavior could reach proportions (both in intensity and duration) found nowhere else in the animal kingdom. Mistakes in encounters with the dominant males are not only potentially fatal, but, equally important for their evolutionary consequences, they can have traumatic effects on mating behavior and thus lead to sterility.

The strain of this type of social situation must tax the discriminating power of the brain, at times, to breaking point. Consequently, there is good reason to believe that ability to adapt to social requirements could have played a more potent part in the evolution of our mental powers than has been evident heretofore.

Not only is this social activity much less prominent in some species of social monkey (e.g., howlers and spiders) than in others (e.g., macaques), but also it is clearly dependent, to a large extent, on the actual situation of a particular group. Mere aggregation resulting from confinement, either by pressure of population (Collins and Southwick, 1952) or by actual physical boundaries, is clearly able to increase the intensity of social encounters, and there is no doubt that in the evolutionary history of a given species there will be major fluctuations of this kind.

It is important to realize that this ability to equilibrate under the appropriate stimulus has also become a propensity, so that there is now a drive for each young monkey to try his hand repeatedly by testing his ability to engage another monkey in an episode and to come out of it unscathed—or even with an enhanced status. This, also, is attention-demanding, similar *in function* to tantrums, crying, etc., in children's behavior. This low-level aggression, or aggression combined with suitable elements of submission, when employed in the instinctive initiation of episodes, can therefore be used to attract attention as well as being the means of coping with the attention of other monkeys.

Just as the young use threats to initiate episodes during their maturation, so also may the female entering on the sexually active phase draw the attention of her prospective consort to herself. This was so in the London macaque colony (Chance, 1956), but Carpenter describes lip and facial gestures as the soliciting behavior of females in the Santiago colony. Such differences may be real and reflect different elements of instinctive behavior, blended in various ways by social "tradition." On the other hand, he may have been misinterpreting these gestures. Very much more detailed ethological analysis is required before this type of problem can be resolved.

I have introduced this example here to draw your attention to the very close relationship that has been observed between mating behavior and the two other components of equilibration to threat, namely, aggressive approach and the tendency to flee. Courting females threaten the males, at the same time combining with this behavior, at the moments when the male's interest is aroused, varying amounts of presentation and short bouts of running away from him, as well as another submissive gesture, crawling up to him. The male, suitably aroused by such behavior, follows the female and briefly mounts her. Full mating takes place only after this behavior has died down and the two are relaxed and spending much time together.

Comparative studies of behavior are always illuminating. Our analysis (Chance and Grant, in preparation) of encounters between rats has revealed that these are made up of the components of the same three drives: aggressiveness, a tendency to flee, and the mating drive. These encounters are resolved by successful mating, if the meeting is between members of the opposite sex and the female is in oestrus. If between members of the same sex, or a male and an anoestrus female, by one rat's fleeing successfully or submitting by rolling over on its back, thus allowing the other rat to assume a dominant posture, crouched over the body of the submissive rat from one side. These two postures are the consummatory acts of the flight drive and aggressive drive, respectively, at low intensities. As might be expected, therefore, the "episode" comes to an end when the dominant rat moves away.

Mounting appears sporadically and quite often in the encounters between two rats of either sex, and both male and female mount each other in encounters between rats of opposite sex, though the male attempts are more frequent. This is evidence that in both sexes the drive to mate is aroused, together with the drives of aggression and flight.

The difference between the postures available to rat and social monkey is striking and important for us to understand. The female rat's copulatory posture (lordosis) is shown by her only during oestrus, as a direct result of a high level of circulating oestrogens. In contrast, both sexes of social monkeys (macaques and baboons) possess and use frequently in encounters between any combination of the sexes, both copulatory stances—mounting and presentation.

The triad of motive (flight, aggression, and mating) provides the substratum upon which agonistic encounters are built in both rats and monkeys, but in monkeys the female copulatory stance is available to both sexes and serves by what is known as "ritualized displacement" (i.e., the taking-over into the repertoire of one drive the gestures serving the functions of another) as the submission posture, as well as being, in another context, the female mating stance. Mounting also serves as the consummatory act of aggression in low intensity episodes between monkeys. Both the sexual gestures (mounting and presentation), therefore have been taken over into the agonistic context to serve as means whereby status resolution may occur quickly, so preventing a rapid rise of tension. Overt sexuality thus, more often than not, gives expression to the relative status of two monkeys and is not, in these circumstances, evidence of true mating.

For social monkeys, therefore, status, though of greater concern to them than sexuality, also involves expression by sexual gesture more than in other species of mammal.

The distinctive quality of the behavior of social monkeys lies in the ambivalence of their social response, which, under threat of moderate intensity, switches their attention to the dominant animal and impels them to move toward the center of dominance in the group. This pronounced cohesive movement is only an exaggerated overt aspect of the preoccupation of every monkey with his status, once his social awareness is aroused.

SPECIAL FEATURES OF THE BOND-FORMING SITUATION

The preoccupation of social monkeys with their hierarchical status is an aspect of excited behavior. It is as if at the slightest provocation their attention was deflected to this aspect of their surroundings and thus heightened their social awareness. Sociability in monkeys, other than aspects associated with what is broadly described as comfort activities (nest-building, grooming, huddling at rest, etc.), all at less excited levels, or the rather simple nursing responses described by Harlow (1958), is thus an aspect of rank; but the individual's reaction to this situation is dependent on other variables present or absent at any given moment and may take a number of forms, two of which have been noted, one by Chance and Mead (1953), and the other by Kummer (1957).

ANLAGE OF CONCEPT-FORMATION

The sexually mature male that is, nevertheless, in a subordinate position, occupies a unique place in the group. The situation about to be described is maximal in a group with fluid sociosexual relations, such as that so far recorded for *Macaca mulatta*, and less frequent where harems are present to apportion the females between the males. The social propensity of the male second in rank keeps him in the vicinity of the overlord monkey, and his sexual maturity in this position subjects him to a motivated conflict resulting from the ever-present sexually receptive consorts of the overlord. All three social drives—flight, aggression, and mating—are in this instance active and balanced, primarily because in the social encounters between mammals, such as rats and monkeys, all three drives contribute to the form of excited social encounters but also because, in this specific situation, sexual stimuli from active females is an added element evoking the drive to mate. The final resolution of this situation compatible with optimal reproductive performance involves the correct modulation of all three drives over a considerable period of the life of the animal. This behavior will be selected on the basis of a breeding premium. The opportunity to mate with a female at the height of her receptivity, when ovulation is due, comes when, having judged the correct moment to exert his dominance, he displaces the overlord. Such a "Claudian" situation needs must be once and final. It is a final yes or no— a single binary step, in modern electronic terms—which comes only after the assessment of many variables.

There is one special aspect of this situation, however, to which I want to draw your attention for further discussion. The successful equilibration in this situation demands an awareness of two aspects that may be evolutionarily significant for animals in no other situation so far identified in the natural condition of any other species. First, he must orient himself not merely in relation to the overlord but to two individuals, the overlord and his consort. Second, the consort is always changing as the females go in and out of oestrus, so it is important in the total social framework of events in the colony to know, at any one moment, which female is the preferred partner. A situation that, when more than one female is coming to her peak of sexual receptivity, is not a simple matter. This means, essentially, assessing the relation between two external varying features of the environment before this monkey relates his own behavior to either. It seems almost as if the situation demands the recognition of formal content in the changing continuum of interindividual relationships in order to make possible an evolutionarily adequate response. This possibility that monkeys could make a response based on such a discriminatory assessment should receive careful scrutiny in the hope that it will ultimately be possible to find out whether, given the right types of cues, they are capable of this response.

ANLAGE OF TOOL-USING

The second of the special ways of behaving in relation to the bond-forming awareness of rank has been noted by Kummer under the term "protected threat." It frequently happens that monkeys (or rats, for that matter) that are in a group and are threatened displace the tension so engendered by threatening another animal lower in rank. This behavior, which in rats takes this form alone, in monkeys can be so arranged that the original threat from the more dominant animal can be deflected onto a third party rather than onto the monkey that was threatened in the first instance. The property of monkeys to, as I put it earlier, try their hand at or exercise the faculty of entering into social "episodes" with other monkeys, extends to this situation and can be seen in colonies of macaques and baboons. Kummer (1957) has, however, identified a unique feature of this in his colony of baboons in the Basle zoo, namely, that on occasion a monkey lower in rank than the recipient will work himself into a position between the recipient and an alpha animal so that, after arousing the alpha animal to awareness of his position, he can deflect threats aroused against himself onto the recipient and so gain a trick, so to speak, in the competition for rank.

Two monkeys may be playing, or otherwise occupied together, when one or both are alarmed and they both run to the alpha animal; the one that reaches him first may then invoke protected threat toward the latecomer. As Kummer writes:

Owing to the tendency of seeking out the high ranking animal during excitement, the place most aspired to is close to the high ranking animal. The part played by the actor in protected threat consists partly in preventing the recipient from seeking out the high ranking animal. This can be deduced from the following observation; during the threats which are often of long duration, the recipient sometimes runs back and forth in a semicircle, the centre of which is the high ranking animal. The actor accompanies him, allowing a small time lag, in a curve of smaller radius.

The recipient has occasionally been observed trying to break through to the high ranking animal. This was successful only once and led to an exchange of roles between the actor and recipient. Protected threat can also be called *a struggle for a place near the high ranking animal* [1957].

It is as if the actor were exploiting a use value of the relationship engendered between himself and two other monkeys. If so, it is an "anlage" of tool-using, and tool-using may have come about as a transfer of this propensity in the field of social exploitation to that of the subject's relation to physical objects. In this new context the attributes of an object (the tool) could have been seen to have an effect on some material if applied by the subject's own activity.

Using concepts inherent in one set of data to enhance an awareness of relationships in other realms of experience is a simple, if frequent, component of originality and appears to have taken place, if the interpretation just presented can be ultimately validated, in the early stages of man's developing awareness just as it does today.

Ethology has revealed analogous shifts of one element of behavior from one context to another, as when one act normally evolved in the repertoire of one drive is performed as a displacement activity when another drive is in control of the behavior. This may lead to the performance of this act in a different situation.

An example is the "fanning" activity of the male three-spined stickleback, *Gasterosteus aculeatus* L., which, autochthonously expressed, is a nest-ventilating activity that serves to aerate the developing eggs. It has been shown conclusively that this movement is employed as a displacement activity during the sexual phase, before any eggs are present in the nest. It occurs as such when the sex drive of the male is thwarted because the female will not respond to his courtship (Tinbergen and Iersel, 1947).

In contrast to those instances in which only one "displacement activity" occurs, other cases have been cited in which the thwarting of a certain drive, or the conflict between two particular drives, may provoke any one of several different kinds of displacement activity. These are known as "alternative displacement activities." This state of affairs may have been the more primitive, the instances of single displacement activity being the result of selection during phylogeny.

In the higher apes, motor elements that are unconnected with any specific stimuli form the basis of adaptive behavior rather than stimulus-response patterns. As Schiller (1957) points out, their organization consists of serialization or condensation more than of selection. These motor elements can be regarded as "emittances" dependent upon the internal state of the organism rather than as responses dependent on specific external stimuli.

Whether tool-using came about by the operation of motor pattern or by awareness of a potential relationship, the logic of ethology would suggest that a necessary, if not a sufficient, cause would be the transfer of a behavioral pattern, normally operative in one context, to another.

ADDENDUM

The hypothesis put forward by Washburn (1959) and foreshadowed by Oakley (1957) that a threefold enlargement of the brain has taken place during the Pleistocene (from about 500 to 600 cc., represented by the brain of *Australopithecus*, to that of modern man, which is approximately 1,500 cc.) seems to be a reasonable deduction from present evidence; especially after the recent discovery of *Zinjanthropus* by the Leakeys at Olduvai. This enlargement was, of course, mainly the growth of the cortex.

These authors ascribe the selective advantage and cause of this enlargement to the two factors that emerged in the behavior of man during this period, namely the use and making of tools. This supposition is supported by the specialization of the cortex characteristic of man, as evident in the exceptional enlargement of the hand area of the motor cortex.

It is necessary, however, to issue a caveat fully explained by Chance and Mead (1953), since cortical maps of the kind referred to are made from the accessible surface and may be seriously modified when they are extended to include the surface of the cortex covering the invaginations of the sulci. As more than half the surface area of the cortex is invaginated in this way, considerable reservation must be held about maps constructed from the exposed parts of the surface alone.

It would seem that a threefold increase in the size of the brain in 1,000,000 years, equivalent to 50,000 generations—assuming a generation was twenty years for most of the Pleistocene—bespeaks a very rapid selection rate. In comparison with the evolution of the leg of the horse, for example, the time taken for man's brain to treble its size is about 100 times as rapid. A question that should, therefore, be asked at this stage is whether such a rapid rate of selection would require a special breeding system.

In an earlier part of this communication and elsewhere (Chance and Mead, 1953), I have argued that a potent influence causing enlarging of the cortex and related parts of the amygdala, which is found in man, could have been the result of competition for dominance, such as can be seen most acutely in the social behavior of present-day macaques and baboons under certain circumstances. The more intense this competitive behavior is, the more it is correlated with a breeding premium, which means a very rapid rate of selection for the characteristics that lead to dominance, the most important of which is the ability to control motive expression at high levels of social excitement. This latter faculty,

TABLE 2—PROBABLE FEATURES OF

Period		Habitat	Habit
Upper and Middle Paleolithic	*Australopithecus Homo*	Open savannah, taiga, and steppe	Hunting
Lower Paleolithic		Parkland and more movement into the open savannah	Expansion of brain, making possible emergence of cultural adaptation
1 Million Years			
Pliocene	Prehominids	Parkland with increasing excursion into open country	"Act complexes" were gradually dissociated from their emotive background and became available as exploratory movements. The "act complexes" themselves broke up so that the component movements are now separately available for exploratory behavior
12 Million Years			
Miocene		Forest	Little diversity of exploratory behavior in new situations because different movements were bound together in rigid "act complexes" evoked only under specific motivation
25 Million Years			

SOCIAL LIFE OF PLEISTOCENE MAN

Group Size	Group Structure	Posture, Body Size, and Mother-Child Relationship
Tool specialization increased productivity through hunting, and	possibility of larger group assemblages arose again	Upright posture present. Small body size. Mother-child relation changed. Mother required to hold and care for feeding of child
Relatively large aggregations were possible but became smaller as body size increased	Group size diminished and became dependent more and more frequently on a greater number of other factors than hierarchical order between males	
20–200 individuals aggregating into larger hordes at special points (e.g., water sources)	Groups arranged around a hierarchical core of males?	Posture became upright
Model group, 20–30 individuals		Child still actively clings to mother

dependent on an enlarged amygdala, would also be a predisposing mechanism for the development of "tameness," the suggested basis upon which co-operative social life can emerge in hunting communities (Washburn, 1959).

This type of social development need have been only a phase in man's development, and I am inclined to think that if it had played a role it would be likely to have antedated the period of maximum cortical expansion. Then it would have served as a necessary preliminary period of selection, assisting the background rearrangement of hereditary factors that could predispose man's ancestors for the rapid change that occurred during the Pleistocene.

Perhaps one way in which we might decide whether this type of selection did precede Pleistocene enlargement of the cortex would be to know whether *Australopithecus* had a large amygdala.

BIBLIOGRAPHY

BASTOCK, M., D. MORRIS, and M. MOYNIHAN
1953. "Some Comments on Conflict and Thwarting in Animals," *Behaviour*, 6:1.

CARPENTER, C. R.
1934. *A Field Study of the Behaviour and Social Relations of Howler Monkeys* (*Alouatta palliata*). ("Comp. Psychol. Monogr.") 10:48–168.
1942a. "Sexual Behaviour of Free Ranging Rhesus Monkeys (*Macaca mulatta*)," *J. Comp. Psychol.*, Vol. 23, No. 1.
1942b. "Societies of Monkeys and Apes," *Biol. Symp.*, 8:177–204.

CHANCE, M. R. A.
1955. "Sociability of Monkeys," *Man*, 55:162.
1956. "Social Structure of a Colony of *Macaca mulatta*," *Brit. J. Anim. Behav.*, 4:1.

CHANCE, M. R. A., and E. C. GRANT
In preparation.

CHANCE, M. R. A., and A. P. MEAD
1953. "Social Behaviour and Primate Evolution," *Symp. No. 7, Soc. Exptl. Biol.*

COLLIAS, N., and C. SOUTHWICK
1952. "A Field Study of Population Density and Social Organisation in Howler Monkeys," *Proc. Amer. Phil. Soc.*, 96:143.

HARLOW, H. F.
1958. "Development of Affection in Infant Monkeys," *Proc. XVth Internat. Cong. Zool.*

IMANISHI, K.
1957. "Social Behaviour in Japanese Monkeys (*Macaca fuscata*)," *Psychologia*, 1:47–54.

ITANI, J., and N. HAZAMA
1953. "Observations on the Behavioural Development and Mother-Baby Relation of the Japanese Monkey." Communication Zool. Inst. Coll. Sci., Kyoto University.

KUMMER, H.
1957. "Soziales Verhalten einer Mantelpaviangruppe," *Schweiz. Zs. f. Psych.*, Vol. 33.
OAKLEY, K.
1957. "Tools Makyth Man," *Antiquity*, 31:199.
SCHILLER, P. H.
1957. "Innate Motor Pattern as a Basis of Learning," *Instinctive Behaviour I.U.P.*, pp. 264–87.
TINBERGEN, N., and I. IERSEL
1947. "Displacement Reactions in the Three-spined Stickleback," *Behaviour*, 1:56–63.
WASHBURN, S. L.
1959. In this volume.

THE EVOLUTION OF TERRITORIAL BEHAVIOR

HEINI P. HEDIGER

I T CAN be assumed that the natural history of territoriality in the animal kingdom represents the introduction to the first chapter of the history of property in mankind. A piece of land or a section of space was most probably the very first thing that living beings took possession of and that they defended even against their own kind.

The surface of our earth is basically a complex system of mosaics, as can be seen readily on every flight: man's real estate is divided up into many squares or similar figures. Animal territories cannot be recognized with such ease and clarity, but careful studies have shown that among animals, also, each individual or organized group of individuals, whether flock or herd, inhabits, as a rule, a space of specific size—one piece of a mosaic, which has to be conquered and defended, chiefly against members of the same species and, to a much less degree, against others.

The further apart two species are in the zoölogical system, the less is one a threat to the territory of the other. Every species occupies its own mosaic system, with units of specific size. One must conceive, therefore, of as many superimposed mosaic systems as there are animal species in a given region. Tools as property, naturally, come very much later than territories.

The unit of the territorial mosaic, the individual or social property, forms the primary possession of all organisms. In many species this simple ownership is not a permanent one but is merely temporary. Many fishes, reptiles, birds, and mammals have clearly limited territories only during their breeding seasons; for the remaining time, the borders become vague or disappear completely. There are also species that are not bound to territories or that have territories with curious distortions in regard to space and time. In all classes of vertebrates, however, examples of permanent territories exist, which will here receive special attention.

In 1949 I attempted to survey this problem, and, more recently, other authors have published data on the territorial behavior of various mammals. Regarding the territoriality of primates, C. R. Carpenter has taken the lead with his report on howler monkeys (1934) and gibbons (1940). In 1958 he published a splendid survey of territorial research.

With these notes I merely wish to indicate that "territorology" today has

FIGURE 1
A Berber tribesman buying a stuffed sheep gut to ward off evil demons.

become a broad and fairly well-cultivated field of science, in which ethology, animal psychology, and ecology are successfully combined. It seems to me that ethnology, physical anthropology, and sociology can also gain in various ways from territorology, especially since human behavior can never be understood as something isolated, but only in its phylogeny as revealed by comparative studies.

Here I shall call "territory" merely that section of space that is defended by the occupying individual or social unit (clan, herd, etc.) and that has a definite size (within limits typical of a species) as well as a specific internal structure.

As a rule, small animals have small territories and big animals big ones. If we compare carnivores and herbivores of equal body size, we find always that the former have larger territories than the latter, while the internal structures are mainly alike and represent a system of fixed points with connecting lines (Hediger, 1950, 1955).

In order to occupy and defend a territory, or a circumscribed region, it is necessary to render it recognizable by marking its borders. Today we employ the following methods for such territorial demarcation: (1) optical, (2) acoustical, (3) olfactory, and (4) a combination of the methods listed above.

This sequence is not arbitrary, but corresponds largely to the relevant evolutionary direction among vertebrates. The optical method of territorial demarcation predominates among lower vertebrates, that is, fish and reptiles. Among birds the acoustic method plays a prominent part in addition to the optical, and among mammals olfactory methods predominate up to the prosimians and some New World monkeys. Within the order of primates we find remarkable variety in the methods of territorial markings: among higher, or at least simian, primates, from the platyrrhine *Alouatta* to the catarrhine gibbon and all three great apes, the acoustical method has acquired greatest importance. Man, however, secondarily marks his living space optically, even though he has not completely given up olfactory means. In Morocco, for example, I observed that some Berbers purchase very smelly, oily stuff from their witch doctors, which they hang, in pieces of sheep gut, onto all four corners of their houses to keep away evil demons (Fig. 1). More civilized populations use optical means of demarcation, such as street names, house numbers, etc. Just as do reptiles and birds, man wants to define his living space, mostly for recognition by his own fellow beings and not so much for the information of different species. A cat in our garden or pigeons on our roof disturb us little, but our feelings as owners of a territory are most violently activated if we encounter a fellow being unannounced at night in our living space.

Mrs. Meyer-Holzapfel, in her study of the origin of man's property concept (1959), has pointed out that the German word for property, *Besitzen*, literally means to "sit on." In this connection it seems remarkable that many primates have developed special sitting structures in the shape of ischial callosities, so that one could almost call them *Sitztiere* ("sitting animals"). Man, too, has a sitting structure, represented by his powerful gluteous musculature. No matter what the anatomical explanations for these specializations may be, to the comparative psychologist they suggest some connection with the original meaning of possession. Furthermore, primitive stools, besides weapons that were indispensable for survival, belong to the earliest inventions of man, and this in all races, from the simple stool of the chief of a primitive tribe to the throne of a modern king. By mounting the throne, one takes possession of a large territory.

Territorial behavior is designed to prevent the loss of contact among reproducing units. Within the territory, the specific "social distances" act effectively against any dissolution of the group. Aggressions, and indications thereof, or threats, prevent any dangerous crowding of territories.

Besides the spatial and individual cohesion of the group, warning sounds relating to the presence of enemies always are among the first needs for mutual information. No more is required so long as the food consists only of plants and small animals. However, as soon as it is necessary to obtain large quantities of meat and to overcome large prey by joint action, then more differentiated means of communication also are indispensable to such co-operative activities. It is here that we find a biologically strong motivation for the development of language.

I. THE ACT OF SITTING AND ITS ANATOMICAL STRUCTURE

If it is correct that the ability to sit on something represents an advanced characteristic, then in a comparative survey of the animal kingdom we must necessarily find that the position that we call "sitting" occurs only in the more highly developed groups. It is, furthermore, necessary to define what "sitting" means.

I was unable to find any definitions of "sitting" in dictionaries or encyclopedias. A tentative definition must therefore be attempted. No doubt everybody will agree that it implies a posture of the body that differs from lying. Certain species of fish can lie, but there seems to be no example of a sitting fish. To sit means to repose in a position in which the ventral surface is lifted off its base, the body weight resting on the lower part of the trunk—be the tail turned over ventrally or dorsally—completely freeing the frontal extremities. Consequently, no fish can sit, not even the sea horse (*Hippocampus*). Although this fish can take up a vertical position in the water, it has no sitting surface. *Hippocampus* is merely able to anchor itself by its tail. The mud skipper (*Periophthalmus*) also is unable to sit; it has to rest its ventral surface on the ground.

The case of the next highest class of vertebrates, the amphibia, is different. Urodela, in principle, behave like fish, although many can abide on land. Sitting does not yet occur among animals living in water. Some Anura, that is, frogs and toads, can undoubtedly lift their ventral surface off the ground if they rest their weight on their forelegs. Some Anura are even capable of lifting one of the two front legs for short periods—for example, in order to cram food into their mouths or to help along the skin-shedding process. No amphibian, however, will get past the three-legged position.

The same applies to reptiles. No snake, tortoise, or crocodile can sit; neither can any lizard. Some lizards are able to move bipedally, however (e.g., certain Agamidae, Varanidae, etc.), but not a single reptile can repose in a sitting position; there is therefore no "sitting" proper in their case.

Birds do rest on their hind extremities, leaving the wings free, but there is no sitting organ, not even in the penguin, which is merely able to rest on its feet and short tail.

Among mammals none of the primitive forms can sit, nor can any of the Insectivora or the Chiroptera. Certain marsupials, ungulates (e.g., Hippopotamidae, Tapiridae), and carnivores can rest their posteriors upon the ground and hold one or both of their forelegs free for some time, but, as for example the kangaroo, no true sitting structure exists; no ungulate can take its weight off its front legs in a sitting position, and the situation regarding carnivores is basically the same. Dogs, bears, and cats are able to sit even while freeing their front legs, but they cannot pursue any of their habitual activities while doing so. Some of the rodents can, however, and they can also use both arms to hold their food. At the same time, to my knowledge, there is not a single rodent that actually reposes in this position. The sitting position serves only the process of feeding and watching (avoidance of enemies).

The sitting position proper seems to be the privilege of the prosimians and of the primates. Only after walking upright has been mastered does sitting (in addition to lying, as the sleeping position) become the dominant posture during feeding time and for other important occupations. In man a great deal of thinking and practically all writing is done in a sitting position.

Special sitting structures in the shape of ischial callosities or especially developed parts of the musculature (*gluteus maximus*) are encountered only in the higher and most highly developed primates. Only in these does the sitting position also acquire a specific psychological importance. In man it is often associated with social superiority and the demonstrative emphasis on possession. The superior may invite the inferior to sit. The superior disposes of seating accommodation of special distinction (the throne). There is a comprehensive literature about the organs of locomotion and their functions; walking in an upright position and the history of its development have been the subjects of intensive studies. Surprisingly little attention, however, has been given so far to the sitting position and the anatomical structure of sitting or to its biological and psychological importance, although anthropologically it seems of great significance. B. Rensch in a few words pointed out the importance of the sitting position and its influence on different organs of the body (Rensch, 1959, p. 56).

II. METHODS OF TERRITORIAL DEMARCATION

As already mentioned, there are—roughly speaking—at least four methods of demarcating individual or communal property in the animal kingdom. In primates, at the lower end of the scale, we still find the olfactory method throughout, which no doubt has primitive traits, while at the upper end of the scale the acoustic method prevails, either predominantly or exclusively. This no doubt represents some connection with other acoustic signals, that is, language. The olfactory method of demarcation used by prosimians (Fig. 2), by means of urine and gland secretions, is closely connected with the fact that they are mainly macrosmatic, nocturnal animals, so that optical markings would be impractical. As the primates were getting progressively microsmatic and diurnal, they ac-

FIGURE 2
A female ring-tailed lemur (*Lemur catta*) in the typical attitude of demarcation.

cordingly had to give up the use of scents. The olfactory method was replaced by the acoustical one, which, furthermore, is much more practical in thick vegetation than is the optical.

As early as 1944 (Hediger, 1944, p. 173), I described, on the basis of many years' observations, how the slow loris (*Nycticebus*) used to walk importantly around its freshly cleaned territory (i.e., cage), thoroughly wetting it with urine. Galago and saimiri urinate on their hands and then moisten the branches below them. Galago even rubs urine into the palms of his hands and feet.

In addition, in many prosimians—as also in many rodents, ungulates, carnivores, etc.—urine is by no means an unimportant excretion, which, after filling up the bladder to a determined degree, has to be released out of a physiological need. It is, rather, biologically a very important substance—a means of demarcation—a limited amount of which is deliberately deposited in certain fixed points of the territory. This deliberate use of the urine is based on localized urination, which is usually coupled with localized defecation. As I have repeatedly described (1944, 1950, etc.), among all the higher vertebrates two completely differing manners of urination and defecation can be distinguished, namely the localized and the diffuse, and I am particularly anxious to characterize these two types, because their distinction is important for the assessment of human behavior, including psychiatric study. In child psychiatry completely erroneous theories about the nature of *enuresis nocturna* have arisen out of ignorance of these simple facts, which are observable in every zoo, and in consequence quite hopeless therapeutic theories have been established.

In the territory of the localized type we find fixed points to which the animal repairs for the specific purpose of urination, or of urination and defecation. Even sick and weak animals will at times still painfully drag themselves to such fixed points to urinate and to defecate. There are no such fixed points in the territory of the diffuse type. That is to say, here again the inner physiological organization is topographically reflected in the organization or foundation plan of the territory. Elsewhere (Hediger, 1956) I have described in greater detail how a territory can, in a certain sense, be considered the projection of an organism over and above the body proper.

As has already been hinted, it is characteristic for many prosimians that the urination and defecation points in their territories be well defined; the places of urination can be identical with the points of territorial demarcation. The further we ascend the chain of primates, starting from the prosimians, the less this territorial and associated behavior pattern appears. Neither the more advanced platyrrhines (like *Cebus*, *Alouatta*) nor the catarrhines (from the cercopithecoids upward) belong to the localized type any longer, but to the diffuse.

This is also the circumstance that is to blame for the fact that neither monkeys nor apes can be house-trained. Only on very rare occasions does this seem to have been achieved. In zoo life we are constantly up against this unpleasant problem; monkey cages are perpetually dirty, and, particularly among anthropoids, we encounter most repulsive habits: they play with and throw excreta, frequently eating it in appreciable quantities. Without any doubt, the chimpanzees are the worst offenders in this respect. We have a rich literature on such behavior, which poses a problem in every zoo. In my opinion, the only solution consists in keeping these highly developed primates on sufficiently widely meshed iron grating, so that the excreta and urine will immediately pass through and out of reach, as is the case in their natural habitat. In nature—at any rate in the case of all those species living in trees—excreta and urine pass through the branches and reach the ground and thus immediately escape the animal's attention. Only in captivity do they remain in full view on the unbiological, solid floor, within reach of the ape, leading not only to the repulsive behavior outlined above but also to frequent reinfection with parasitic worms.

It must be emphasized that our nearest relations in the animal world unmistakably belong to the diffuse type. There are no fixed defecation and urination points in their territories, and, accordingly, such matter is not used for demarcation—as is the case among many prosimians. Localization in human habitations is a modern institution, which, for white men, is only a few hundred years old. By nature man is clearly of the diffuse type. One has only to think of sanitary conditions during the Middle Ages or of the desperate efforts needed in former colonies to introduce a fixed point in the service of public hygiene among primitive peoples. In several parts of the tropics I have seen how the inhabitants were compelled to install a water closet in their village, in order to conform to the rules laid down by government officials, who were without the slightest success in enforcing its proper use.

It is therefore quite wrong to conclude that careless defecation among schizophrenics or bed-wetting (enuresis) among maladjusted children is based on the unhealthy decay of human instincts (see, e.g., Ora Meyerhardt [1951]). Such an instinct (of localized urination and defecation) has never existed in man or in his nearest animal relations, the higher primates. These unhealthy disturbances can therefore on no account be the consequence of any decay of human instinct of any kind. The localization of a water closet in human habitations is the result not of any instinct but of modern hygiene.

Incidentally, some prosimians—as for example, *Lemur catta*—do not use urine but a gland secretion for the olfactory demarcation of their territory. At the Zurich zoo I have been in the habit for years of demonstrating their demarcation behavior to students. It is only necessary for me, with some students, to approach the cage (which is 4 meters wide, 4 meters high, and 4 meters deep) with deliberation, to obtain the following results of demarcation on the wire meshing that forms the front of the cage: The animal responsible immediately approaches the wire at a determinate spot on the lower left, turns and does a hand stand and, with tail lifted, presses the opening of the perineal gland against the cage. Approximately another eight spots in the cage are treated in the same manner, especially door corners, the most obvious approaches that might be taken by potential rivals.

Protruding branch stumps on the climbing tree are treated in the same manner. The position from which the gland secretion takes place is always the hand stand. A similar position is taken for this purpose by some quite different animals (e.g., some of the Viverridae).

For the ring-tailed lemur, too, the olfactory redemarcation of territory when man approaches is by no means an idle gesture. The only outsider tolerated in the well-defined territory of the lemur in our zoo is the keeper. On one occasion that I recall, he was accompanied by a volunteer who wanted to help him with the cleaning. She was immediately bitten in the leg, so severely that one of the larger arteries was opened, necessitating protracted hospitalization. When territorial defense is at stake, even small and apparently harmless animals and birds may become dangerous to man.

The ring-tailed lemur provides, further, an example of territorial defense undertaken by the female. This usually occurs only in such animals as are devoid of any well-defined sexual dimorphism, for example, also, certain Viverridae, Felidae, and rodents (*Castor*), etc. In species of marked dimorphism, territorial demarcation is customarily up to the male. W. Fiedler, incidentally, reported in 1957 the behavior relating to territorial demarcation of the ring-tailed lemur and other animals at the Zurich zoo.

III. SOCIAL ASPECTS

As it has generally proved fruitful to take stock of biological data from as many different points of view as possible, I should like to raise here a few other points that come to a zoo director's mind in this connection. Intrinsically, certain prosimians, as, for example, the large lemurids of Madagascar, are exceptionally decorative and interesting animals, of great value as exhibits. It would therefore be well worth while to keep a large group, say twenty or thirty, on a monkey island or monkey hill. However, I cannot recall ever having seen such a thing in any zoo, nor do I think it feasible. The reason for this is no doubt the fact that prosimians—unlike many Cercopithecidae, for example—never occur in large groups, but live paired or in rather small families.

Social units cannot be increased at will. Their volume is determined in ways similar to that, for example, of the size of territory. Prosimians apparently never live in larger societies, just like their predecessors the insectivores, except when these latter can move in three dimensions, like the Chiroptera. The habits of insectivores—or at any rate of those living on the ground—seem to preclude the foundation of substantial groups. This seems to apply even to the small insectivorous platyrrhines. Only the herbi- and frugivorous higher platyrrhines, who have no problem of food supply, seem to be able to live in larger communities, as, for example, the capuchin and howler monkeys.

At the Zurich zoo we have endeavored for years to build up a substantial group of *Lemur catta*, but we have never succeeded in keeping two mature males in one group, not even father and son. Since the young were born in the surprising proportion of five males to one female, we were always forced to sell the maturing males before the father would attack them as rivals.

In contrast to the Cebus monkeys, *Lemur catta* hardly seem to distinguish individual zoo visitors; they do, however, recognize their keepers. A Cebus more than thirty-five years old used to greet me in the morning by loud whistling. It is a fact that he identified me at once at a distance of over a hundred meters, even among groups of roughly a hundred people. I stress that I had never brought him any food; it was merely a case of meeting an old acquaintance. This emphasizes the extraordinary gift of observation possessed by these capuchin monkeys. From the account given above it may be deduced that they also register the smallest differentiations of behavior and expression among their own kind.

I believe that the extent and intensity of interindividual relationships among the higher primates is usually grossly underestimated. This has been demonstrated, for example, by the meticulous observations that Hans Kummer has made of a group of baboons at the Zurich zoo (1957). Of these I wish to single out one here: it has been proved that even an individual animal's sleeping position is regulated by social hierarchy. I quote as follows:

When embraced in sleep, it is not the larger animal which lets its chin rest across the nape of the other, but the one of higher rank. The one of lower rank—even when it is larger—plays the role of the young and rests its head sideways unto the chest of its sleeping companion [Kummer, 1957].

It further transpires that, the higher the rank of an animal, the more peacefully it will sleep, and, correspondingly, the lower its rank, the more it will toss and turn, that is, the greater its restlessness.

Another very characteristic indication of strong individual differentiation described by Kummer (p. 85) consists in the various behavior patterns observed in the care of the skin. Not every animal may search the skin of all the others. On the contrary, even this social activity follows strict rules. Young females may work the skin of the alpha animal only with a forefinger (touch inhibition), whereas young males may not touch it at all, only watch it. These touch inhibitions in the females (retention form of grooming) disappear when sexual maturity is attained. Only then does mutual searching of the fur become normal.

Kummer's observations at the Zurich zoo have also confirmed the belief that the oestrous female baboon may be served by only one specific male, namely, the alpha animal. Even at an advanced age the visibly weakening alpha animal would not under any circumstances allow his two much stronger rivals to take possession of a female. Only the young females that had sexually matured after the climax of the alpha animal's development had taken place had a chance of seeking out one of the males that, without a doubt, were the alpha animal's physical superiors.

One gained the impression that the older females remained imprinted on the mind of the old alpha animal, without his obvious senile decay entering into the matter. Naturally, we must not generalize from the situation of these Papio hamadryads at the Zurich zoo. On the contrary, this probably represents an isolated case. It is, in fact, the first time in my zoo experience that I have ever been able to observe an aging ape or monkey being able to cling to his favored alpha position with such obstinate persistence. During his last few months and weeks, nevertheless, it could be observed that the females neglected the now obviously senile alpha animal more and more in favor of his rivals. What is surprising in this case is that the old male, who is now really only a shadow of his former self, has not been killed or even wounded by his rivals. The reason for this seems to be his willingness to make concessions, and he is slowly but definitely handing over his power to his successors. I cannot help thinking of the situation of some senile village chief in a primitive country, who in view of his prestige is still in power, though clearly he is his successors' physical inferior.

In many fields man acts as a powerful catalyst for animals and activates latent capabilities and reactions in the latter that would otherwise never develop. In this connection I would only mention taming, training, and domestication, which are immense fields of behavior that can only take their origin from man and are unthinkable in the contacts of animal with animal. It is, however, not possible to expand further here on this theme of the stimulating influence of man on animal.

Nevertheless, I should like, in passing, to raise one other point relating to the sociology of primates, since it may be of general biological, and therefore also of anthropological, interest. I am referring to certain peculiarities in habits of reproduction. Ethologists usually divide animal behavior as a whole into the inherited or instinctive and the acquired or learned. On the basis of the great wealth of existing evidence, we are inclined, and indeed entitled, to assume that everything relating to such elementary matters as reproduction is instinctive, in particular the way in which the mating act is fulfilled; it seems plausible that here in particular, if I may so express it, nature must not take the risk of a specific individual's ability to learn how to mate. An act of such importance for the preservation of the species must be independent of the hazards of individual experience, it must needs be inborn. For the sake of certain preservation, such behavior must be instinctive, independent of the uncertainties of the process of learning. Countless facts prove this. And yet this biological and logical hypothesis has no absolute validity. Here again there are exceptions to the rule, in particular among apes, certainly among chimpanzees.

Any zoo biologist must notice how rarely we have succeeded in breeding chimpanzees in zoölogical gardens, although sexually mature pairs have been kept in captivity with relative frequency. If I am not mistaken, the first success in breeding chimpanzees was registered in 1915, a memorable birth that occurred in Mme Abreu's establishment in Havana, Cuba. Since then, innumerable healthy pairs of chimpanzees, intrinsically capable of reproduction, have been kept in zoos on all five continents, but actual results have lagged far behind expectations. The number of chimpanzee births lags far behind that, for example, of giraffes and hippopotami.

This must surprise the zoo biologist. In my opinion it is based on the following facts: Fully grown chimpanzees are hardly ever caught in Africa, and consequently cannot be exported. The rule is, rather, for babies or barely weaned young, whose parents have been killed, to reach the zoos, where, over the years, they develop into sexually mature specimens. In this manner, that is, through the importation of unknowing young animals, the chain of natural tradition is interrupted. The young that have grown up in isolation literally do not know what to do with their sexual urge upon maturity. This situation leads to the most unbelievable methods of masturbation—indeed in the presence of both sexes. On the other hand, it may then happen by chance that the two sexes unite functionally and mate.

In many cases, mature pairs, out of ignorance, never get past the stage of sterile masturbation. I had such pairs under observation for years on end. The female used to bite pieces of wood off the cage furnishings in the presence of a sexually mature masturbating male, in order to introduce them into her vagina. It was obvious that the pair, in the absence of an example, were not acquainted with the natural mating process. This knowledge is not inborn in the chimpanzee—nor, presumably, in some other anthropoids—but must be acquired. This thesis is based on voluminous data from experiences in zoölogical gardens, although I admit that at first glance it seems rather improbable.

What, however, is the situation regarding humans? It is a fact acknowledged by many ethnologists that many of our contemporaries among primitive peoples ignore the connection between mating and pregnancy. I myself met such tribes in the Pacific Islands thirty years ago. Is it not, after all, necessary even in our own civilized human society to enlighten each young generation anew about the facts of life? If the complete sexual behavior pattern were inborn, this would obviously not be necessary. The well known story about a girl who was afraid of getting a baby because she had been kissed by a young man is more than a silly anecdote; I regard it as one more indication that sexual behavior is not inborn in the hominids but has to be learned. In a free-living chimpanzee family under natural conditions, each young one has the opportunity of observing sexual behavior in mature animals. Tradition and imitation play a very important part in these highly developed primates, as has been demonstrated by K. J. and C. Hayes (1952), among others.

We are told by psychoanalysts and psychiatrists that an extraordinary number of severe psychic disturbances in children have evolved from the fact that they have observed coitus in their parents, misunderstanding or somehow misconceiving it, and consequently experiencing a serious trauma. How can behavior that we have inherited and that is instinctively familiar to us conceivably produce a trauma? Only, in my opinion, because the behavior in question is quite unknown to us and only becomes familiar through learning processes and information. At any rate, in the whole animate world I do not know a single further example of observation of an instinctive action provoking a trauma. Apparently coitus, in man and in chimpanzee, is not an inherited, instinctive action but is a behavior acquired individually, with the help of tradition and of imitation.

There are still other behavior patterns in the breeding biology of the chimpanzee that apparently have to be learned and that are not inborn, for example the carrying of the young. On June 29, 1955, the first chimpanzee baby was born at the Zurich zoo, to a mother who had herself been imported as a young animal but who, over several years, had been able to observe periodically from her own cage the mating of an older chimpanzee pair, the female of which was sterile. The male finally fertilized the young female mentioned above.

The female was apparently born with the knowledge that one could seat the young on one's back from a certain age on but she did not know exactly how. Thus she often grabbed the child with both her arms in such a way that it was facing her, and lifted it over her head onto her back. The young therefore sat pickaback, facing backward. This impractical way of carrying the young had several disadvantages. Whenever the mother had to pass under an obstacle, such as through a low door, there was always the risk that the young, looking backward, would not see the obstacle and would bruise its head. It therefore constantly had to turn its head 180 degrees in order to see in the direction in which the mother was moving and to be able to observe all obstructions in time to avoid them. Thus the poor chimpanzee child, during several months, had to sit the wrong way whenever carried on its mother's back.

On September 17, 1955, another female chimpanzee, who had grown up in the same cage as the one described above, had a baby (Fig. 3). This second mother,

FIGURE 3
Chimpanzee M. inspecting vagina of Chimpanzee L. immediately before birth of young.

apparently by chance, took her baby on her back in the correct manner, facing front. From that moment the first mother changed her behavior and carried her young correctly too. Unquestionably, the other mother, who was also a friend, had here provided an incentive to adopt the only practical course. Indubitably this behavior was not inborn but had to be acquired. This experience perfectly agrees with the interpretations made by K. J. and C. Hayes in 1952 on the importance of imitation in man-apes. Apparently imitation plays a far more important part than has previously been believed.

The second mother chimpanzee referred to, by the way, was utterly helpless toward her placenta. When her baby was born, she fled from it with a penetrating cry to the farthest spot in the cage. As she did so, the umbilical cord snapped. Only after a few seconds did she look at the baby with interest, going toward it and taking it into her arms. As regards the placenta, she obviously did not know what to make of it. She treated it, so to speak, as a twin, taking the bloody clump into her arms, until finally the keeper succeeded in getting it away from her.

Goma, the gorilla baby born at the Basle zoo on September 23, 1959, was held upside down by her mother, so that she could not nurse it. For this reason the precious baby—the second gorilla ever born in a zoo—had to be raised artificially.

The facts given above are, in my opinion, important evidence that behavior regarding mating and raising of the young does not seem to be innate in the most highly developed primates; a great deal has to be learned individually. This may seem a paradox; however, it appears necessary in the development toward the reputedly most highly developed being, *Homo sapiens*, for the inherited, instinctive behavior patterns to recede more and more into the background, and for acquired behavior to predominate more and more. This in no way contradicts the available evidence of brain development: the paleencephalon has been overgrown more and more by the neencephalon. In certain respects man has become impoverished and uncertain in his instincts. This loss is being compensated by thinking processes—often in a fatal manner.

I should like to give you a quite different example of the loss of inborn habits in favor of the acquired during the course of the phylogenesis. Most animals, even desert animals, from the reptile to the cercopithecoids, can swim. The apes, however, and man himself, are not born with this gift; they have to acquire it painfully. Whereas, for example, the rhesus or proboscis monkeys are naturally excellent swimmers—as I was able to observe at the New Orleans zoo, among other places—all apes lack this instinct. At the Bronx zoo in New York, the famous gorilla Makoko, the first male gorilla to attain sexual maturity in captivity, sank like a stone when he fell into the confining moat. At the Chester zoo in England, a shallow moat has been serving as a safe means of isolation for a large group of fully grown chimpanzees. After all, man too has to make an effort to learn to swim.

IV. ELEMENTS OF SPEECH

Before enlarging on the subject of animal speech, in particular the speech of primates, I must recall a man who, notwithstanding his dilettantism, has done some remarkable pioneering on this subject; I am referring to the American R. L. Garner, whose book, *The Speech of Monkeys*, although it had several editions and has, incidentally, also been translated into German, has nevertheless fallen into neglect and, in fact, has never been taken seriously. Garner started as early as 1884 the systematic study of sound expressions by animals in the zoölogical gardens of Cincinnati, New York, Philadelphia, Chicago, and Washington. To my knowledge, he was the first scientist who endeavored to record objectively animal sound expressions. At the time—1890—no modern sound-reproducing apparatus was yet in existence, so Garner had to use an ancient phonograph; by doing this, however, he inaugurated a new method, which is still valid today.

I am not going to enlarge on the quite interesting speech studies by Garner, nor shall I discuss the fascinating research done by Carpenter, Imanishi (1957), and others, but I would like to venture here to construct a primitive animal language purely theoretically, through making use of the experiences I have gained in zoos and with free-living animals in five continents over a period of thirty years.

When searching for the simplest possible animal language, we have to realize that even *Homo sapiens* still uses some very simple language. The vocabulary of pidgin English in the Pacific Islands comprises approximately only sixty words— yet this has proved sufficient to translate the Bible, for example. The Central African word *Niama* has an extraordinary number of different meanings: in general it means "meat," and in particular it may refer to anything from an antelope moving through the plain to a tin of corned beef. I am giving this example only in order to demonstrate that we may assume conditions in the animal world to be very simple if even man can use a single word so widely, giving it such a variety of meanings, and if a whole human language can be so simple.

Once it is established that the principal activity of free-living wild animals consists in noticing a menacing enemy as soon as possible and escaping in time (Hediger, 1950, 1959), one may logically deduce that a special sound expression also exists for this decisive, primordial activity that surpasses any other in importance and has a wide application among animals. I refer to the *warning signal* or enemy-detecting sound, which is not always identical with the signal for retreat but often precedes it.

As is generally known, the first "word" in animal language is no doubt the one meaning "enemy." Literature is full of expressions like "warning sound," "alarm call," "danger signal," etc. Even among some fish such elementary warning sounds have been detected; the splash sound of the fleeing frog has often been described. Many reptiles hiss or whistle when enemies are detected in any dangerous degree of proximity, and danger signals among birds have been thoroughly analyzed by the ornithologists. Frings and Jumber (1954) have introduced their practical application as a method of pest control.

Many birds give different signals depending on whether an enemy threatens from the air or from the ground. The chaffinch gives detailed information on the enemy in his warning signals (Marler, 1956), etc.; starting from the elementary danger signal, one can, in fact, detect some other specific ones. It is further characteristic of the warning signal—which is equally common among mammals— that it is one of the first, or possibly the first, applicable to more than a single species. The warning call of the peacock can alarm the whole jungle for a great distance, and the "barking" signal of the roe deer will warn the whole neighborhood, often to the annoyance of the hunter.

The timely avoidance of enemies is the individual's first duty, not only in order to protect its own life but, thereby, for the perpetuation of the species. All the rest, like feeding or mating, can be delayed, but escape from an attacking enemy is not to be put off. It is therefore not surprising if the signal for "enemy" is the first and most important.

More than thirty years ago, on the upper course of the Sepik River in New Guinea, I was deeply impressed at hearing a primeval danger and escape signal emitted by *Homo sapiens*, that is, the Papuans, who were still living in the Stone Age and could hardly have had any previous contact with whites. They had apparently noticed our small craft, which was riding at anchor in the river, only when their narrow dugouts reached the open water after passing a belt of reeds. At that moment they emitted terrified shouts and, like startled animals, disappeared back into the reeds.

The second "word" urgently required by an individual seems to me to be the *mating call*, which in primitive cases appears to have been identical with the assertion of *territorial possession*. The throating of the red deer represents the assertion of territorial occupancy, a challenge to rivals, and a lure to females. The situation is similar regarding many other mammals and birds. From this central meaning there can again be increasing differentiation.

I hold the "word" associating *mother and child* as the third one of elementary importance. In contrast to the primates, many animal mothers are unable to carry their young around continuously. Many, such as the hoofed animals, are forced to deposit their offspring periodically and seek them out again. They thus remain in instinctive contact. If the young feels menaced or hungry, it can call its mother, and, in turn, the mother is capable of coaxing her young toward her.

A fourth, *social sound*, seems to have developed from this elementary mother-child sound, probably in consequence of expanding communities, expressing attendance to other members of a group and keeping it *au fait* with individual displacement. From this, special calls of departure, return, etc., have developed (e.g., among social birds).

A fifth "word" may, I think, be assumed for *food*. This could also mean feeding, drinking, hunger, etc., and further indicate prey, booty, hunting mood, etc.

If we try to put ourselves into the situation of a free-living wild animal—not humanizing it but, under careful consideration of the respective biological facts, also allowing for the ecological aspect—we can thus, I think, express everything that the situation requires. Admittedly, five words or signals offer modest possibilities. On the other hand, the situation of a free-living mammal is also relatively simple. It has to be continuously on the lookout for potential enemies; it has to carve out a territory for itself and to keep and defend it; and it has to find a mate, raise its young, and provide the necessary sustenance. These are the sum total of its essential activities.

Maybe the simplicity of the animal situation and the consequently modest vocabulary required can be even more vividly demonstrated by visualizing the variety of subjects that are excluded from animal conversation: everything that daily fills our newspapers, that is, apparel, traffic, finance, technical developments, professions, politics, anything intellectual like science, religion, art, music, history, literature, the past, and the future. Animal language can indeed be simple; fundamentally, five words, that is, signals, seem quite enough.

If we check through all significant data known to us about animal systems of communication, all knowledge of animal "speech"—starting from the excellent research done by K. von Frisch (1956), about the bees, to the classical observations by C. R. Carpenter (1934, 1940), about, for example, the gibbon—then we shall find in all these animal languages the five elements mentioned above. The theoretical construction corresponds, therefore, to the empirical experience. The five elements of "speech" become more and more differentiated in the course of development, and numerous secondary new elements occur.

Something quite decisively different, however, is necessary for a true elementary language to develop from single emissions of sounds, and that is consciousness. Several biologists, for example, A. Portmann (1951, p. 74) and even Konrad Lorenz (1953, p. 10), are of the opinion that all animal sounds are pure interjections, without any desire for communication, comparable, at best, to the human exclamatory cry or shout. If somebody hits his finger with a hammer, he will cry out or curse, whether he is alone or in company. On experiencing sudden pain, the cry simply escapes him without any desire for communication whatever.

Both Lorenz and Portmann claim that no animal sound passes this stage and has therefore only the importance of an interjection. This is no doubt the case with many animal sounds; but I am firmly convinced that on different systematic levels this stage is passed, that the animal can consciously, deliberately make communications in order to achieve certain desired reactions in other animals. Strangely enough, examples manifest themselves most obviously not in intraspecific but in interspecific contacts. I do not know yet whether this is coincidence or has a deeper reason.

Lorenz himself (1953, p. 13) gives a few examples in animals, in this instance dogs, which in his opinion can be interpreted only as the animal's conscious communication with man: he describes how a dog nudges his master with his nose, goes to the tap, put his paws onto the sink, turns to his master, and whimpers. Therein Lorenz sees, certainly rightly, a perfectly conscious expression of the wish for water. Such behavior of an animal toward man therefore represents an acquired, purposeful, and subjectively projected one.

Strangely, however, misunderstandings sometimes arise between animals when they use means of communication among themselves that derive from man and are meant for man. In this connection Lorenz observed a poodle who was greatly afraid of an approaching boxer; the weaker poodle tried to appease the enemy by giving him his paw. A Sealyham terrier, by begging, asked a female Alsatian in heat to be allowed to serve her. In these two cases the "language" used by the animals was certainly not understood by their own kind.

Lorenz sees the case of the greatest approximation to human speech known to him from observations of animals in those chimpanzees of M. P. Crawford (1937), which, after "asking" each other for their respective co-operation, finally succeeded, with united effort, in getting hold of a container of delicacies. This obviously transcends a mere interjection and bears the stamp of intended, deliberate communication. I may add that such cases of useful co-operation are known from numerous occurrences at the zoo and the circus, where animal and man live together in the closest contact. It is a daily occurrence for animals to take the initiative in certain situations in a meaningful, understanding manner, as I know from my own experience. Usually, however, such observations are not taken seriously—understandably so—but are regarded as hunters' stories or fairy tales, as they are not made under the usual "precise laboratory conditions" but emanate from a rather unscientific environment.

Robert M. Yerkes describes in his chimpanzee book (1945, p. 192), which is a classic, how a charge in his primate station refused solid food because of an inflammation in its mouth. A careful examination by one of Yerkes' colleagues had not shown anything unusual, and the scientist made ready to leave the cage, when the chimpanzee in question (Moss) held him back by his clothes. The ape once again opened its mouth wide, using one finger of the other hand to point out the place on its upper jaw where a small swelling indicated the source of pain. Yerkes offers the following comment: "Our examiner naturally felt somewhat chagrined at having to be assisted in diagnosis by the animal himself."

Corresponding cases of understanding and co-operation between animal and man are very frequent in dealings with large animals, both at the zoo and at the circus. Usually they are not published, as they are mostly experienced by persons who lack any formal biological training and whose reports would therefore not be taken seriously in scientific circles. From this it follows, in my view, that scientific research in general and ethological research in particular should not be confined to the laboratory but should also extend to the zoo and the circus, to those animals that under normal conditions cannot be kept in a laboratory. Whenever such work has been attempted, it has proved most fruitful and inspiring, as was the case, for instance, with the detailed observations made by Bernhard Rensch and his associates on the Indian elephant (1954).

From these observations it transpired that any well-trained elephant will take in acoustically as many as from twenty-one to twenty-three different orders and execute them and that elephants generally are surprisingly good learners and have an extraordinary memory.

I do not, however, wish to go into detail here, but rather to extract what seems relevant for our purpose from examples already given, namely, the fact that the maximum in communication has so far been observed in animal contact with man. Lorenz' dogs were able to communicate more clearly with man than with their own kind; Yerkes' chimpanzee turned to man with his toothache; Crawford's chimpanzees were induced in the course of an experimental situation to co-operate successfully; the elephant will obey up to twenty-four different orders only when they are given by man, etc.

As applicable to so many other facets of animal-human relations, here again—in the field of communication—man is the powerful catalyst and stimulator of latent animal ability.

The question now arises whether free-living animals (primates) under natural conditions also use means of communication that are more than a cry and are of a conscious, deliberate nature. I consider it unlikely. K. J. and C. Hayes (1954, p. 300) think it possible

that chimpanzees are capable of enough communication to permit several kinds of cooperative enterprise which might be typical of very primitive culture. An individual could go and get one or more others to bring them to a place were there was something to be done: a heavy load to be transported, a large animal to be attacked, or a good supply of fruit to be picked. If the nature of the task were not immediately apparent to the newcomer, he might be shown what was wanted. If he did not understand the technique to be used, he could ask for a demonstration. If he were reluctant to work, he might be coerced.

Chimpanzees could probably communicate well enough for some kinds of organized group hunting: they might, for instance, be able to surround a herd of animals and stampede them over a cliff. We doubt however that they could arrange for certain individuals to wait in ambush while others drove the quarry to them. Their communication would probably be inadequate to deal with events remote in time or space.

I fully subscribe to the interpretation made by these two experts on chimpanzees; I would go even further in that I do not believe that a co-operative effort like Crawford's experiment would occur among free-living animals. If a tempting fruit cannot be reached on one's own or if a branch required for nest-building cannot be broken off by one's self, then the attempt is given up and a substitute searched for—which the tropical vegetation offers in such great profusion. Although I certainly do not underestimate their latent capabilities, I cannot visualize a group of chimpanzees (or of similarly gifted beings) undertaking an organized hunt, since this would require a plan projecting into the past, present, and future. A communal hunting expedition of primates can be organized only on the basis of previous experience and has to take into account the future behavior of hunter and hunted.

J. B. S. Haldane (1954, p. 98) has most aptly characterized the difference between animal signaling and human speech, as follows: "When a child tells its mother 'I am hungry' or 'I am sleepy,' it is still an animal. When it says 'This is what I have done this morning,' then it begins to be a man."

One can scarcely imagine a group of hominids giving organized chase to a herd of animals that they use for food without possessing a system of communication vastly superior to the five elements referred to earlier, and without conscious speech. This, however, was not required so long as no actual demand for meat existed and therefore no necessity for finding any large prey. I therefore expressed the opinion in the introduction to this paper that the beginning of meat consumption on a large scale, with the consequent necessity for overcoming a large prey by joint action, might well have considerably enhanced the (latently existing) development of language. None of the other activities pursued by the anthropoids under review seem to require any differentiated speech, and I believe that this is proved in the free-living chimpanzees, gorillas, and orangutans.

V. TERRITORY

In 1958 C. R. Carpenter made an exhaustive description of territory and territoriality in his contribution to the volume *Behavior and Evolution*, in the course of which he enumerated thirty-two different meanings and functions of territorial behavior. If I nevertheless take the liberty of returning to this subject, I am doing so because the territory enables us to grasp the grandiose simplicity of the systems of animal communication, especially if we take into consideration the concept of social distance and the importance of imitation and of the contagiousness of emotions.

As related by C. R. Carpenter (1958, pp. 242 ff.), the extent of a territory is regulated by an individual or by the organized group of individuals (swarm, herd, pack, etc.). Propagation is insured by protecting the respective animals from the two extremes of either too many or too few mates. This spatial organization of individual animals, however, also insures sufficiently close confinement for each animal to see and hear what the others are doing—say, for example, in a group of monkeys. Then there is imitation and the transfer of mood or emotion. In this manner a minimum of communication is already achieved, which often resembles or equals the "optimum." It may, for example, prevent some of the animals from dozing instead of feeding and then being hungry when the rest of the group is ready to move on. The animals will use the same source of water at the same time, and care of the body, escape from enemies, etc., are also synchronized. This does not require any complicated language.

Naturally an animal society does not extend over an entire territory but occupies only a small part at a time. Some factor must therefore be instrumental in holding the group to a definite spot within the territory at any one time. K. Imanishi (1957), for example, indicated an area of 1–8 square kilometers (⅓–3 square miles) for the territory of the Japanese *Macaca fuscata*. Within such a territory, however, the group will occupy only about 100–200 square meters (120–240 square yards). The question arises, then, What is this factor? Imanishi assumes that it consists in specific calls or sounds, of which his associate Itani was able to distinguish over thirty in this particular species. Naturally, vocalization plays an important part in this matter among monkeys. But, in my view, they exclusively express a general element of behavior, namely, a social code (social distance).

In my contacts with animals of all kinds, both free-living and in captivity, I have noticed that certain spatial displacements occur in accordance with certain rules and are predictable, and this knowledge can therefore be exploited. In zoo and circus life it is sometimes of great importance to move animals spatially in the desired manner by the use of very simple manipulations and by obeying a certain code, for example, by bearing in mind the respective escape distance or critical distance.

Here I wish to emphasize only one of these biological "distances," namely, the "social distance" mentioned above, as this makes an essential contribution to the permanency of such an animal society, causing imitation and transfer of mood, which in turn make a more exact means of communication unnecessary. Such means of communication (or speech) therefore appear secondary, almost a luxury, and certainly not a factor of primary necessity. Social distance is an utterly primitive element of social behavior, which is already encountered in many nonvertebrates. Among the vertebrates it exists in all stages, from the fish to the gorilla. It is the maximum distance that individuals of one society will move from one another, which is occasioned by that power that, for instance, keeps together a school of herrings or a herd of zebras. Among herring and most fish this is regulated optically; among higher primates optical regulation is complemented, or possibly substituted for, by acoustical elements, as described by Imanishi.

Social distance in animals reminds me of an elastic rubber band, which invisibly connects all members of a group. This social distance is specific and can be measured exactly in meters and centimeters. If this band is stretched over and above its specific value, the result will be an unhealthy reaction. Among flamingos, for example, an atypical extension of social distance usually represents the first symptoms of serious illness.

Social distance can also be characterized as the counterpart of individual distance, which is, however, irrelevant for our purpose; it furthermore occurs only among animals of the "distance type," as opposed to those of the "contact type." Some animals—from fish to mammal—seek or at least tolerate substantial bodily contact with their companions, particularly when resting; these are the contact animals (some owls, parrots, porcupines, monkeys).

Distance-type animals, however, except in contact with their young, do not tolerate any bodily contact with their kind; in fact, they meticulously keep a specific distance from each other (swallows, blackheaded gulls, deer, etc.).

Thus, territorial behavior of a group insures the right degree of distance and contact within its biotope; and social distance, the right degree of distance and contact between the individuals within their territory.

SUMMARY

1. We have demonstrated a few aspects of the complex evolution in territorial behavior and of sociology in primates, which the biologist cannot fail to observe at the zoo.

2. In contrast to the various methods of locomotion and the upright walk, the sitting position, which is specifically characteristic of the primates, has so far been given very little attention. A few comparative-psychological observations are dedicated to the sitting posture, which is realized by means of certain anatomical characteristics.

3. While territorial demarcation by olfactory means is widely used among macrosmatic mammals and prosimians, the acoustical method achieves prominence among the higher primates.

4. Prosimians have so far mostly been observed as small social units (in pairs, families); larger groups as a rule form among the higher primates (from the Cercopithecoids upward).

5. Anthropoids (and man) have to acquire individually the knowledge of certain manners of behavior, like the mating process and swimming, whereas this knowledge is inborn in less highly evolved primates.

6. We defend the thesis that, in certain cases, the systems of communication, that is, "language" among animals can be more than a simple cry or interjection and can consist of conscious, deliberate communications. Under the catalytic and stimulating influence of man these latent possibilities achieve an importance vastly superior to the minimum required in the respective animals' natural habitat, under natural conditions.

7. Five elements of speech that by purely theoretical reasoning have been found to be the most essential are in fact contained in all animal systems of communication investigated up to date and receive added differentiation in the course of evolution, in accordance with the requirements imposed by the respective living conditions. These are the five sounds or signals: (a) warning signal (enemy), (b) mating and territorial possession, (c) mother-and-child contact, (d) social contact, and (e) announcement of food.

8. Territory and social distance are important factors in holding the units together, so the power of imitation and transfer of mood can act as "speech-saving" devices.

BIBLIOGRAPHY

CARPENTER, C. R.

1934. *A Field Study of the Behaviour and Social Relations of Howling Monkeys.* ("Comp. Psychol. Monogr.," Vol. 10, No. 2., ser. 48.)

1940. *A Field Study in Siam of the Behaviour and Social Relations of the Gibbon* (*Hylobates lar*). ("Comp. Psychol. Monogr.," Vol. 16, No. 5., ser. 84.)

1958. "Territoriality: A Review of Concepts and Problems." In A. ROE and G. G. SIMPSON (eds.), *Behaviour and Evolution.* New Haven: Yale University Press.

CRAWFORD, M. P.

1937. *The Cooperative Solving of Problems by Young Chimpanzees.* ("Comp. Psychol. Monogr.," Vol. 14, No. 2.)

FIEDLER, W.

1957. *Beobachtungen zum Markierungsverhalten einiger Säugetiere,* 22: 57–76.

FRINGS, H., and J. JUMBER

1954. "Preliminary Studies on the Use of Specific Sounds To Repel Starlings (*Sturnus vulgaris*) from Objectionable Roosts," *Science,* 119: 318–19.

FRISCH, K. VON

1956. "The 'Language' and Orientation of the Bees," *Proc. Amer. Phil. Soc.,* Vol. 100, No. 5.

GARNER, R. L.

1905. *Die Sprache der Affen* ("The Speech of Monkeys"). 2d ed. Dresden: Übersetzung von W. Marshall.

HALDANE, J. B. S.

1954. "La Signalisation Animale," *Ann. Biol.,* Vol. 30, Fasc. 3–4.

HAYES, K. J., and C. HAYES

1952. "Imitation in a Home-raised Chimpanzee," *J. Comp. Physiol. Psychol.,* 45: 450–59.

1954. "The Cultural Capacity of the Chimpanzee," *Human Biol.,* 26: 288–303.

HEDIGER, H.

1944. "Die Bedeutung von Miktion und Defäkation bei Wiltieren," *Schweiz. Zs. f. Psychol.,* Bd. 3, Heft 3.

1949. "Säugetier-Territorien und ihre Markierung," *Bijdragen tot de Dierkunde,* 28: 172–84.

1950. *Wild Animals in Captivity: An Outline of the Biology of Zoological Gardens.* London.

1955. *Studies of the Psychology and Behaviour of Captive Animals in Zoos and Circuses.* London.

1956. "Instinkt und Territorium." In *L'instinct dans le comportement des animaux et l'homme.* Paris: Fondation Singer-Polignac.

1959. "Die Angst des Tieres." In *Die Angst.* Zürich-Stuttgart: Rascher Verlag.

IMANISHI, K.

1957. "Social Behavior in Japanese Monkeys, *Macaca fuscata.*" *Psychologia: Intern. J. Psychol. Orient,* Vol. 1, No. 1.

KUMMER, H.
1957. "Soziales Verhalten einer Mantelpavian-Gruppe," *Schweiz. Zs. f. Psychol. und ihre Anw.*, Beiheft 33.

LORENZ, K.
1953. *Verständigung unter Tieren.* Zurich.

MARLER, P.
1956. "The Voice of the Chaffinch and Its Function as a Language," *Ibis*, 98: 231–61.

MEYERHARDT, ORA
1954. *Untersuchungen über den Mechanismus der Enuresis nocturna.*

MEYER-HOLZAPFEL, M.
1959. "Die Bedeutung des Besitzes bei Tier und Mensch," *Inst. f. Psycho-Hygiene Biel, Schweiz.*

PORTMANN, A.
1951. *Biologische Fragmente zu einer Lehre vom Menschen.* Basel.

RENSCH, B.
1954. "Zähmung und Dressurleistungen indischer Arbeitselefanten," *Zs. f. Tierpsychol.*, 11: 497–510.

1959. *Homo sapiens: Vom Tier zum Halbgott.* Göttingen.

YERKES, R. M.
1945. *Chimpanzees: A Laboratory Colony.* New Haven: Yale University Press.

SOME FACTORS INFLUENCING THE SOCIAL
LIFE OF PRIMATES IN GENERAL AND
OF EARLY MAN IN PARTICULAR

ADOLPH H. SCHULTZ

THE TITLE of our symposium seems somewhat vague to a physical anthropologist, used to terms that can be defined precisely. Since this is my first venture into social anthropology, I had to begin by consulting dictionaries for the exact meaning of "social," but found merely that it "appertains to society" and is synonymous with "companionate." These definitions evidently do permit a wide variety of interpretations, since most people still make a distinction between, for example, a *society* wedding and a *companionate* marriage. The words "early man" present similar puzzles. At once I was reminded of the proverbial "early bird that catches the worm," especially with my belief that all "early men" did catch more parasitic worms than were good for them. I am also far from certain in knowing at which stage of his evolution "early man" began to correspond to whatever exact definition may be decided upon for that no longer clear word "man." With these critical remarks I merely wish to explain why at times my discussion may seem to go astray and not bear directly on whatever other specialists expect from the general title of this symposium.

The social life of early man, like that of any other animal, was unquestionably determined and limited by his zoölogical status, that is, his morphological and physiological heritage. Any attempt to visualize the behavior of a species of the past must first of all consider the relevant general conditions of behavior characterizing the entire group of animals, of which the particular species is only one representative, even though possibly a specialized one. Since man is a primate and developed from somewhere among the Old World simian stock, his social behavior, too, must have evolved from within the range of social variations possible to this mammalian group. At all times man's social life had been profoundly influenced by such typical catarrhine features as the retention of grasping hands, highly developed mimetic musculature; lack of a real breeding season, together with single, slowly maturing offspring; chief reliance on sight and neglect of the sense of smell; prolongation of all periods of life, etc. The basically catarrhine nature of man formed his social behavior as much as it did his bodily construction.

As human anatomy has to rely upon comparative-anatomical studies of non-human primates for its full meaning, so the investigation of the evolution of man's behavior is dependent upon our knowledge of the behavior of monkeys and apes. The last few years have produced an exceptional number of highly interesting attempts to trace the emergence of man together with the development of his social behavior, especially in some chapters of *Behavior and Evolution*, edited by Roe and Simpson (1958); some of the contributions to the French colloquium on "Les processus de l'hominisation" in 1958; the American symposium on the evolution of man's capacity for culture, edited by Spuhler (1959); the new German book by Rensch (1959), *Homo sapiens; Vom Tier zum Halbgott,* Heberer's comment on the "Tier-Mensch Übergangsfeld" (1958); and the survey by Count (1958) of the biological basis of human sociality. Never before has there been such intense and widespread interest in the very problems we have chosen as focus of our symposium. Thirty-five years ago the late anthropologist G. Dorsey had published a best-seller entitled *Why We Behave Like Human Beings* (1925); today we should be able to answer this same great question more fully and soundly, if we pool the accumulated experiences of the many different anthropological specialties—what we hope to achieve by this symposium.

When a primate morphologist thinks also of the behavior of primates, he will naturally consider first of all the means by which these animals can perceive and enjoy the world they live in, that is, their *senses*. To all mammals the environment must appear very differently according to their anatomical specializations. Whales, for instance, have practically no sense of smell, very poor eyesight, and extremely limited tactile sense, but their sense of hearing is highly specialized for their exclusively aquatic environment. Among primates the well developed *tactile sense* has gradually become localized. In the mostly nocturnal prosimians we still find many vibrissae distributed on the face and the forearms as essential aids for literal contact with the environment. In the suborder of simian primates the tactile hairs play at best a most insignificant role. The strepsirhine prosimians, distinguished by their common possession of a rhinarium, still rely extensively on this specialized tactile organ, present in many other mammals. Even the Melanesian delight in rubbing noses (Fig. 1) can no longer approach the delicate tactile sensations of a rhinarium. The highly sensitized dermatoglyphic covering of the palms and soles reaches its full development only in simian primates in direct connection with their almost exclusive preference of the hands and feet for tactile exploration. With the great thickening of the soles in bipedal man this function became concentrated in the hands alone.

The *sense of smell* still plays an important role in the life of all those prosimians in which not only is the olfactory apparatus still far better developed than in any simian primates, but there are also various specialized skin glands, secreting odoriferous substances, used for marking territories and pathways. In the suborder Simiae odoriferous glands have been found only among such lower platyrrhines as marmosets and night monkeys, in which they seem not to function before maturity and hence serve most likely as sexual attraction. In view of the fact that in all recent catarrhines the sense of smell is poorly developed, it seems certain that "early man," too, had derived no great benefit from this sense.

To the best of our knowledge all simian primates are distinguished among mammals by having acquired *color vision* in various degrees of perfection, and many prosimian as well as all simian primates can see stereoscopically, an indispensable faculty for arboreal animals, which have to judge distances before jumping. The ability to see in the dark, well developed in the many nocturnal prosimians and in the single night monkey *Aotes*, is lacking in all other primates, which are therefore quite helpless and easily panic-stricken at night. Nocturnal species are in general not social animals but tend to associate ony as sexual partners or as parent and young. In significant contrast to this, all diurnal primates live in groups of varying and, for the most part, considerable size. In daylight all diurnal primates rely most of all on their excellent eyesight, which becomes of greatest advantage to a group spread and moving in trees and thereby gaining many different and constantly changing viewpoints, from which any danger is bound to be quickly detected by one or another member of the group. The speed of reactions to visual perceptions appears to be much more rapid in most monkeys and apes than in modern man and may still have been so in early man. The latter also seems to have benefited from a better visual memory than most

FIGURE 1
Papuas rubbing noses (*after A. A. Vogel, 1954*).

of us possess today, as proved in later stages of human evolution by the remarkable ability to draw from memory alone.

The *sense of hearing*, especially the capacity to determine the direction of sound, seems to be most highly developed in such nocturnal prosimians as galago, aye-aye, and tarsier, with their huge and extremely mobile outer ears, which in some forms can also be completely folded over the auditory openings during sleep. Many monkeys still can abduce their outer ears as part of a threatening attitude, but it is very doubtful that these structures are of significant aid in sound-direction finding. Among all higher primates the ear musculature has degenerated so much that the outer ears have become useless decorations, varying between mere vestiges, as in orangs, and huge flaps, as in chimpanzees. While the sense of hearing is of vital importance to all primates, it has not become highly perfected in any simian species but has remained merely adequate for the range of sounds produced by themselves.

It is beyond any doubt that throughout his evolution man never deviated from this order in the relative roles of the main senses, an order that is valid in all catarrhines. The least important role has always been played by the sense of smell and the most important role by that of vision.

The sense of hearing is certainly not of vital help for simian primates in avoiding danger and in escaping predators. Snakes and owls approach noiselessly, and leopards and ocelots stalk their prey at night too silently to wake a monkey out of his notoriously sound sleep. Man-eaters among the large cats invariably get their human victims without having been heard and undoubtedly did so in the days of early man. The great importance of hearing for primates is primarily connected with their *own sounds*, and the simian primates are by far the noisiest of all mammals, at least if judged by the total amount of noise produced throughout the year. From this fact, incidentally, the novice gains the impression that monkeys and apes are the most abundant mammals in the jungles, in which all other mammals are silently hidden except during their rutting seasons. Sounds are the essence of primate life: When a member of a group gets caught by a predator, it usually can still scream for help, with the result that the entire group is alarmed by a pandemonium of sounds. The discovery of a potential danger is immediately broadcast by the entire group with reverberating and persisting noise, as every big-game hunter knows to his own advantage.

Without the hearing of sounds, produced by their own kind, monkeys and apes would never have become the intensely social animals that they are. Sounds of a surprising variety serve continually for the contact between the members of a group, for the orientation of mother and young, for the information of the entire group about possible danger, and, last but not least, for scaring enemies of different or the same species and even for warning rival groups away from territories already occupied. The amount and variety of information that can be exchanged by means of sounds in the highly social catarrhines surpasses that in any other mammals and culminates in human speech. The primatologist regards *language* not as the result of something radically new and exclusively human but rather as a quantitative perfection of the highly specialized development of man's central nervous control of the anatomical speech apparatus in the larynx, tongue, and lips, the latter being as good in an ape as in man. The orgies of noise, indulged in especially by howlers, guerezas, gibbons, siamangs, and chimpanzees, seemingly so repetitious and meaningless, are probably at least as informative to the respective species as most after-dinner speaking is to *Homo sapiens*.

The expression of emotions and transmission of information are by no means limited to sounds and the hearing thereof but result, in catarrhines generally, as much from a great variety of postures and gestures. Crouching down, presenting buttocks, extending hands in pronation, exposing teeth partly or fully, raising eyebrows, protruding lips, shaking branches, pounding chest, dancing in one place, walking backward, etc.—all are actions full of definite meaning. Among catarrhines the oral and ocular facial muscles have become differentiated with increasing complexity and thereby have provided additional means for the expression of feelings and intentions, readily understood by others (Huber, 1931), especially in combination with sound. The long lists of different postures, gestures, and facial movements characteristic of monkeys and apes have not yet been compiled, but any careful observer realizes that they represent an intricate and voluminous "silent vocabulary" of great aid in social intercourse.

In the perfectly adapted arboreal life of monkeys and apes, the limited variety of sounds, together with the great variety of meaningful gestures and facial expressions, is fully adequate for all social life within such close contact as permits seeing and hearing these detailed means of communication. As soon as the early hominids had ventured into open spaces, had begun to use and even make tools, and had co-operated in hunting, the total variety of all means of expression needed additions, which could come only from an increase in sounds, since the comparatively little changed anatomy had already been fully used for all possible gestures, etc. With the disappearance of an outer tail many eloquent means of intercommunication became lost and could be replaced only by greater reliance on the vocal apparatus. Gestures have always persisted in human evolution, but they have become overshadowed by an infinitely greater variety of sounds in increasing numbers of combinations.

Bipedal posture and locomotion undoubtedly represented the first and most decisive evolutionary change of hominids, but it is by no means such a radical innovation as is commonly assumed. Bears, weasels, and many other mammals can and do *stand* erect for raising their level of sight, and so can all monkeys. *Walking* on the hind legs alone, with the trunk naturally held so that the center of gravity is perpendicular above the center of support, is easily possible for at least *Propithecus* among the prosimians, for *Ateles* and *Lagothrix* among the platyrrhines, and for gibbons, siamangs, chimpanzees, and gorillas. Even the orangutan can readily stand and walk erect on its feet, which are extremely specialized for climbing trees (Fig. 2). Without ever having been trained for it, healthy young gorillas in captivity play by running around upright on their hind legs for minutes at a time, only to drop back on all fours for a quick run, to sit upright for a while, and to resume bipedal locomotion again and again, exactly as a human child who is also as yet incapable of maintaining an upright posture for more than brief spells. Ontogenetically as well as phylogenetically erect bipedal locomotion can develop only from occasional brief to habitual long action, but never through an intermediate half-upright posture. Many different primates *might* have gradually developed bipedalism after their preparation of a pronounced division in function in the upper and the lower limbs. The propelling force in jumping is mostly provided by the hind limbs alone (Fig. 3), most clearly shown by *Tarsius*, which has proportionately longer legs than has man. Only the extreme brachiators, like gibbons or spider monkeys, can throw themselves through space by their arms alone. Man's erect locomotion was prepared for by the shortening and widening of the trunk and the associated shift of the spinal column toward the center of the trunk (Fig. 4), a basic trend common to all higher primates and present already in *Oreopithecus* (Schultz, 1960). In addition, the iliac blades of man, though broad, as in pongids, remained short, turned from a frontal to a sagittal direction, and the sacrum shifted somewhat ventrally and far caudally (Fig. 5). The useless phalangeal parts of the toes II–V started to become vestigeal in hominids as soon as they began their terrestrial career. Quickly they perfected still other typically simian conditions, facilitating erect posture, such as the bending of the spine at the lumbosacral border (Fig. 6) and the ontogenetic retention of the fetal forward position of the occipital condyles.[1] Judging by the australopithecids, the erect posture preceded the acquisition of a well-balanced head, but in the *Pithecanthropus* stage of hominid evolution all significant adaptations for bipedal walk were already fully developed.

Monkeys and apes use their *hands* for catching animals and picking vegetable food, which is conveyed to the mouth with the hands. The nursing young are held with a hand, and food or young is frequently carried in one hand even during locomotion. The hands play a very effective role in fighting and, of course, in grooming, nest-building, and other daily activities. This differential use of the extremities was the long-present inducement for bipedal walk. When the earliest hominids had left the forest, the need for a higher level of vision than that in quadrupedal position led to the upright posture and even to erect walk more and more frequently, and thereby the hands became free for purposes other than locomotion and, we can be sure, were rarely idle. It was no radical innovation for Dawn men to use their hands for picking up rocks or clubs as ready defense to overcome the lack of large teeth. Nearly every captive macaque delights in carrying new objects around its cage, and apes are entertained for hours by a blanket or a bucket, which they will not let out of their hands without a fight.

In all catarrhines the thumb is rotated in prenatal life about 90 degrees and

---

1. For a much fuller account of these morphological changes connected with the erect posture of man, the reader is referred to the writer's papers 1950c and 1957.

FIGURE 2
Orangutan carrying her infant while
walking upright (*after*
H. Wendt, 1954).

FIGURE 3
Chimpanzee jumping in upright posture
(*after I. T. Sanderson and G. Steinbacher, 1957*).

thereby becomes truly opposable even to the index finger. In platyrrhines the thumb has no real opposability but is merely abducable, and the extremely opposable thumbs of some prosimians act against the fourth fingers, while the second are greatly reduced. The hands of man are especially well adapted for holding objects as well as for delicate manipulations because neither have the thumbs been shortened, as in many monkeys, nor have the fingers II–V been lengthened, as in all brachiators. With thumb and index finger any baboon can extract the sting from a scorpion, and every chimpanzee a thorn out of its skin— and this more dextrously than most of us—but their thumbs are of less aid in a powerful grasp than man's, on account of the relatively weaker thumb muscula-

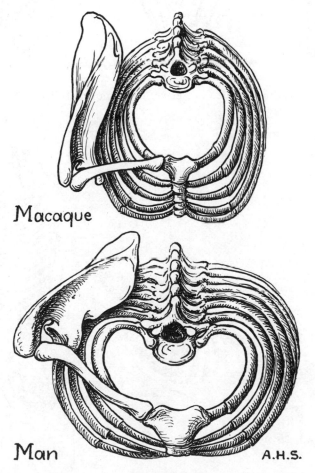

Macaque

Man

A.H.S.

FIGURE 4

Cephalic view of thorax and right shoulder girdle of adult macaque and man (*after Schultz, 1957*).

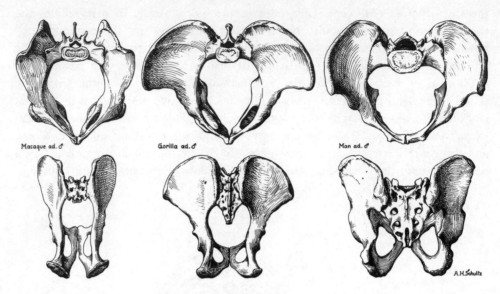

FIGURE 5

Cephalic and dorsal views of pelves of macaque, gorilla, and man.

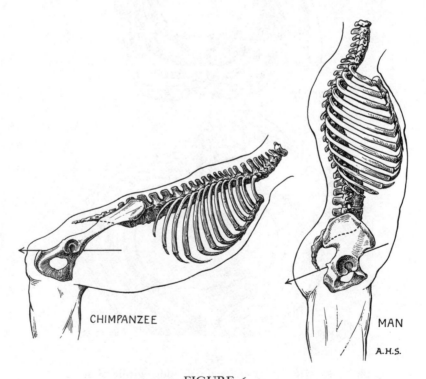

FIGURE 6

The position and size of the pelvis and the curvature of the vertebral column
in an ape and in man (*after Schultz, 1957*).

ture and the difference in the proportionate lengths of the opposing digits (Fig. 7). There can be no doubt that anatomically our hand itself has undergone no significant change since the days of early man. After our typically catarrhine hand had been freed from any routine function of locomotion, it could perform more varied and finally more skilful manipulations exclusively by means of a greatly improved nervous control.

The grasping hands of simian primates, together with their great range in arm movements, can readily be used also for *throwing* objects. In hunting howler and spider monkeys, I frequently had to dodge dead branches and bunches of foliage that, if not thrown, were then certainly dropped deliberately by these monkeys

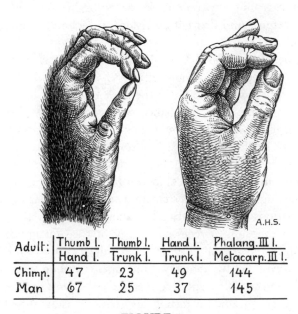

Adult:	Thumb l. / Hand l.	Thumb l. / Trunk l.	Hand l. / Trunk l.	Phalang. III l. / Metacarp. III l.
Chimp.	47	23	49	144
Man	67	25	37	145

FIGURE 7

The opposability of the thumb in a chimpanzee and in man and averages of some proportions of the hand. The total thumb length is much shorter in relation to the total hand length in the ape than in man, but in relation to the trunk length the thumb has practically the same length in both, while the total hand length has greatly increased in the ape, and this in its phalangeal and metacarpal parts.

whenever they had been driven into the crown of some high tree from which they could not escape except by coming down toward the hunter. Carpenter (1935) has recorded very similar experiences with platyrrhines, and Hornaday (1922) has given a vivid account of baboons throwing stones. Once I had stalked an orang mother and her half-grown offspring, and, though well hidden, my presence became suspected by the youngster, which had approached very closely. The old ape stood upright on a limb and with both hands broke thick branches and threw them deliberately and with good aim at my hiding place, quite evidently to provoke a movement and exposure of whatever danger she suspected. An old male chimpanzee that had lived in the Washington zoo for twenty-five years was famous for regularly throwing most effectively and accurately potatoes, apples, his drinking cup, and even his feces at any member of the audience who dared to laugh in front of his cage. The psychologist Klüver (1937) experimented with a capuchin monkey that intentionally picked up and threw a mouse, attached to a string, beyond some fruit outside its cage, just to rake in this fruit by means of pulling mouse and fruit within reach. I have seen several other captive apes and one old mandrill throw objects at the public with great force and good aim. I mention these experiences merely in support of my conviction that the earliest men, capable of carrying any odd rocks or clubs in their hands, would have thrown them as defense and fled before risking an enemy's coming close enough to be hit by rock or club.

If early man, before he had fire, really did retire to caves at night, he could drive off a prowling leopard far more effectively by a shower of thrown stones than by waiting until it *might* be hit in the dark by a rock in the hand. Furthermore, the earliest hunters had few chances of overtaking swift prey to hit it to death with a rock in the hand but could stalk unsuspecting, stationary game until it was within reach of thrown stones. It seems most likely that *throwing* objects came sooner and more easily than pounding with objects or using them as "lengthened arms" in the form of clubs or lances. This can hardly be proved directly by archeologists[2] but must remain a matter of relative probability supported by observations on comparative behavior. Soon after these statements had been read at the symposium, I received a copy of the "inaugural lecture" of the animal psychologist Kortlandt (1959) containing many varied and detailed descriptions of *throwing* by monkeys and apes. Among the most significant accounts of this remarkable report are those of a young chimpanzee at the Amsterdam zoo that "attained a hitting accuracy considerably better than that of average children of comparable physical development," of the chimpanzees of the Chester zoo that "often aim in front of a moving target . . . even smashing two windows of the Director's car as he drove past," and of the experiments at the San Diego and Rotterdam zoos, in which captive-born chimpanzees "were suddenly confronted with an aggressively behaving leopard or tiger and in both cases anything at hand was thrown at the large cat . . . as an instinctive reaction resulting from a conflict between fleeing and fighting impulses."

In contrast to most mammals, including the majority of prosimians, there is no real *breeding season* in tarsiers, Cebid monkeys, and all catarrhines, a fact of profound influence for social life, as has already been discussed fully in many recent publications. Some seasonal fluctuations in the relative number of births have

2. The discovery of the throwing of clay pellets at zoömorphic targets by Neanderthal man, reported by Professor A. C. Blanc in this symposium, is of special interest in this connection.

been reported for various monkeys and even for man, but generally the two sexes live together all year round, and pregnancies can result at any season. Among the Simiae only the marmosets are exceptional in this, as in many other respects (multiple young and paternal care of infants). According to recent reports, the Japanese macaque also seems to have a quite restricted breeding season, but most likely on account of the pronounced climatic seasons in the home of this most northern of all macaques. Among apes copulation has been observed as occurring with great regularity not only throughout the oestrous cycle but even well after pregnancy had commenced (Miller, 1931; Schultz and Snyder, 1935). The continual presence of sexually receptive females, together with the helplessness of infants for a relatively long period, necessitated coherence in families and clans with a division of duties. For a relatively very long time the mother will give continual devoted care to her young. This proverbial "monkey-love" is manifested most extremely by the common tendency of females to kidnap infants not their own. In moments of danger it is the mother who flees with her young, while the father covers the retreat with bluff or attack, and this in species with great sex differences in size (baboons, gorillas, etc.) as well as in those in which the males differ comparatively little from the females in strength (many monkeys, gibbons, chimpanzees, and men). Again we find that even in modern man this basic rule is still valid, and in view of the lack of any contrary evidence we are justified in assuming that early man, too, was governed by these same general factors, determining the social life of all simian primates.

Aside from those few mammals that have become specialized for huge bulk, primates are clearly distinguished by their pronounced trend toward *prolonging all periods* of their individual lives (Fig. 8). Prenatal life lasts only about six weeks in *Tupaia*, which still can produce two or more offspring three times a year. Among the highest primates the period of gestation for the normally single young has increased to roughly nine months, and this in the great apes as well as in man. The state of maturity at birth is much more advanced in the lemurs and monkeys than in apes and man (Fig. 9). Measured by the conditions in the former, the average differences in the great immaturity of the newborn of apes and men are insignificant,[3] in spite of what has been claimed in the literature. There can be no reasonable doubt that early man had just as helpless newborns as we produce today and that therefore parental care and group protection was fully as necessary then as now. The clear and general trend toward prolongation of all main periods of *post*natal life has reached its outstanding extreme in modern man, who has to get along with merely his milk teeth for at least his first six years, apes for three years, and most monkeys for only about one year. The diet of apes and primitive man is strictly limited while the food can be bitten off

---

3. This has been demonstrated by the writer in a series of reports, referred to in his review of ontogenetic changes in primates (1956*a*), and is supported by recent, new findings.

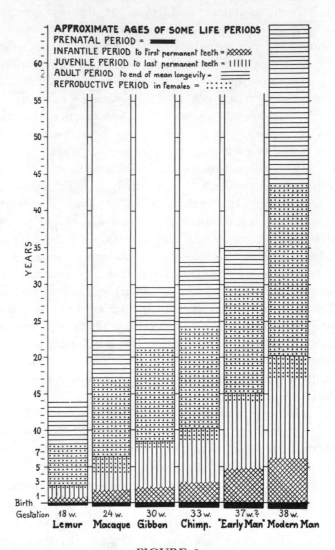

FIGURE 8

Diagrammatic representation of the approximate average durations of some periods of life among recent primates, based upon data assembled by Schultz (1956a), and the most likely corresponding duration in early man.

and masticated with only the small and fragile deciduous teeth, hence they rely for much longer periods than do other mammals on the addition of mothers' milk—for over two years in chimpanzees and for three and more years in orangs and in some races of man (Fig. 10). Among Alaskan Eskimos, children formerly often nursed until they were four or even five years old (Spencer, 1959). This is consequential not only for long and close contact between mother and young but also because it greatly prolongs the interval between pregnancies, inasmuch as lactation generally prevents conception.

The onset of sexual maturity also tends to occur steadily later in life among primates (Fig. 8), thereby increasing the minimum interval between generations, which naturally is one of the primary factors determining population growth and evolutionary change within a given unit of time. As far as known, most primates become sexually mature well before they are fully grown and even before their dentition has been completed, though there seem to be some minor specific differences in this respect. In view of the prevailing sexual dominance of the strongest males in most simian groups, the potential male breeders, not yet fully grown and still without fully erupted canines, have little chance for reproduction but are provident, immediate substitutes in case the leading protector is incapacitated through one cause or another. If the gestation period is added to the average age of full sexual maturity, we obtain the shortest possible interval between generations, which equals about five years in Old World monkeys, at least ten years in apes, and eighteen years or more in civilized man. This last extreme has most likely been reached quite recently and had not yet been fully developed in early man. The average duration of life has also become greatly increased in the higher, as compared with the lower, primates and has reached an extreme quite recently in the civilized races of modern man, without,

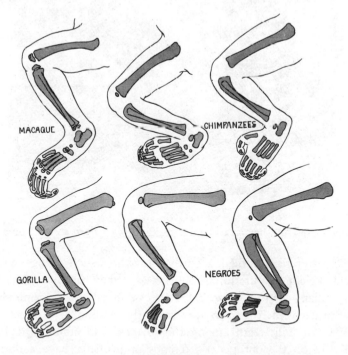

FIGURE 9

Tracings of X-ray photographs of the lower extremities of some newborn primates. For chimpanzee and man the least and the most ossification in full-term fetuses is shown (after Schultz, 1957).

however, having in any way improved the durability of tissues and organs. Among wild monkeys and apes and even in uncivilized man, really senile individuals are comparatively scarce, though occasional specimens are found with clear symptoms of senile degenerations. To insert in Figure 8 approximately comparable data for "early man" is not as arbitrary as it may seem in view of the regular, gradual shifting of these data in only one direction, from the lowest to the highest primates. It is justified, furthermore, by some observations regarding

FIGURE 10
Papua mother nursing her infant and a suckling pig (*after A. A. Vogel, 1954*).

relevant racial differences in man, according to which such ontogenetic processes as dental and skeletal maturation still proceed somewhat more rapidly in, for instance, Australians than in whites. It is also permissible to assume that infancy lasted longer in early men than in apes from the finding of a larger percentage of markedly worn milk teeth among the former than among the latter. Such comparative data on the ontogenetic tempos of primates have a direct bearing on social life. The extremely slow maturation of all higher primates, culminating in man, demands unusually prolonged parental care and protection. Even the period of nursing has increased in apes and natural man to a degree unique among all mammals, so that the young are bound to their mothers for years and thereby gain a long period of imitative learning from adults. Any species with such slow rates of reproduction as have apes and men, with their single offspring, would soon become extinct if the young were not protected throughout the long period preceding the age of reproduction. This protection is most effectively provided by the combined alertness and keen vision of an organized social group, especially since primates are not equipped with great weapons,[4] such as horns or claws, or with the outstanding speed of many other mammals.

On my five collecting trips to jungles of America and Asia, I have always found monkeys much more in evidence and apparently more numerous than any other mammals. This impression is due to the fact that monkeys are merely the noisiest and many the gaudiest of all mammals and do not promptly hide quietly or flee upon the approach of man, except when they have been persistently hunted. From my field experience I have become convinced that at least tropical rain forests could easily support far greater monkey populations than actually exist. It is only in areas with marked seasonal changes and possible forest fires at the end of long droughts that the modest density of primate populations seems to be influenced by the fluctuating food supply available throughout the year. The total of all present non-human primate populations probably does not surpass the more than two and a half billion human beings of today, though the former are represented by nearly six hundred different species, as against the single species of the latter. The causes of this stationary or possibly even diminishing *population* of nonhuman primates consist of geographical factors—such as climate, areas with suitable conditions for mode of locomotion, food, etc.—and, at least as important, of the basic factors of fertility, or rate of reproduction, in relation to mortality.

In regard to the first factors mentioned I have little to contribute except my conviction that many catarrhines are hardy creatures, not closely restricted to tropical or even to temperate zones, but able to survive, if necessary, in seasonally cold climates, as, for example, *Rhinopithecus* in Northern China or *Macaca mulatta* in the thriving outdoor colony of Baltimore, maintained for many years by Dr. C. Hartman. Mountain gorillas, some gibbons, and some *Colobus* monkeys live at altitudes where *Homo sapiens* requires at night the protection of blankets and fires. It is particularly in the peripheral, cooler regions of catarrhine distribution that monkeys invariably spend their chilly nights sitting in mutual close embrace to prevent waste of bodily heat. Whenever the temperature remains at night near that of the body, monkeys and apes prefer to sleep separately and lying down on their sides or prone, that is, in a horizontal position for what amounts to nearly half their lives!

The possible expansion of the home territories of primate species is certainly

4. The long canines of adult male monkeys and apes are not very dependable weapons, since they become broken, abscessed, or even lost, especially after the enamel has partly worn off, far more frequently than they do in carnivores.

not limited by water of moderate width or current, since many monkeys are good swimmers (as I have witnessed repeatedly in Central America), as has been reported in the literature (e.g., by Krieg, 1948) and as can be observed in many zoos. Anthropoids, though not in the least afraid of water, usually do not seem to be able to swim without having been trained. Natural barriers to the migration of monkeys and apes are lack of fairly continuous forest and drinking water and lack of shade. As every successful animal dealer has had to learn, most monkeys and apes will not stand exposure to tropical midday sunlight for any length of time but have to find shade after a while. Suitable conditions for the night are equally essential. Typical diurnal, arboreal monkeys retire for the night to the comparative safety of carefully selected trees. Once I surprised a group of Panamanian capuchin monkeys at dusk dropping one by one from the lowest branch of a tall tree into the dense crown of a palm with a very thorny stem, which could never have been ascended by a predator and which the monkeys could leave in the morning only by jumping down into lower bushes. Nests of a crude sort are constructed by only a few prosimians and by the three great apes. Rocky clefts and niches with limited and hence readily guarded accessibility are used as refuges for the night by only some species of baboons and macaques, and even these few kinds will never go deep into dark caves under normal conditions. No chimpanzees ever deserved the name "troglodytes," which has been given to them, and none would survive many nights in caves, in which they would be easy prey for leopards and hyenas, especially since many apes snore resoundingly. Incidentally, in many regions of the total range of early man caves were not sufficiently numerous to shelter enough "cavemen" to maintain a viable population. For routine usage and before the added protection of fire, early hominids found greater safety during the night in trees than in caves and, even as bipeds, could climb trees as easily as natural man still can today (Fig. 11).

Population growth depends primarily upon *fertility*. The latter seems to vary extensively among primates according to our few available data. In some monkeys and in gibbons, I found only about 12 per cent of all adult females pregnant, among howler monkeys 20 per cent, in langurs 30 per cent, and in macaques 50 per cent (Schultz, 1944) or even more by other reports. Most nonpregnant females of the same local groups were accompanied by young of widely varying ages, proving the lack of definite breeding seasons and supporting the conclusion that new conceptions do not follow soon upon the termination of pregnancy, provided the offspring lives and is being nursed. Under the most favorable conditions of captivity, macaques can produce during their period of fertility no more than 7 or possibly 8 descendants, if the early loss of some has not shortened a period of sterility due to lactation. We know that in modern mankind a woman *can* have twice as many pregnancies during her greater number of fertile years, but it is exceedingly rare that all her children will survive to puberty. The number of prior pregnancies varies in Pueblo Indian women, over forty years old, between 0 and 14 and averages 9.4, but infant mortality is very high (Aberle, 1931). Rasmussen (1927) encountered an old Eskimo woman who had had 20 children, of whom 5 grew up, the others having died early. Gusinde (1948) mentions on old Congo pygmy who had lost all her 11 children. Among Melanesians, Powdermaker (1931) reported an average number of children per

FIGURE 11
Australian boy climbing a tree (*after C. P. Mountford, 1951*).

woman of only 2.9 and found that 12 per cent of all women were sterile and 20 per cent of all children died before marriage. In the Bushmanlike East-African Tindiga, Kohl-Larsen (1958) found 1—10 children per woman, but evidently very few attained their reproductive age, since this hunting tribe is rapidly decreasing in total number. From these and many other relevant reports on "natural man," it appears that fertility in man as well as in monkey always was at least adequate for possible population growth, which, if lacking, must have been prevented by a death rate equal to or surpassing the birth rate. In an excellent book on *Population Problems*, Thompson (1953) has reached practically the same conclusion, stating that "from time immemorial the number of people living in any given area has been determined not so much by the level of the birth rate as by the level of the death rate."

Mortality can be highly selective as to age and sex, and, since the conditions of social life are directly influenced by any changes in the composition of a population according to age and sex, some remarks are inserted here about the all-too-few data which have become available in regard to the age- and sex-ratios among primates in their natural habitat. Most of the voluminous records on primate material in my files are based upon specimens collected in the jungle without any conscious preference for age or sex in order to represent true population samples. Sex, even of the youngest specimens, could always be determined from the corpse, and age from the skeleton. With all my admiration for my old friend Carpenter, with whom I shared many of my field experiences, I doubt that even the most powerful binoculars can determine age and sex of monkeys moving in changing light high in dense forest anywhere nearly as reliably as can direct observations on dead specimens. In attempts to estimate the age or sex of living individuals, the observer is bound to be influenced by behavior and size, though both these factors are variable and that of size is occasionally very misleading. My data on collected population samples are also far from ideal, since differences in behavior might have resulted in unnatural representations of sexes or ages in spite of the best intentions of the collectors. When hunted, adult males do not flee as promptly as do females, but in their escape they are not burdened by infants, since the latter are never hidden and abandoned by their mothers, as in so many other mammals. These facts are mentioned merely as possible explanations for the, at times, considerable discrepancies between the well-known data of Carpenter, Nissen, and other field observers and those based upon my records on dead specimens. According to the latter, immature individuals (= infants + juveniles) constitute from about 20 per cent to a maximum of 40 per cent of the populations of various wild monkeys and apes, percentages that correspond roughly to those in most populations of recent men but do not reach such extremes as the 52 per cent of human beings below twenty years in the population of the United States in 1850 or the percentage nearly as high reported for Greenland Eskimos (Pearl, 1930), or the even 57 per cent of children among North-Canadian Indians, living chiefly by hunting (Wissler, 1942). It is significant also that among the macaques of Santiago Island (Puerto Rico), which were practically free of parasitic and infectious diseases and knew no large predators, Carpenter (1942) found the immature to form about 50 per cent of the population. These data on the surprisingly modest proportionate number of young among many monkeys and apes again support the conclusion that infantile and juvenile mortality must be at least as high in the latter as it is known to be in recent primitive man, who also has mostly stationary or decreasing populations.

The composition of the population by *sex* according to all available data changes with age not only in man but also in apes and monkeys. Among the latter this sex ratio, or the number of males per 100 females, is not culturally altered as it is in some human societies. It is all the more significant, therefore, that the sex ratio decreases with age in nonhuman primates, just as it does in man without artificial interference, such as the custom of killing or exposing unwanted girl babies.[5] Evidently it is a generally valid rule that males have a higher mortality rate than do females, and in some species this sex difference must be very pronounced, indeed, to produce the great preponderance of adult females. For instance, in series of Central American monkeys, totaling nearly a thousand, the sex ratio equals in howler monkeys 67 for the immature, whereas it is only 57 for adults, and in spider monkeys these figures even drop from 118 for the immature to 61 for adults (Schultz, 1959). Among 224 chimpanzees, for which I have exact records, the sex ratio of the young is 91 and that of the adults 75. Even among gibbons, which are distinguished by having practically no morphological secondary sex differences, this ratio decreases with age from 115 to 108 (Schultz, 1944). In South African Negroes the sex ratio of all children under fifteen years is 101, whereas that of adults over fifty years is only 66, and for Switzerland the corresponding figures are 101 and 83. These few examples suffice to show that the stronger sex proves to be universally the weaker one in the course of years or else meets with more accidents while still young.

Even under the best of laboratory conditions many pregnancies of captive primates fail to reach full term, and thereby a considerable part of the reproductive period becomes wasted and the maximum possible number of offspring is reduced. According to Yerkes' (1943) extensive experience with chimpanzees, about one out of every three conceptions ends in death before or at birth, and Hartman (1932) found practically the same proportion in his large colony of macaques in Baltimore, which had been maintained under nearly ideal conditions for many years for the purpose of studying reproduction. This high prenatal death rate in nonhuman primates equals that prevailing in civilized man, according to our best clinical authorities, and there is no justification for doubting that natural man forms no exception in this respect. Though we cannot expect any reliable statistics for the latter, we do have many relevant claims, such as that by Gusinde (1948), who states that among Congo pygmies miscarriages and stillbirths are very common. Since most dead embryos and fetuses are promptly expelled, there seems to be little chance to encounter such cases among wild primates. It is all the more significant, therefore, that we have already found several instances of intra-uterine deaths among wild-shot monkeys of quite a variety of species.

Irregularities in early development, producing congenital malformations of one kind or another, are far from limited to civilized man, as is commonly assumed.

5. Among Eskimos, Chinese, and ancient Romans (Russell, 1958), girls have sometimes been permitted to die at birth, causing unnaturally high postnatal sex ratios.

I have found such cases, with frequencies unheard of in man, among some populations of wild monkeys and apes. Here I can merely refer to the published instances of polydactyly, syndactyly, and oligodactyly in baboons, gibbons, and chimpanzees (Schultz, 1956b). I might also recall the interesting occurrence of an extremely pronounced oxycephaly combined with the lack of both thumbs and both great toes in a young chimpanzee from Cameroon. This syndrome, well known in man, had so handicapped this ape that he fell out of a tree during the pursuit of his group (Schultz, 1958). Of special interest also is an adult wild gibbon we had shot in Siam that had one arm very incompletely formed, containing only a slender proximal part of the humerus (Schultz, 1944). A practically identical profound malformation has just been found in one of the adult Neanderthal skeletons of Shanidar in Iraq, according to my interpretation of the preliminary description of this important find given by Stewart (1959). I am convinced that this case, too, is an incidence of *unilateral peromelia*, well known in recent man and reported for at least three other primates.

The already mentioned modest proportion of young in many primate populations may be partly accounted for by the fact that certain birds of prey, snakes, and the smaller cats will snatch, preferably, such young monkeys as are bound to stray from the protection of the group whenever the notorious curiosity of the young has become stronger than their primary timidity. Such accidents, however, can hardly occur with a frequency sufficient to produce an infant mortality resulting in a more or less stationary population. Far more effective are the minute enemies in the form of the great variety of parasites that have been found in primates (Stiles, Hassall, and Nolan, 1929), of which many are very pathogenic, particularly in the young. Malaria, filariasis, and a great many other parasitic diseases have been reported for monkeys of the Old and the New World, and this often with very high frequencies. In all probability yaws is widespread among African apes and, like malaria, will at least temporarily incapacitate infected individuals so that they cannot keep up with their group and, as single animals, become more exposed to predators. From extensive surveys and tests, the epidemiologist Clark (1952) reached the conclusion that many wild monkeys must have had yellow fever at one time in their lives and had recovered, while others undoubtedly had succumbed to it. It has also become known that an epidemic of yellow fever wiped out entire populations of howling monkeys in parts of Brazil in 1947 and that in all probability the same disease was responsible for the marked decrease in the number of monkeys on Barro Colorado Island between the census taken by Carpenter (1934) and that taken later by Collias and Southwick (1952). The parasitologist Cameron (1958) has recently stated that man certainly had acquired from his prehuman ancestors his malarial parasites, pinworms, and lice and, most likely, also his taenias, hookworms, ascarids, and filariae.

That arthritis, osteitis deformans, sinus infections, dental diseases, and even arterial lesions have not developed with civilization in recent man, but are at least as prevalent in many kinds of wild monkeys and apes, has already been proved

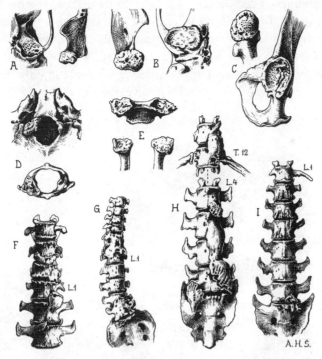

FIGURE 12

Examples of arithritic changes in skeletal parts of adult wild catarrhine monkeys and apes: A = gibbon; B = orangutan; C = gibbon; D = gibbon; E = same gibbon as A; F = baboon; G = gibbon; H = proboscis monkey; I = macaque (*after Schultz, 1956*b).

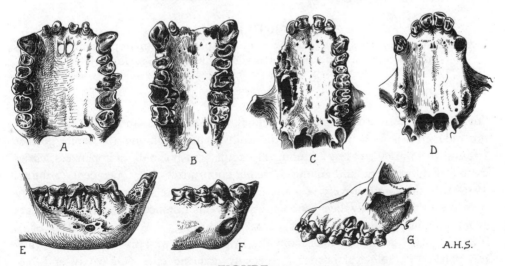

FIGURE 13

Examples of pathological conditions in the dental apparatus of adult wild apes: A = old gibbon; B = old gorilla; C = chimpanzee (caries on incisors); D = chimpanzee; E = old orangutan; F = same gorilla as B; G = orangutan (*after Schultz, 1956*b).

by abundant findings (Figs. 12, 13, and 14).[6] For instance, among 233 wild gibbons, I found marked chronic arthritis in 17 per cent of all skeletons, but this
percentage changes markedly with age, being only 2 in juveniles but 55 in the
series of the oldest specimens with very worn teeth and closed sutures (Schultz,
1944). Destruction of the dental apparatus also advances rapidly with age in all
primates, and apes, at least, frequently outlive the durability of their misnamed

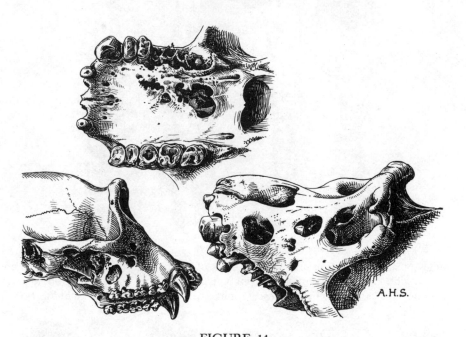

FIGURE 14

Extensive maxillary sinus infection in a wild chimpanzee and multiple sinus infections
and destruction of dentition in a wild gorilla (*after Schultz, 1956*b).

"permanent" teeth. For instance, I found alveolar abscesses among 186 adult (but
not old) gorillas in 16 per cent of the skulls, whereas among 107 senile gorillas
I found them in 60 per cent. Among 110 adult (but not old) chimpanzees, caries
existed in 13 per cent, and among 62 senile chimpanzees in 31 per cent (Schultz,
1956b). In the comparatively few and mostly incomplete skeletal remains of early
man there have already been encountered several instances of arthritic changes
(e.g., Krapina, Shanidar) and of dental decay (e.g., La Chapelle, Rhodesia).
Ten out of 28 adult skeletons from the Copper Age of Hungary showed various marked pathological changes, especially arthritic ones (Gáspárdy and Ne-

6. The enormous number and variety of diseases that can occur in nonhuman primates and
that are, of course, best known from their occurrence in captive ones have recently
been described systematically by Ruch (1959).

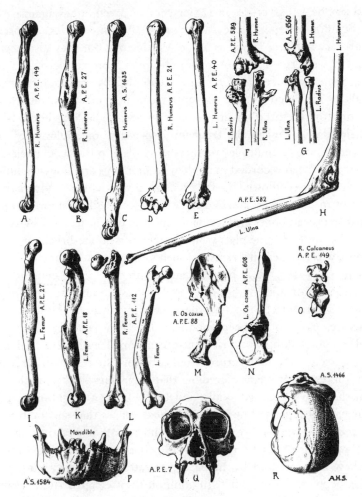

FIGURE 15

Examples of more-or-less well-repaired fractures in adult wild gibbons
(*after Schultz, 1944*).

meskéri, 1960). It seems certain, therefore, that pain and suffering has existed throughout human evolution, merely varying in prevalence now and then according to racial immunity, environmental conditions, or dietary habits.

That crippling accidents are not at all rare in the life of wild monkeys and apes is proved by the many more or less well-repaired fractures one finds in every large series of skeletons (Fig. 15). The frequency of fractures, as of diseases of bones and teeth, increases markedly with age. Among 233 wild gibbons, I encountered healed fractures in only some older juveniles, but in 28 per cent of fully grown (but not old) adults and in 50 per cent of the oldest adults, some of which had as many as seven repaired fractures. My survey of 100 skeletons of orangutans shot in the wild lists healed fractures in 12 per cent of juveniles, as against 34 per cent of adults (Schultz, 1941; and a few later cases). Among the less arboreal African apes fractures are not as common as in the Asiatic apes, but they also become much more frequent with age and also are significantly more numerous in males than in females. Some of these fractures have undoubtedly resulted from fights between rivals, as indicated by their greater frequency in males, but this accounts probably only for fractured fingers, toes, or an occasional long bone. Incidentally, intratribal fights also explain the frequently torn ears of adult males. The many cases of severe and even multiple fractures in skulls, hip bones, clavicles, sternums, and ribs that have been recorded in adult wild monkeys and apes (Schultz, 1956*b*) must have been caused mostly by falls when animals had misjudged the strength of a branch or mismanaged a hurried leap. This seems all the more probable from the fact that fractured bones are decidedly most common in such swift and daring acrobats as gibbons and some platyrrhine brachiators. Bone-breaking accidents are nowhere nearly as frequent in terrestrial man as in arboreal primates. For instance, Smith and Jones (1910) found healed fractures in only 1 per cent of about three thousand skeletons of ancient Nubians, and corresponding figures for other human populations are rarely much higher. Among the fossil remains of man, repaired fractures have so far been found in only few instances (e.g., ulna from Oberkassel). The striking contrast between arboreal and terrestrial primates in regard to the frequency of fractures implies a corresponding difference in mortality from this cause. It seems incredible that some apes in the jungle can and do survive smashed jaws, cracked skulls, and badly broken thighbones at least long enough for natural repairs. The bodies of those others that succumb to accidents are rarely found on the wet ground of the rain forest, where they disappear in a few days. As soon as the early hominids had become bipeds and had invaded open country, they were favored by much lower rates of incapacitating or fatal accidents than occur in arboreal life. In addition they escaped the prevalent jungle diseases of malaria, yellow fever, etc., which counteract population growth in forest-dwelling primates.

Because early man's attitude toward death represents a prominent "paleopsychological" problem in our symposium, a few remarks may here be inserted concerning the fate of injured, sick, and dying nonhuman primates, especially also since the latter are more frequent than is commonly assumed. Every zoo and primate laboratory has witnessed instances of the pitiful devotion of simian mothers to their sick infants and knows the long struggle needed to take a dead or even decomposed baby away from the mother, who will clutch the corpse to her breast day after day. Sick or wounded juvenile and adult monkeys, incapable of keeping up with the group, search instinctively for a hiding place anywhere in a cluster of dense foliage, or, if they have fallen to the ground, in the deepest niche among roots or rocks. If any cleft or cave is within reach of their strength, they may soon be found in the remotest and darkest corner thereof; here they quietly remain until recovered or dead, safe from molestation by companions of their own kind and by flies, attracted to their wounds, and hidden from predators stalking by sight or ear. The deeper the cleft in the hillside, the more cooling to fever and the more likely to supply water, the only nourishment they crave while infected teeth or sinuses or broken jaws and limbs preclude any solid food. Zapfe (1954) has recently collected some remarkable evidence showing that many different mammals that do not ordinarily enter dark caves will, under stress, venture far into long cavernous passages, frequently to perish and thus gradually to contribute to the accumulation of the dense masses of bones that have been recovered from many caves and clefts in all parts of the world. Professor von Koenigswald has recently told me of the huge numbers of teeth of pleistocene orangs found in Chinese rock clefts unsuitable for routine occupancy by man or ape. These fossilized teeth of orangs are nearly all from adults. The best explanation for this seemingly quite unnatural occurrence is von Koenigswald's hypothesis that the big pleistocene orangs, when sick or dying of old age, had entered those narrow, dark, and moist fissures, never approached by any healthy orang. Most of our rich Pliopithecus material comes from "Spaltenfüllungen," and the remains of many other fossil primates have been recovered from former rock clefts that would never have been chosen as sleeping quarters by healthy individuals, and into which they had not been dragged by hyenas or washed by floods but had dragged themselves in desperation when death was approaching. There is much in favor of this hypothesis that caves and clefts, wherever they exist in primate territories, have served as last retreats for even monkeys and apes. The early hominids were no exceptions but also withdrew to the best available hiding places as soon as they became too weak from one cause or another to live with their group. It was not until the later hominids became encouraged by the light and protection of fire that they began to use caves, instead of trees, for the nocturnal retreat of those healthy individuals who could be sheltered therein. The primary role of caves, for primates connected only with illness and death, may very well have influenced the later behavior of "cave men," especially their attitude toward the skeletons found in the innermost darkness.

The *diet* of nonhuman primates does not differ as radically from that of natural man as has been claimed. Most prosimians and some New World monkeys eat more worms, insects, frogs, lizards, and birds' eggs than plant food, and at least some animal food is consumed occasionally by all primates, with the possible exception of the specialized Colobinae. Some marmosets and macaques stalk and consume small fish and other aquatic animals in shallow water; gibbons have been reported to catch birds even in flight; and I have repeatedly seen the chimpanzees I formerly kept kill and eat mice. Stevenson-Hamilton (1912) mentions baboons' having killed a small antelope and, with apparently increasing frequency, lambs and ewes. Krumbiegel (1955) reports a remarkable case of two chimpanzees' tearing down a large nest of wild bees and quickly jumping down to escape getting stung while a third chimpanzee was rolling the nest along the ground away from the bees. This, incidentally, is only one of an abundance of examples of co-operation among apes, which is curiously still doubted by some inexperienced authors. The tapeworm *Anoplocephala gorillae* has been found in the intestines of mountain gorillas. It has been found, otherwise, only in small rodents and ungulates of the same region, so it seems highly probable that some of these small animals are occasionally eaten by gorillas (Stiles, Hassall, and Nolan, 1929). A change to a fish or meat diet is frequently followed by new parasites, which may, at least at first, be very pathogenic for their new hosts. For instance, some trematodes occur in human beings only after fishes have been eaten raw or undercooked, and certain nematodes are very commonly acquired by Eskimos from eating walrus and bears (Cameron, 1958). Many more such examples have become known and demonstrate that changes in diet, like changes in environment, can have disadvantageous as well as beneficial consequences that may hinder rather than favor population growth.

It is generally true that the quicker and more radical a change, the greater becomes the potential danger to the health of a population not yet selected for and adapted to the new conditions. It seems very doubtful to me that early hominids had at any time or place changed abruptly from a nearly all-vegetable diet to a mostly meat diet. Like all other primates, early man lived on whatever food nature provided, and, after having left the dense forests and ventured into open country, he found fewer edible plants but more small animals with which to supplement his original menus. The first bipeds in their probably winterless and droughtless homeland were as yet indiscriminate gatherers of food of all kinds, from berries, roots, and insects to small vertebrates. Only after having learned to throw stones and use clubs and spears could they add occasional larger animals whenever their gradually overpopulated and exhausted territory necessitated such effort and risk. This stage of man's dietary evolution has persisted with but little improvement to this day in some remnants of primitive food-gatherers of tropical countries. Only such hardy early men as survived their invasion of subarctic regions had by necessity to rely chiefly on meat for winter food supply and, in addition, on the skins of larger mammals for warmth and thus had acquired an exceptionally one-sided diet. No matter how quickly and radically the dietary conditions may have become altered, they were certainly not accompanied by corresponding changes in man's masticatory apparatus. Even though many minute distinctions between the dentitions and jaws of early and recent men have been described, there is not one detail which can be proved to be connected with a change in diet. The same human dentition is just as useful for the rice diet of a Malay as for the meat diet of an Eskimo and did not change essentially between whatever raw diet australopithecines had and the cooked diet of modern Europeans. While the diverse preference for and quest of food can influence social life extensively, it seems to have had remarkably little effect on our dental and digestive apparatus.

The *variability* of a species can influence its social behavior to a significant extent. All anthropoid apes and many species of lower primates are surprisingly variable, indeed in many respects more variable than recent man. In general body size, cranial capacity, body proportions, and coloration of skin and hair all apes possess enormous ranges of variations even among individuals from very limited regions (Schultz, 1947). In a large series of spider-monkey skulls from one region, which will soon be published (Schultz, 1959), I found many with remarkably high and bulging foreheads and others, collected from the same camp, with frontal profiles running straight back from the supraorbital ridge. If some of these striking variations had come from widely separated localities, one would have been tempted to regard them as different species. A few decades ago some taxonomists described incredible numbers of subspecies, species, and even genera of orangutans, chimpanzees, and gorillas whenever they had obtained a few skulls from new localities. After having seen a great many large local series of ape skulls, I have become fully convinced that extremely few of all these names for races or species have any justification, and, fortunately, most of them are no longer in use (Figs. 16 and 17).

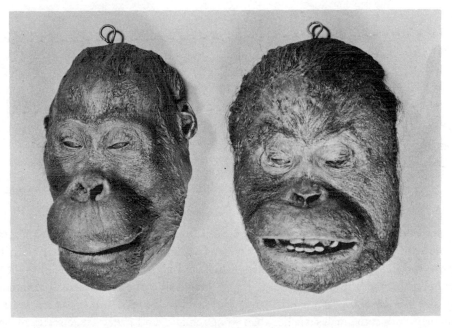

FIGURE 16
Death masks of two adult female Bornean orangutans showing variations
in head formation (*after Schultz, 1950*b).

The classification of fossil men has been even worse than that of the recent apes, but we have come to realize that much of the old nomenclature was not only quite unnecessary but was actually misleading in that it elevated mere individual variations to the rank of racial if not specific characters (Howell, 1957). It seems most likely that hominids were just as variable as are all pongids. There is no need for theories of race mixture or of waves of new immigrants whenever we find an

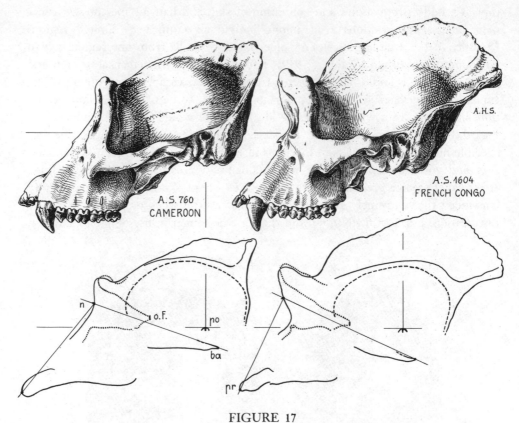

FIGURE 17

Side views of two adult male lowland gorillas and sections of the same showing frequent variations (*after Schultz, 1950a*).

extremely modest random sample of a local population of early man to contain some variations more marked than expected by investigators unfamiliar with the great variability in many nonhuman primates. In view of this variability of all higher primates, the common practice of diagnosing the sex of fossil fragments by size can be quite erroneous. Among adult chimpanzees, for example, one frequently finds some males smaller than some females, and every large series of wild pongids contains in either sex some evident runts as well as exceptional giants. The *average* sex difference in size can be extremely different among primates, and in some species females surpass males even in average body weight, a fact that may quite likely influence their sexual behavior.

As everybody who has worked with living monkeys and apes readily admits, these animals vary in temperament and intellect as widely as they do in size and form. There is no reason, of course, for assuming that early man was exceptional in this respect. Among the five chimpanzees I had kept for many years there was one small female who was far superior to the others in mental alertness, enterprise, and inventiveness, even during her advanced years. In the same way, we can be certain, every group of early man contained occasional individuals surpassing the others in mental faculties and able to create some cultural progress. The latter was desperately needed at the critical time when the first true hominids had for one reason or another abandoned the accustomed protection of the dense forest with but modest size, strength, and speed and without even the large canines of other catarrhines. All they could rely upon at first was the emancipation of their hands, freed for the use of tools, and the old simian endowment of timely discovery of danger by the many quick eyes of closely co-operating social groups, as well as the intensifying trend to prolong the years of dependency of the young on the old, with its corresponding gains from long-continued guidance and imitative learning.

BIBLIOGRAPHY

ABERLE, S. B. D.
1931. "Frequency of Pregnancies and Birth Interval among Pueblo Indians," *Amer. J. Phys. Anthrop.*, 16:63–80.

CAMERON, T. W. M.
1958. "Parasites of Animals and Human Disease," *Ann. New York Acad. Sci.*, 70: 564–73.

CARPENTER. C. R.
1934. *A Field Study of the Behavior and Social Relations of Howling Monkeys.* ("Comp. Psychol. Monogr.," Vol. 10, No. 2.)

1935. "Behavior of Red Spider Monkeys in Pamana," *J. Mammal.*, 16: 171–80.

1942. "Societies of Monkeys and Apes," *Biol. Symp.*, 8:177–204.

CLARK, H. C.
1952. "Endemic Yellow Fever in Panama and Neighboring Areas," *Amer. J. Trop. Med. & Hyg.*, 1:78–86.

COLLIAS, N., and C. SOUTHWICK
1952. "A Field Study of Population Density and Social Organization in Howling Monkeys," *Proc. Amer. Phil. Soc.*, 96:143–56.

COUNT, E. W.
1958. "The Biological Basis of Human Sociality," *Amer. Anthrop.*, 60:1049–85.

DORSEY, G. A.
1925. *Why We Behave like Human Beings.* New York: Harper & Bros.

GASPARDY, G., and J. NEMESKÉRI
1960. "Paleopathological Studies on Copper Age Skeletons Found at Alsónémedi," *Acta Morphol. Acad. Sc. Hungaricae*, 9:203–19.

GUSINDE, M.
1948. *Urwaldmenschen am Ituri.* Wien: Springer-Verlag.

HARTMAN, C. G.
1932. *Studies in the Reproduction of the Monkey Macacus (Pithecus) rhesus.* (Carnegie Inst. Wash. Publ. 433, "Contrib. to Embryol.," Vol. 23.)

HEBERER, G.
1958. "Das Tier-Mensch-Uebergangsfeld," *Studium Generale*, 11:341–52.

HORNADAY, W. T.
1922. *The Minds and Manners of Wild Animals*. New York: Scribner's.

HOWELL, F. C.
1957. "II. The Evolutionary Significance of Variation and Varieties of 'Neanderthal' man," *Quart. Rev. Biol.*, 32:330–47.

HUBER, E.
1931. *The Evolution of Facial Musculature and Facial Expression*. Baltimore: Johns Hopkins Press.

KLÜVER, H.
1937. "Re-examination of Implement-using Behavior in a Cebus Monkey after an Interval of Three Years," *Acta Psychol.*, Vol. 2, No. 3.

KOHL-LARSEN, L.
1958. *Wildbeuter in Ostafrika: Die Tindiga, ein Jäger- und Sammlervolk*. Berlin: D. Reimer Verlag.

KORTLANDT, A.
1959. *Tussen mens en dier*. Groningen: Universiteit van Amsterdam.

KRIEG, H.
1948. *Zwischen Anden und Atlantik*. Munich: C. Hauser Verlag.

KRUMBIEGEL, I.
1955. *Biologie der Säugettiere*. 2 Vols. Krefeld: Agis Verlag.

MILLER, G. S., JR.
1931. "The Primate Basis of Human Sexual Behavior," *Quart. Rev. Biol.*, 6:379–410.

MOUNTFORD, C. P.
1951. *Braune Menschen, Roter Sand*. Zurich: Orell Füssli Verlag.

PEARL, R.
1930. "Some Aspects of the Biology of Human Populations." In E. V. COWDRY (ed.), *Human Biology and Racial Welfare*, pp. 515–52. New York: P. Hoeber.

POWDERMAKER, H.
1931. "Vital Statistics of New Ireland as Revealed in Genealogies," *Human Biol.*, 3:351–75.

PROCESSUS DE L'HOMINISATION, LES.
1958. Colloques Internat. Centre National de la Recherche Scientifique, Paris.

RASMUSSEN, K.
1927. *Across Arctic America*. New York: Putnam.

RENSCH, B.
1959. *Homo sapiens: Vom Tier zum Halbgott*. Göttingen: Vandenhoeck & Ruprecht.

ROE, A., and G. G. SIMPSON
1958. *Behavior and Evolution*. New Haven: Yale University Press.

RUCH, T. C.
1959. *Diseases of Laboratory Primates*. Philadelphia: Saunders Co.

RUSSELL, J. C.
1958. "Late Ancient and Medieval Population," *Trans.-Amer. Philos. Soc.*, n.s., Vol. 48, Part 3.

SANDERSON, I. T., and G. STEINBACHER
1957. *Knaurs Affenbuch*. Munich: Droemersche Verlagsanstalt.

SCHULTZ, A. H.

1941. *Growth and Development of the Orang-utan.* (Carnegie Inst. Wash. Publ. 525, "Contrib. to Embryol.," 29:57–110.)

1944. "Age Changes in Variability in Gibbons," *Amer. J. Phys. Anthrop.*, n.s., 2:1–129.

1947. "Variability in Man and Other Primates," *Amer. J. Phys. Anthrop.*, n.s., 5:1–14.

1950a. "Morphological Observations on Gorillas." In *The Anatomy of the Gorilla.* (Henry Cushier Raven Mem.) New York: Columbia University Press, 227–54.

1950b. "The Specializations of Man and His Place among the Catarrhine Primates," *Cold Spring Harbor Symp. Quant. Biol.*, 15:37–53.

1950c. "The Physical Distinctions of Man," *Proc. Amer. Phil. Soc.*, 94:428–49.

1956a. "Postembryonic Age Changes." In H. HOFER, A. H. SCHULTZ, and D. STARCK (eds.), *Primatologia*, 1:887–964. Basel: Verlag Karger.

1956b. "The Occurrence and Frequency of Pathological and Teratological Conditions and of Twinning among Nonhuman Primates." In H. HOFER, A. H. SCHULTZ, and D. STARCK (eds.), *Primatologia*, 1:965–1014. Basel: Verlag Karger.

1957. "Past and Present Views of Man's Specialization," *Irish J. Med. Sci.*, August, 1957, pp. 341–56.

1958. "Acrocephalo-oligodactylism in a Wild Chimpanzee," *J. Anat.*, 92:568–79.

1959. "Age Changes and Variability in the Skulls and Teeth of Central American Alouatta, Cebus and Ateles," *Proc. Zool. Soc. London, 1959* (in press).

1960. "Einige Beobachtungen und Masse am Skelett von Oreopithecus im Vergleich mit anderen catarrhinen Primaten," *Zs. f. Morphol. u. Anthropol.*, Vol. 50 (in press).

SCHULTZ, A. H., and F. F. SNYDER

1935. "Observations on Reproduction in the Chimpanzee," *Bull. Johns Hopkins Hosp.*, 57:193–205.

SMITH, G. E., and F. W. JONES

1910. *Report on the Human Remains.* ("Archaeological Survey of Nubia: Report for 1907–1908," Vol. II.) Cairo.

SPENCER, R. F.

1959. *The North Alaskan Eskimo: A Study in Ecology and Society.* (Bur. Amer. Ethnol. Bull. 171.) Washington.

SPUHLER, J. N.

1959. *The Evolution of Man's Capacity for Culture: Six Essays.* Detroit: Wayne State University Press.

STEVENSON, HAMILTON J.

1912. *Animal Life in Africa.* New York: Dutton.

STEWART, T. D.

1959. "Restoration and Study of the Shanidar I Neanderthal Skeleton in Baghdad, Iraq." In *Yearbook 1958, Amer. Philos. Soc.*, pp. 274–78.

STILES, C. W., A. HASSALL, and M. O. NOLAN

1929. *Key-Catalogue of Parasites Reported for Primates. . . .* (Hygienic Laboratory Bull. 152, U. S. Treas. Dept. Publ. Health Service.) Washington.

THOMPSON, W. S.

1953. *Population Problems.* 4th ed. New York: McGraw-Hill.

Vogel, A. A.
  1954. *Papuas und Pygmäen.* Zurich: Orell Füssli Verlag.
Wendt, H.
  1954. *Ich suchte Adam.* Hamm (Westf.): Grote'sche Verlagsbuchhdl.
Wissler, C.
  1942. "Human Cultural Levels." In E. V. Cowdry (ed.), *Problems of Ageing,* pp. 77–90. Baltimore: Williams & Wilkins.
Yerkes, R. M.
  1943. *Chimpanzees: A Laboratory Colony.* New Haven: Yale University Press.
Zapfe, H.
  1954. "Beiträge zur Erklärung der Entstehung von Knochenlagerstätten in Karstspalten und Höhlen," *Geologie* (Berlin), No. 12, pp. 1–60.

SOCIAL BEHAVIOR OF BABOONS AND EARLY MAN

S. L. WASHBURN AND IRVEN DeVORE

THE PURPOSE of this paper is to present a brief account of the daily life of baboons to serve as a background for the discussion of the social life of early man. The preliminary version of the paper, which was presented at the conference, was based on approximately two hundred hours of observations in the game reserves of Southern Rhodesia.[1] After the conference Washburn went to Kenya Colony and joined DeVore, who had been there for some months. Both continued to study baboons for the following six months, and the present version of this paper is based primarily on the more extensive data collected in Kenya. Full descriptions of baboon behavior will be published elsewhere, and here an attempt has been made to outline only those points that proved to be of greatest interest to the participants of the conference on "The Social Life of Early Man."

TROOP SIZE

Baboon troops range in size from 9 to 185. The commonest size is between 30 and 50 and is composed of approximately 5–10 adult males, 10–20 adult females, and juveniles equal to the number of adults. A typical count from a troop near Victoria Falls is 5 adult males, 12 adult females, 14 juveniles, and 2 new infants—total 33. Count of a slightly larger troop from the Royal Nairobi National Park showed 5 adult males, 10 adult females, 14 juvenile males, 6 juvenile females, and 3 infants—total 38.

Estimates by the Tanganyika Game Department, estimates for troops in the Wankie Game Reserve (Southern Rhodesia), and carefully repeated counts in the Royal Nairobi National Park all give an average troop size of 36–40. But in the Amboseli Reserve in Kenya (at the northern base of Mt. Kilimanjaro) the average troop numbered 80. It was here that the two largest troops (170–85) were counted. Small troops of from 9 to 13 were seen in the Wankie Reserve, Tsavo Reserve (Kenya, not far from Amboseli), Amboseli, and Nairobi. The very large troops

1. The original study of baboons in the Rhodesias was financed by the Wenner-Gren Foundation for Anthropological Research. The second trip was part of a study of the origin of human behavior supported by the Ford Foundation. We wish to thank the foundations and the numerous people who helped us in Africa, especially J. Desmond Clark, L. S. B. Leakey, B. L. Mitchel, and Stephen Ellis.

were seen only in Amboseli, but troops of over 80 were found wherever careful counts could be made.

Much larger troops have been reported, and we have seen 450 baboons around one water hole; but this was an aggregation of three separate troops. Even though the animals from one troop may be immediately adjacent to those from the next, the troop members will not mix. The actual situation can be understood only if the troops are counted repeatedly and watched as they come to or leave the water hole. From a single count it is not possible to tell whether one is seeing a temporary aggregation of several troops or a single large one. A further complication is that some of the large troops divide temporarily, and these subdivisions (often with a peculiar age distribution) may be mistaken for whole troops. The range of size given here (9–185) is based on troops that were repeatedly counted and where the neighboring troops were also known. We believe that the small troops (five troops, numbering 9–13) represent the limit for independent, viable groups. The restricted geographical distribution of the large troops shows that they are un-usual, but a much more extended survey would be necessary to establish an upper limit with any confidence. One trained observer (G. Savard, personal communica-tion) reports a group of 1,000 in Ethiopia, but there is no way of deciding whether this was a single troop or a temporary aggregation of several troops.

Oakley (see his essay in this volume) estimated the group size for australo-pithecines as between 10 and 200. This corresponds almost exactly to the range of size observed in baboons. Since both are plains-living, primarily vegetarian forms, the comparison is of particular interest. Sahlins (1960) has estimated the size of bands of primitive human hunters to be from 20 to 50. The local group in recent gathering and hunting people appears to be no larger than that in baboons, show-ing that the human way of life does not necessarily result in an increase in size of the local groups.

The comparison may also be put in terms of population density. In Nairobi Park there are approximately 10 baboons per square mile. Certainly, in parts of Amboseli, in the reserve at the north end of Lake Manyara, in parts of Uganda, and in Kruger Park (South Africa), the density is much higher. But even the Nairobi figure of 10 per square mile is higher than estimates for preagricultural man, which suggest something on the order of 5–10 square miles *per person* (Clark, 1959; Deevey, 1960, p. 196). In other words, troops of baboons may ex-ceed in size the bands of primitive hunters, and the density of baboons may reach a hundred times that attributed to ancient man. All the evidence suggests that in tropical Africa baboons were much more numerous than humans until the begin-nings of agriculture. Even today there are many more baboons than Masai in the Masai Reserve.

Man's success comes from hunting and the diversity of custom that allows him to adapt to many areas, permitting a single species to inhabit most of the earth. But the numerical success, which is so dramatic today, may be much more recent than is often suggested. It should be remembered that the range of the baboons and the closely allied macaques was almost exactly the same as that of presapiens man. It stretched from Europe to Japan and to the Cape of Good Hope. In this vast area baboon-macaques were probably more numerous than men until the last glacial advance, and even then continued to outnumber men in the tropics (Sanderson, 1957, p. 120).

RANGE

Baboons' activities are restricted to a small range[2] of approximately 3–6 square miles. Large trees near water are selected for sleeping; some troops sleep in the same trees night after night, but others move frequently. The troop descends from the sleeping trees shortly after sunrise and leaves for the daily circuit of some 2–4 miles. The ranges of different troops overlap, sometimes extensively, and there is no evidence that troops defend a territory. However, habitual daily routines tend to keep troops apart. Even in Amboseli, where several troops come to the same water hole and may be around it at the same time, they tend to use the surrounding area differently. Two water holes at Amboseli were connected by a lush, grassy area. Of the five troops that frequently came to this small area, three used one part and two the other. In leaving this water hole three of the troops usually moved on a variety of routes to the north or west while the other two moved in opposite directions. When the sleeping trees near this water hole were utilized, the three troops used two groups of trees, while the other two troops went to a different grove of trees nearby. The general situation seems to be that a particular troop occupies a small range (and preferred places in it) much more frequently than do other troops, but there is much overlapping at the edge of ranges. Vervets (*Cercopithecus aethiops*) and small troops of baboons slowly moved away from large baboon troops, but no fighting between baboon troops was observed.

Clearly, the area occupied by a whole troop of baboons is less than that estimated as necessary to support a single human hunter. In a reconstruction of the social life of early man, hunting is the best clue to range. All the living large carnivores move over much larger ranges than do baboons, and no human hunter could restrict his activities to a small area. The small animals found at Olduvai with the skull and tools of an australopithecine (Leakey and Bartlett, 1960, p. 433) might have been killed incidentally while food-gathering in a small area. But while the range of *Australopithecus* may have differed little from that of the living baboons, the men of the Middle Pleistocene, who definitely hunted large mammals, must

2. Our use of the terms "range" and "territory" follows the technical distinction made between them by zoölogists. An animal's range is the area over which he customarily travels in search of food, whereas his territory is any portion of the range that he defends. "Every kind of mammal may be said to have a home range, stationary or shifting. Only those that protect some part of the home range, by fighting or aggressive gestures, from others of their kind, during some phase of their lives, may be said to have territories" (Burt, 1943, p. 351; see also Bourlière, 1956).

have looked for game and pursued their quarry over many miles. The primary evidence for the reconstruction of the range of australopithecines and man will come from their diet.

DIET

Baboons are almost entirely vegetarian. They eat a wide variety of fruits, buds, leaves, grasses, and roots. Eggs, nesting birds, some insects, and larvae are also eaten. A small live animal in the grass will also be killed and eaten. We saw two newborn Thompson's gazelle, two half-grown hares, and three nestlings of ground-nesting birds killed in this way. Although the same baboon troops passed beside fresh carrion on several occasions, they made no attempt to eat it. The normal diet is overwhelmingly vegetarian, and animal food accounts for less than 1 per cent. The readiness to eat meat is present, however, and it is easy to see how the acquisition of a simple weapon by *Australopithecus* could expand the baboon kind of diet to include the killing of many more small creatures (Clark, 1959; Leakey and Bartlett, 1960).

Baboons do not share food. After a baby is weaned, it gathers all its own food. Food is neither carried nor stored. Hewes (1959) has called attention to the importance of carrying food, but this is so awkward for a quadruped that baboons do not carry anything for more than a few yards. For short distances, food, or objects, may be carried in the mouth, in the hand, between body and elbow, or, as was observed once, tossed ahead and picked up. The presence of stones in Sterkfontein that had been carried for miles from a river gravel is evidence for bipedalism, and the structure of the pelvis supports this inference. It is hard to believe that animals that carried stones did not also carry food and thus initiate an important stage in freeing man from the necessity of eating his food where he found it. Carrying food, whether meat or vegetable, opens the way to storage, sharing, and division of labor, so that the presence of carried stones in australopithecine deposits suggests that their economic way of life may have advanced far in the human direction. The ability to carry water could greatly increase mobility; terrestrial monkeys, such as baboons, must stay within about two miles of water.

In summary, a wide variety of vegetable foods, garnered in a small area, effectively supports a large population of baboons, whereas hunting requires a much larger range. In spite of tools, transporting food and water, and division of labor, it was not until very recently that man outnumbered baboons in tropical Africa.

POPULATION STRUCTURE

The populations of vegetarian baboons, living on small ranges, are compact, inbred social systems. Most of the time the members of a troop stay within a few feet of one another. Many baboons live a lifetime without being more than three miles from where they were born and without ever being out of sight of another baboon. In every phase of the troop's activity, whether moving, eating, resting, grooming, or playing, baboons are close beside one another. This compact social unit is inbreeding, and many troops can be distinguished by the similarity among the troop members. Troops are characterized by a predominance of individuals that are similar in color, length of hair, and form of face and tail. In over 1,200 hours of observation, we saw only two individuals change from one troop to another; both were adult males. Only three solitary baboons were seen (two females and a male); all these were either very sick or badly hurt and trying to rejoin a troop. This small, localized, inbred group is in sharp contrast to the human tribe, in which rules of exogamy and relations between local groups result in a breeding population that is much larger than the local group. The large tribe, composed of more or less exogamous groups, is unique to man, and nothing comparable to it is found in nonhuman primates. In fact, such an organization probably could not exist without language.

In summary, the baboon troop is mostly inbred and constitutes a complete social system. Small groups of hunting humans are related to one another in a great variety of supralocal associations that fundamentally change the breeding structure of the species. In reconstructing the social life of early man, how can we date the disappearance of the compact, inbred society? Human hunting is incompatible with the kind of society that does not allow any of its members to leave the group. When hunting, one or a few men must leave the band, sometimes for days, and the hunters of the Middle Pleistocene could not have been living the same kind of group life as did the nonhuman primates (see below, "Home Base"). At the present time, inbreeding cannot be determined from the scanty fossil record, but the widespread use of the same kind of tools suggests communication at a level unknown in baboons. The spread of custom implies communication, and the problem of the change from the inbred troop to much larger units may eventually be solved by archeological data.

SUBGROUPS AND PLAY

The baboon troop is subdivided by age, sex, and individual preference. For example, as a large troop moves along, the lesser adult males are first, then come the juveniles and females, then the most dominant males and the females with small babies, followed by more females and juveniles, and finally by the other adult males. The order is clearest when the troop is moving rapidly and may vary considerably when the troop is moving slowly, feeding as it goes. Some individuals prefer each other, and these will walk together, feed close by, and sit together when the troop is resting. Such preference groups frequently consist of an adult male, an adult female or two, and some infants or juveniles. (Groups of this kind may have given rise to the stories of "harems," but these preference groups are temporary associations and limit sexual activities in no way.) The juveniles play together, and in the large troops there may be several play groups of different ages.

Play is an important activity, which occupies many hours every day. It is almost entirely interpersonal (chasing, mock fighting, pulling), and play with objects is almost nonexistent. We have seen playing baboons pull a rope, take a piece of cloth, or pull on parts of a car, but these rare acts seem more exploratory than playful. Although baboons turn over stones looking for food, they do not play with the stones. Branches may break off when they are feeding or gesturing defiance, but they do not throw them or play with them. Baboon play builds social skills but not manipulative skills. We believe that manipulative play with objects is essential to the development of tools and that manipulation is inhibited by quadrupedal locomotion.

MOTHER-CHILD RELATIONS

The motor development of the newborn baboon baby is more advanced than that of the human infant and enables the baby to cling to the mother. The baby baboon may be helped a little on the first day or two, but a quadruped that must walk several miles every day cannot use its hands to carry its infant. Bipedal locomotion is essential to the human mother-child relationship; mothers who cannot carry things cannot carry babies. The psychological consequences of the change from the monkey pattern to the human are profound. Bowlby (1953) has described the mental defects arising from deficient maternal care in man. He says that the first six postnatal months are the most important in man. In a baboon the comparable developmental stages are *in utero*, and, when the baby baboon is born, it has the reflexes and motor development that enable it to help determine its own relationship to the mother. In the baboon, species-specific behavior is guaranteed by pre- and postnatal events that are very different from those of man. The helpless human infant is exposed to maternal whim, custom, or vagary in a way that is true of no other primate.

At least a part of this momentous change in the role of the mother can be detected in the fossil record. Clearly the reason man must be born in such an immature state is that the pelvis will not permit the birth of a larger head. Selection that favored larger brains also had to favor earlier birth, but earlier births were impossible unless the mother was already bipedal and able to hold the baby. The fossil record shows that the australopithecines were bipeds with ape-size brains. Their young could easily have been born with brains that were 40–50 per cent as large as the adult size and with a motor development comparable to that of a monkey or ape, which would have allowed the baby to hold on to the mother. Although it may have begun at this time, it would not be necessary to postulate the human mother-child relationship among the australopithecines. But, with the large-brained men of the Middle Pleistocene, a human kind of mother-child relationship must have been established. Their larger brains required both that the infant be born earlier and that it be carried and cared for by a bipedal mother.

In the infants of monkeys and apes the great toe is very important in holding the mother. In newborn Old World monkeys the foot is specialized to hold the mother's hair. The great toe may be abducted to a degree impossible later on; the ankle is bent so that the foot faces inward, and the tarsal region is relatively elongated. In man bipedal locomotion makes this kind of adaptation impossible. This is another line of evidence showing that the human mother must have taken more responsibility for holding the baby. If the australopithecine foot was fully evolved for bipedal locomotion, the australopithecine mother must have held the baby more than is the case among monkeys or apes. This would have prepared the way for the great change in mother-child relations that was necessitated by the evolution of the large brain.

SEXUAL BEHAVIOR

Among baboons the female cycle averages around thirty-four days (Asdell, 1946; Harms, 1956, pp. 623–24), and oestrus lasts approximately a week. In the beginning of oestrus the female mates with juvenile males and the less dominant adults. She actively solicits the attention of the males and may mate with several in close succession. In the later part of oestrus, the female forms temporary consort relationships with the dominant adult males. These consort pairings may last a matter of hours or days and usually dissolve peacefully. However, fighting may occur if a male tries to break up the consort pair. A full description of the complicated sex life is given elsewhere by DeVore (in preparation), but the pattern is similar to that of the *Rhesus macaque* (Carpenter, 1942; Altmann, 1960).

The baboon's pattern of mating differs from the human family in that no lasting male-female relationship is established, and there are no economic ties or other social controls. Oestrus disrupts all other social relations; the female leaves her preference group and her infant (if she has one) to form a temporary consortship with a male. Her position within the troop is altered both by her oestrus and by the status of the male with which she is paired. We can see no way that oestrus behavior could be combined with the care of an infant that is still economically dependent upon the mother. The physiology of the human female has become radically modified, with the endocrine control of behavior being greatly reduced (Beach, 1947; Ford and Beach, 1951). The apparent difference between the sociosexual behavior of man and monkey has been minimized by the use of the words "family," "harem," and "jealousy" to describe the behavior of monkeys and apes. Actually, oestrus, multiple mates, and no economic responsibility present a pattern that is fundamentally different from that of man.

The origin of the human family pattern presents three problems: (1) the evolution of a helpless, slow-growing human infant, (2) loss of oestrus, and (3) the male's role as an economic provider. It has already been shown that the human mother-child relationship must evolve after bipedalism and together with large brains; that is, by the Middle Pleistocene. At the moment, there seems to be no direct evidence on the time of the loss of oestrus, but we may speculate that this occurred early, together with bipedalism and a lengthening of the period of infant dependency. It has already been suggested that oestrus is incompatible with continuing child care. By the same token, it can be argued that prolonged receptivity in the female was necessary before a lasting male-female relationship of the human type could be formed (Count, 1958; Sahlins, 1960). In this view, oestrus is associated with rotating mateship; the family, with noncyclical receptivity.[3] The male's role as an economic provider had certainly appeared by the Middle Pleistocene, when men were killing large animals. Hunting large animals was probably based on co-operation, and the band must have shared in the eating.

By the Middle Pleistocene there is direct evidence of hunting and indirect evidence for co-operation, division of labor, and sharing of food. This human pattern differs on each of these points from that of baboons, who do not hunt, share, or co-operate, and where there is no sexual division of economic activity.

We are tempted to date human notions of range and territory from the same time. Earlier, we indicated that baboons do not defend a territory, but occupy a small range. However, we have seen baboons drive vervets from fruit trees. The sources of vegetable food are normally so widespread that the overlapping of ranges does not appear serious, but with the hunting of large animals the matter is entirely different. If strangers hunt game, or even disturb it, scaring it from its normal routes, the plans of the local hunters are ruined. Hunting man requires a large area free from the interference of other hunters. When man became a hunter, his relation to the land changed from one in which a small range was adequate to one that demanded a large territory. Hunting large animals made children and females economically dependent. A young baboon receives no food from other members of the troop, and, once it is weaned, it is economically independent, but in a band of hunters children are dependent on adults for a substantial portion of their food. So the relation of the human child to adults differs from that of the monkey in two ways: it is more dependent both physically and economically.

ECONOMIC DEPENDENCE

The relation of the infant monkey or ape to its mother is guaranteed by biology—by the infant's reflexes and the mother's drives and physiology. A close

3. The gibbon troop is composed of an adult male, adult female, and their young (Carpenter, 1940). This grouping bears a superficial resemblance to the human family, but it is produced by an entirely different mechanism. Except for a mating pair, adult gibbons are extremely antagonistic. This adult antagonism is a primitive species-spacing mechanism, comparable to that in tree shrews and some lemurs.

mother-child relationship lasts only as long as lactation. No such direct biological bonds bind the human mother to her older children, or the human father to his offspring. Although female monkeys appear to learn part of their maternal behavior patterns, and older juvenile females hold and carry infants before they have any of their own, the role of learning, culture, and custom in determining the care of the young is vastly greater in man than in any nonhuman primate. In the evolution of society, the most important rules are those that guarantee economic survival to the dependent young. Human females and their young are efficient gatherers, so the crucial customs are those that guarantee the services of a hunter to a woman and her children. That the resulting family bonds are much more than sexual is shown by the fact that custom in contemporary hunter-gatherer groups provides that new families may be formed only around males who have proved themselves as economic providers. The maturing human male is dependent upon the adult males not only for food but for years of instruction in the techniques of hunting. The human male matures sexually from about twelve to fourteen years, but he reaches full social and physical maturity much later, from about eighteen to twenty. The wide variety of customs that insure this delay in social maturity all have the same biological function: to delay the production of children until the male can provide for them. As Schultz (this volume) has outlined, biological maturation in the monkeys, and even more in the apes, is delayed in comparison to that in other mammals. This biological delay in development is greatest in man, and a considerable social delay, determined by custom, is added to the biological.

The economic advantages of delaying the formation of a new family until the male was a fully efficient, proved provider, however, would be largely nullified if delayed marriage was not accompanied by the incest tabu. From a biological point of view, father-daughter mating amounts to taking a second wife, regardless of economic considerations. Brother-sister mating adds babies without adding an economically responsible, fully socially mature male. It is probably impossible to encourage the sexuality of the young male in mother-son relations while at the same time prohibiting other sexuality in the family.

In addition to creating within the family economic conditions that favored exogamy, hunting as a major activity may have reinforced this tendency by bringing about a new type of relationship between bands. The exclusive control of a hunting territory can be efficiently maintained only with the mutual consent of neighboring bands; excessive fighting over territorial borders both disturbs game and dissipates the energy of the hunters. The exchange of mates between neighboring groups helps to insure friendly relations with them because it disperses persons with close emotional ties among many groups and over a large area. By contrast, the baboon troop is a self-sufficient, closed social system with no supralocal affiliations.

It cannot be proved, of course, that incest prohibitions and exogamous matings arose in the Middle Pleistocene, but it can be shown that the conditions that made such regulation advantageous arose at that time. All data suggest that the killing of large animals is a task for adult men and that, once hunting became important to the group, children had to depend upon adults for many years. Both by increasing the importance of the male as provider and by making control of a hunting area essential, large-scale hunting activity created conditions that favored exogamous mating. The offspring of *Australopithecus* may have been just as independent as those of a chimpanzee, but the children of Ternifine or Peking man depended upon the hunting of adult males, and their survival depended upon the relations between the young and the hunters. It is impossible to date the beginning of the human family or of the incest tabu, but the conditions that made these institutions advantageous in the evolution of the species are concomitant with the hunting of large animals.

DOMINANCE

Dominance in baboons is ultimately based on the ability to fight. Fighting within the troop seldom occurs, because the position of each animal is recognized by the others, and these positions remain stable for considerable periods of time. Adult male baboons are much larger than the females and have large canine teeth. When danger is near, it is they that protect the troop, and as a result they are actively sought out by the younger and weaker troop members. No similar structural difference exists between the sexes in any fossil australopithecine or in man. This suggests that tools had already replaced teeth as the mechanism of fighting and defense before *Australopithecus*.

Among baboons the sources of food are usually widely distributed, and dominance has little effect on food-gathering. The normal spacing of the troop keeps animals sufficiently far apart so that each may gather without interference. Occasionally, a dominant animal may displace lesser members of the troop from a desired location in fruit trees, but the gathering and immediate eating of grasses, buds, and fruits leads to an economic life that no animal tries to dominate. The situation must have been radically changed once tools were used in gathering. Among baboons, digging with a tool would result in a surplus under the control of the larger animals. The use of tools and transporting and storing food must have created problems of distribution that could not be efficiently solved by a social system that relied upon dominance as its only ordering mechanism. With the killing of large animals, the problem of distribution must have become even more severe.

It has been noted that carnivores share food and that a similar habit must have arisen among early human hunters (Washburn and Avis, 1958). But the human situation was far more complicated socially than that of other carnivores. If early men were living in troops that were as large as those of baboons, there would have been perhaps fifty or sixty individuals sharing the meat. No comparable situation exists among other carnivores, and the orderly distribution of food in human society must have presented a new social problem. Tools, carrying, storing, hunting—all these would have led to accumulations of food, which helped the survival of early man. But the use of these quantities of food by all members of the troop required that co-operation and sharing increase and that dominance become less important in social control.

HOME BASE

All human societies have bases where the weak may stay and from which various combinations of individuals may move out to gather, hunt, or fight. In this location are tools, food, and normally some sort of shelter. Implicit in the idea of the home base (whether relatively permanent or temporary) is the idea that some of the group may stay there while others move out. No such "base" exists among the baboons, other monkeys, or apes. When the troop moves out on the daily round, *all* members must move with it or be deserted. We have seen sick and wounded animals making great efforts to keep up with the troop, and finally falling behind. At least five or six of these were killed, and the only protection for a baboon is to stay with the troop, no matter how injured or sick he may be. In wild primates injuries are common (Schultz, 1939; see also his essay, this volume), and animals that are so sick that they can be spotted by a relatively distant human observer are numerous. For a wild primate a fatal sickness is one that separates it from the troop, but for man it is one from which he cannot recover even while protected and fed at the home base. The whole evolutionary impact of disease and accident on the human species was changed when it became possible for an individual to stay in one place and not have to take part in the daily round of the troop. Certainly one of the reasons why it has been possible for man to migrate without building immunity to local diseases is that his way of life allows him to be far sicker than a baboon and still recover. Injuries to the legs are common and are far more serious, of course, for a biped than for a quadruped. It is the home base that changes sprained ankles and fevers from fatal diseases to minor ailments.

SOUNDS AND GESTURES

Among baboons social relations are mediated by many gestures and a few sounds. This very important subject is treated fully elsewhere by DeVore (in preparation) and is mentioned here only because of the great importance of language in human evolution. It must be remembered that the baboon social group is compact and that normally animals are in sight of each other. Some baboon vocalizations, such as a warning bark (which indicates danger others may not have seen), can convey a meaning independent of gestures, but usually vocalizations are subsidiary to gestures. Vocalizations may draw attention to an animal, emphasizing his gestures and body postures, but most communication

SUMMARY TABLE

	Baboons	Preagricultural Humans
Group size . . .	10–200	50–60
Group density . .	10 baboons per square mile	5–10 square miles per individual
Range	3–6 square miles; no territorial defense	250–600 square miles; territorial rights, boundaries defended from strangers
Diet	Almost entirely vegetarian; no food-sharing or division of labor	Omnivorous; food-sharing; men specialize in hunting, women and children in gathering
Population structure . . .	Small inbreeding groups	Tribal organization with local exogamy
Social system . .	Self-sufficient, "closed" system; temporary subgroups based on preference and age	Interband affiliation and dependency, semiopen system; subgroups based on kinship
Play	Largely interpersonal and exploratory	Also interpersonal, but includes considerable play with inanimate objects
Mother-child relations . . .	Intense but brief; infant well developed and in partial control, abduction of toe, etc.	Long; infant helpless and entirely subject to attention of adults
Sexual behavior .	Female oestrus; multiple mates; no prolonged male-female relationships	Female continuously receptive; family structure based on prolonged male-female relations and incest tabus
Economic dependence . .	Infant economically independent after weaning; no hunting, storage, or sharing of food; full maturity biologically delayed	Infant dependent upon adults for many years; hunting, storage, and sharing of food; male maturity both biologically and culturally delayed
Dominance . . .	Sexual dimorphism with large canines in males	Minimum sexual dimorphism, canines reduced; tools replace teeth in fighting and defense
Home base . . .	No base	Improved locations, which are occupied for periods of time
Sounds and gestures . . .	Species-specific communication; largely gestural and concerned with immediate situations	Linguistic community based on speech

between troop members is gestural and without vocal accompaniment. Noises of defiance, anger, fear, frustration, and contentment all exist but are supported by gestures. The atrophy of human ear and scalp muscles probably comes after language, since movement of these muscles is essential in social gesture.

Human language appears to require a large brain, and linguistic ability is greatly limited in microcephaly. It is possible that the rapid doubling of the australopithecine brain into the brain of primitive *Homo* is related to both tools and language, but there is no direct evidence of the latter.

SUMMARY AND CONCLUSIONS

In this paper we have tried to outline some of the ways in which the way of life of contemporary baboons differs from that of man. The main points of difference are summarized in the accompanying table. Although monkeys and apes certainly differ in their behavior from one species to the next, we believe that the main points as given in this table would not be greatly changed by substituting other nonhuman primate species for baboons. For the purposes of this symposium we are interested in the contrasts between Old World monkeys and apes, on the one hand, and man, on the other. If there were great variation in social behavior from species to species of monkeys or if man's social behavior were very similar to monkey's, then the chances of reconstruction of the social life of early man would be very poor, but man is unique in his social life, as he is in his locomotion and intelligence. His ideas of territory, exogamy, and co-operation are unique among the primates, as are his language, tools, and war. Because of the great behavioral gap between man and his nearest relatives, some reconstruction of behavior is possible.

We see two stages of behavioral evolution separating the apes from *Homo sapiens*. The first of these is that of the australopithecines of the Lower Pleistocene. Although these forms were bipedal and tool-making, there is little to suggest that their social life was very different from that of apes or monkeys. They were probably primarily vegetarian, and the small-brained young could have matured rapidly. Perhaps only the rudiments of the human way of life were present. But, by the Middle Pleistocene, large-brained men who hunted big animals were present, and this may well have been the period during which the distinctively human attitudes on hunting, territory, and the family originated. At least the biological and economic problems that ultimately led to the social customs of today had their roots in the hunting societies of half a million years ago.

BIBLIOGRAPHY

ALTMANN, STUART
1960. "A Field Study of the Sociobiology of Rhesus Monkeys, *Macaca mulatta.*" Unpublished Ph.D. dissertation, Harvard University.

ASDELL, S. S.
1946. *Patterns of Mammalian Reproduction.* Ithaca, N.Y.: Comstock.

BEACH, FRANK A.
1947. "Evolutionary Changes in the Physiological Control of Mating Behavior in Mammals," *Psychol. Rev.*, 54: 297–315.

BOURLIÈRE, FRANÇOIS
1956. *The Natural History of Mammals.* Rev. ed. New York: Knopf.

BOWLBY, JOHN
1953. *Child Care and the Growth of Love.* Penguin Books.

BURT, WILLIAM H.
1943. "Territoriality and Home Range Concepts as Applied to Mammals," *J. Mammal.*, 24: 346–52.

CARPENTER, C. R.
1940. *A Field Study in Siam of the Behavior and Social Relations of the Gibbon* (*Hylobates lar*). ("Comp. Psychol. Monogr.," Vol. 16, No. 5.)
1942. "Sexual Behavior of Free Ranging Rhesus Monkeys (*Macaca mulatta*)," *Comp. Psychol.*, 33:113–62.

CLARK, J. DESMOND
1959. *The Prehistory of Southern Africa.* Penguin Books.

COUNT, EARL W.
1958. "The Biological Basis of Human Sociality," *Amer. Anthrop.*, 60:1049–85.

DEEVEY, EDWARD S., JR.
1960. "The Human Population," *Scient. American*, 203:194–204.

FORD, CLELLAN S., and FRANK A. BEACH
1951. *Patterns of Sexual Behavior.* New York: Harper & Bros. and Paul B. Hoeber.

HARMS, J. W.
1956. "Fortpflanzungsbiologie." In H. HOFER, A. H. SCHULTZ, and D. STARCK (eds.), *Primatalogia*, 1:561–660. Basel: S. Karger.

HEWES, GORDON W.
1959. "Food Transport and the Origin of Hominid Bipedalism." Unpublished abstract of paper delivered at American Anthropological Association Meetings, December, 1959.

LEAKEY, L. S. B., and DES BARTLETT
1960. "Finding the World's Earliest Man," *Nat. Geog. Mag.*, 118:420–35.

SAHLINS, MARSHALL D.
1960. "The Origin of Society," *Scient. American*, 203:76–87.

SANDERSON, IVAN T.
1957. *The Monkey Kingdom.* Garden City, N.Y.: Hanover.

SCHULTZ, ADOLPH H.
   1939. "Notes on Diseases and Healed Fractures of Wild Apes and Their Bearing on the Antiquity of Pathological Conditions in Man." *Bull. Hist. Med.*, 7:571–82.

WASHBURN, S. L., and VIRGINIA AVIS
   1958. "Evolution of Human Behavior." In ANNE ROE and G. G. SIMPSON, *Behavior and Evolution.* New Haven: Yale University Press.

NOTES ON THE MENTALITY OF PRIMITIVE MAN

F. M. BERGOUNIOUX

T HE STUDY of manifestations of social life in prehistoric man presupposes that humanity, in the course of a long history, acquired sufficient numerical strength to establish ethnic groups large enough in numbers or importance to necessitate the making of regulations, at least tacitly, for all community life (Bergounioux, 1958).

If we consider the question from this standpoint, it will seem that paleo-sociological research cannot be sure of success until the beginning of the Neolithic, a critical point that in some ways marks the change from man to humanity, following a slow progression in the organization and concentration of groups continuously growing in numbers and accompanied by many changes in individual mentality. Therefore, the term "civilization" cannot legitimately be applied before the existence of cities, the inhabitants (citizens) of which are freely linked to one another (Bergounioux, 1943). Before this we can speak only of fairly diversified "cultures," achieved according to the degree of mental elaboration reached by the members of the small and scattered tribes, without apparent ties with one another. If we adopt generally recognized values for estimating dimensions, this final period in prehistory can be said to have started some six thousand years before the Christian Era. The first villages appeared in Asia Minor and in Egypt (Jarmo, Jericho, etc.). These are no longer a few very large dwellings, as there are in the Ukraine (Timonovka) and in other European regions—remarkable as this attempt of the late Paleolithic was—but are important groups of small houses with their inevitable surroundings of cultivated fields and domestic animals. The sedentary life and the nomadic life of the agriculturist and the shepherd give a picture of the first well-defined and fairly easily interpretable traits of concurrent or rival societies exercising complementary activities.

The Neolithic is the dawn of the day in which we live: on the fringes of our mechanized societies many proofs of this still exist in Africa and in Asia Minor. Nonetheless, many archaic tribes, incorrectly called primitive, provide examples of considerably earlier social states, which are linked to·the late Paleolithic. Tools and weapons of stone are used to the exclusion of all metal implements: hunting, fishing, and gathering of wild fruit provide the essentials of food. Such stagnation is in itself very instructive and shows the slowness with which man progresses when isolated from conquering humanity.

Be that as it may, the first villagers represent the results of sustained effort during hundreds of thousands of years, about which our knowledge dwindles strikingly as we trace back the course of time, becoming virtually nonexistent for a very long period, the same period that appears of major interest to us. If we compare the few thousand years that separate us from the beginning of the Neolithic with the date of the appearance of man on earth, we are struck by the enormous disproportion existing between the two events. If Villafranca man is hundreds of thousands of years removed from us—possibly even a million years— and if Mousterian man, in the first stages of the last Glaciation (Würm), is only about 60 or 70 thousand years distant, we gain some idea of the immensity of the first stage of humanity in relation to the two others: The *archanthropines*, thought to have lived perhaps for 900,000 years, followed much later by the paleoanthropines *sensu stricto*, who are doubtless the terminal stage of the former; the neanthropines are unknown before Aurignatian man (if we exclude the group of presapiens, which is so difficult to interpret), that is, some thirty thousand years ago. As to the beginning of the retreat of the glacial front, which is, as it were, the beginning of the new era (Mesolithic), this can be placed no earlier than twelve thousand years before our era. Thus we are witnessing the phenomenon of the contraction of time, common in all aspects of geology but particularly noticeable here, since it is accompanied in the case of humanity by an expansion of the psychic content, the effects of which increase in proportion to the increase in the mass of humanity. The more men grow in numbers, the more their mutual relations are facilitated and increased, and thus the more their intellectual and moral development is enriched.

However, it would obviously be incorrect to restrict this study to the Neolithic, the terminal point of the progress preceding humanity, and we must, therefore, attempt to give an account of this progess. To mark the steps in the development of the social life of paleohumanity, schematic stages must be established to which the large divisions proposed by prehistoric archeology correspond roughly.

a) Lower Paleolithic.—Very small family groups are formed from the first human generations. Under the pressure of vital necessity, they soon split up and move farther away from one another. This results in almost total isolation of each group (Choukoutien).

b) Middle Paleolithic.—Clans composed of larger numbers are organized for the purpose of common action for a specific goal. (This occurred in the case of the Teshik-Tash paleoanthropines in the *Capra siberica* hunt.)

c) Upper Paleolithic.—With increasing population, the various ethnic groups have more and more frequent contacts, and in certain privileged regions may even agglomerate in urban-type groups (Timonovka).

d) Neolithic.—Actual concentration occurs, grouping men in villages, then in cities. Complementary social activities take place for the common good.

If we are to remain within the limits of this report, it is very important to try to gain an idea of the mentality of all early men and to follow their slow development, which we must attempt to explain. But the almost total absence of documentation makes this work difficult: it is nonetheless indispensable for anyone wishing to give an account of the overwhelming progress accomplished during the last few thousand years, from the time when small human societies, pressed close together in continuously growing areas, begin to enrich one another by constant contacts, leading humanity to the conquest and exploitation of the entire earth.

"Man entered without noise. . . ." This remark by Father Teilhard de Chardin (1923) strikingly expresses the double and troubling reality of our origins. The very first human phenomenon manifested itself, but in such humble guise that an observer had to have great perspicacity to notice it. If we consider merely the anatomical data, in fact, not much difference can be recorded between the first men and the other large primates: the erect posture no doubt was acquired some millions of years ago. *Oreopithecus* appears during the Pontian, and the theory that he is descended from the large Miocene monkeys of Kenya is no longer tenable; research by Dr. Hürzeler (1958), still in progress at the present time, has uncovered this biped with the shortened face, narrow nose, and high forehead. Since we have no information as to his origins, we are forced to conclude that in the Pontian we meet a direct ancestor of humanity for the first time, the result of a long evolution that roots him deeply (doubtless to the beginning of the Eocene period). It is plainly the biped character that brought about the other anatomical traits indispensable to the appearance of human intelligence: the hands become prehensile organs; the jaws assume a more specific, reduced shape for their masticating role; the face shortens; the cranial curve grows. We know absolutely nothing of what occurred during the few thousand years separating *Oreopithecus* from the appearance of *Australopithecus;* but the latter appears to be a hominid branch already in a full stage of development. The cerebral capacity is considerably increased and may amount to 750 cubic centimeters in *Paranthropus crassidens.* We have arrived at the border line of the "cerebral Rubicon," so aptly described by Dr. Henri V. Vallois (1955), the crossing of which was accompanied by the sudden passage from simple psychism to considered psychism.

It is obvious that an anatomical study will not provide valid criteria for differentiation between man and animal: the final transforming mutation was of a neuropsychic order—the sudden increase in the number of neurons in the cervical cortex immediately provided conscious thought with its material substrate, the material from which it drew the magnificant organ that has never ceased to improve. But macroscopic differences in the skull of early man are practically imperceptible to an anatomist, whose means of measurement are rather limited. Thus in the continuation of anatomical development the primates found themselves before a metaphysical threshold that marks a major break in the psychic organization. There is no common measurement for human and animal intelligence;

qualitatively these are different phenomena. To give an account of human intelligence, we are forced to turn to the so-called "emergent" philosophical systems that link these absolutely new and unforeseen qualities to a special material organization. Here we are dealing with a recording of facts more than with an explanation, which will always remain unknown from the strict standpoint of scientific observation. But the large stages of the organization and development of the earth are no more clearly marked: geogenesis, biogenesis, and anthropogenesis succeed one another without any mechanically registerable gap: the phenomenon of complex conscience appears to govern the earth; when man appears, the threshold of thought has been crossed. It is for us to observe and appreciate the reality and importance of this event (Teilhard de Chardin, 1955).

The first vestiges that show the presence of man on earth without any possible doubt are provided by extremely rough tools grouped under the name of "pebble culture." It is no longer a matter of man's occasional use of a boulder or a tree branch for attack or defense but the intentional organization of a raw material for the purpose of achieving a specific goal. Kagerian gravel recovered from old laterities in the High Kafila Basin (80 km. north of Elizabethville) contain quartzite pebbles upon which traces of violent blows can be detected; fashioning is limited to a blow on one side of the pebble, of which very often only one face has been worked. Father Breuil, upon examination of this industry made up of tools with a cutting ridge, has stated that they must have been intended for woodworking (Alimen, 1955). We are familiar with the considerable extent of this practice in Africa; the most varied techniques must have been used from the time of Villafranchian man, as is shown by the discoveries made in North Africa: in the ancient dry lake of Hain Hanech, not far from Sétif, M. Arambourg has taken from black ossiferous clay some forty limestone or dolomite spheroids the size of an orange, the intentional shaping of which cannot be doubted; certain surfaces carry the marks of the point of impact of the striking instrument with which the ball was struck at the most favorable breaking point. It would be easy to lose one's self in conjecture about the uses of these spheroids, but it is certainly legitimate to connect them with the bolas used to lasso certain wild animals (Bergounioux and Glory, 1952). However that may be, the impression given is the same: an absolutely new event has been recorded on earth; it is conditioned by the entry upon the scene of a conscious actor, who is none other than primitive man, the thinking primate, capable by means of a psychic mechanism of "reflection," that is, of turning to himself, of considering at the same time the goal to be attained and the means appropriate for reaching it.

This fact is so important that if confirmation can be found of the existence of pebble culture in the *Australopithecus* layers, these enigmatic beings will have to be classed among the archanthropines, since they have crossed the "cerebral Rubicon."

Doubtless the human phenomenon consists essentially of this unique fact in the history of the earth, the point of departure of the greatest discoveries. Therefore, we do not understand the distinction made between a *"Homo faber,"* primitive, scarcely emerged from the animal state, only just capable of roughly shaping a few pebbles, and *"Homo sapiens,"* who appeared much later and rose to the level of comprehension of the highest spiritual realities in his discovery of art and religion (Bergounioux, 1951). Nothing would seem further from the truth than an interpretation of facts earnestly advocating the psychic homogeneity of humanity from the very first stages of its development, and there is no proof of uncontrollable spirituality to be found in the statement that the roots of all progress that was to take place were present in all early men, awaiting the time when exchanges of individual experience would become possible, such as the comparison of results obtained. It is in his psychism, completely new and original, that man, at the beginning of his journey, was distinguished, as he is today, from all other living beings. Even though he can legitimately be considered a primate, of which he possesses all the anatomical and physiological characteristics, he alone forms a biological group whose originality none will dispute. If human intelligence, capable of reflection, abstraction, and generalization, demands a complex cerebral organization, it is nevertheless not the necessary result thereof. It is not even a "superimposed epiphenomenon," but a phenomenon with no connection whatever with the physiological structures that support it. The subject is governed from the outset in his thinking and his action by a process of integration without any limit commensurate with the means of animal intelligence. Specific and automatic hereditary memory, which is found in varying degrees in all animals, is replaced by educated memory, which, without entirely eliminating the first, definitely relegates it to second place. Every man has it from birth; it is part of his basic patrimony, but he must cultivate it for it to give a full return, and this can be done only by the accumulation of personal experiences and by transmission from other men (Chauchard, 1957). This is doubtless why man can be said to be a social animal. But, although we meet this latter tendency to educative training among many birds and mammals, in their case it is superseded by instinct, which always remains predominant. No matter what perfection we may attribute (sometimes wrongly) to specific memory, it is confined to a small number of gestures made quasi-automatically. It might be said that with man a change of a qualitative order occurs that is opposed to the quantitative order observed among animals. The biosphere has received its crowning achievement, and the noösphere, or sphere of conquering thought, is to spread gradually to the entire planet.

In the absence of documents (apart from the tools of the "pebble culture"), it is necessary to try to recapture the psychological state of these first mutants, suddenly separated from the other primates, taking their first hesitating steps in an unknown world. These were justly called "denatured animals" by Vercors (1952), and the expression is filled with meaning: instead of unconsciously submitting to the oppressive pressure of nature enclosing him on all sides, man felt himself brutally torn from his environment and isolated in the middle of a world whose measure and laws he did not know; he therefore felt obliged to learn, by constant bitter effort and his own mistakes, everything he had to know to survive. The animals surrounding him came and went, indefatigably repeating the same actions: hunting, gathering, searching for water, doubling or fleeing to defend themselves against innumerable enemies; for them, periods of rest and activity succeed each other in an unchanging rhythm fixed by the needs for food or sleep, reproduction or protection. Man detaches himself from his surroundings; he feels alone, abandoned, ignorant of everything except that he knows nothing, no longer forced to obey the laws of the clan, from which he feels irremediably cut off. His first feeling thus was existential anxiety, which may even have taken him to the limits of despair. Without previous experience, his consciousness was necessarily rudimentary and rough, yet it was an authentic human consciousness.

The first stages of humanity have often been compared with the infancy of man himself. From two to seven years there is the mesoblastic stage, which corresponds psychically to a magic state: plunged into his surroundings, the child does not yet unfold his personality; his imitative instinct shows his feeling for universal assimilation (Martiny, 1956).

But points of similarity end here. It is at this period of his life, it is true, that the child begins his education. Narrowly integrated into the family environment, he receives from it not only the first elements of his human culture, which will develop further upon his entry into school, but also the foundations of his education. According to the good qualities or faults of his hereditary patrimony, the influence of which is dominant, he will either advance beyond or stay behind children of his age, and his psychic development will be conditioned by the quality of his surroundings. The speed with which he acquires habits, by imitating gestures and attitudes observed daily, shows the pliability of human intelligence in its new and supple stage. When isolated or when part of an undeveloped environment, a child shows an astonishing slowness in his psychic development. If, like early man, he were more or less without companions, the most elementary notions would be acquired only very slowly and with great difficulty. These observations explain the apparent stagnation of individuals living in a geographical milieu that is inaccessible or part of an ethnic group that is withdrawn upon itself and living on its own resources. "To know" and "to understand" represent two successive processes of the spirit when confronted with reality: reality, accessible through the senses, is raised to the plane of abstraction by the action of intelligence: medieval scholars claimed that "nothing is recorded by intelligence which was not furnished by the senses." It is at this level of assimilation that reality can assume the name of "knowledge." To be "understood," reality must be compared with information already registered as a result of previous experience, and it is by means of comparison that similarities and differences are established that allow us to place an event or fact in its proper place. Thus "value" judgments are formed, which constitute human thought in its personal, original form and involve the responsibility of the individual who formulates them. Such work is thankless and very lengthy. True enrichment of thought is derived from meetings and from discussing results obtained with other thinking subjects. When he was isolated by the force of circumstances, man had to learn everything at his own risk and peril, without being able to profit from the knowledge accumulated with such difficulty by other men.

Among archaic peoples, that is, contemporary peoples who have not developed on the plane of logical and scientific knowledge, a symbolic manner of seeing the world, and thinking about it, and of living has been observed. It remains to be seen to what point the profane mingles with the sacred; this concept does not mean separation from affectivity and concrete experience, which at the subliminal stage contains everything that will differentiate the development of the human spirit. The term "sublogical" is more in accord with this mentality than the term "prelogical," suggested by the first pioneers of ethnology. This total isolation gave man his realization not only of his fundamental originality—of his personal life, the source of all his inner riches, which he was to appreciate more and more—but also of the tragic course of his destiny, which could not mingle with any other. A fourteenth-century theologian, Duns Scotus, wrote: "Personalitas est ultimo solitude" ("personality is the ultimate solitude"). This is also the source of the difference between the individual and the person, the first being a member of a gregarious community to which he belongs without prior choice on his part, the second leaving to the free choice of all the task of deciding in favor of this or that social life, even if in practice we are all members in spite of ourselves of a particular society, which imposes its demands and to which we are obliged to subscribe in order to profit from the advantages it offers, though at the same time we must suffer from its inevitable drawbacks.

The first human societies were very small ethnic groups, the unit of which was the family clan. We can easily imagine these primitive organizations, soon to become rivals. The chief at the head lived surrounded by his wife and children. His first duty was to provide for the immediate needs of this group and to defend it against anyone who attacked it. There was no need for any law except that of his will, and his authority was derived from his physical strength rather than from his intelligence or cunning. Presumably, the first dispersals took place rapidly. The area of the hunt or of crop-gathering, exploited in a completely irrational manner, soon became exhausted, and migration was the common rule. When the children married among themselves the clan became a more complex organism, which demanded a more flexible government, more difficult to achieve, with the result that rivalries were born that hastened the dismemberment of the small primitive society, so that at the end of a few thousand years the greater part of the ancient world had been traveled. We have proof of this in the fact that for the archanthropines two expansion centers can be established, situated at several tens of thousands of kilometers distance from one another in the Far East and in South Africa, and it appears that only the South African branch persisted in time. The apparent independence of these two branches suggested to Father Teilhard (1953) that "an early break must have taken place in the originally common evolutionary front." Actually, one should never lose sight of the relative immensity of the first stage of humanity compared with the others. Stratigraphic correlations are always difficult to evaluate, but even more difficult is the estimation of their duration in absolute time. We do no know the site of the cradle of humanity. Although, for plausible reasons, it would seem to us to be situated in Africa, we should not forget that the most ancient pithecanthropines known were found in Java, in the Villafranchian of the *Djetis* horizon (Koenigs-wald, 1956).

Be that as it may, this relatively rapid dispersal brought about very important consequences for the diffusion of what might today be termed more accurately "culture" than "civilization." The chief of the dissenting clan doubtless possessed eminent qualities, the very qualities that gave rise to his revolt: thus he left, endowed with approximately the same knowledge as that of the old people he was abandoning, to embark upon adventure with his own people and those loyal to him. He knew the methods of cutting and tool-making, of hunting and fishing, the means of preserving food. He made little effort to improve these, being occupied with innumerable necessary tasks. Since he had no contact with those he left behind and since he lived upon his own mental resources, any psychic progress he might have made was rare, as also was its practical application. Thus during very long periods technical development remained the same over very large areas. Proof of this can be seen in the geographical spread of the Acheulean flints, which can be found in almost identical form throughout the ancient world.

In the absence of any wooden remains, the rapid disappearance of which can be readily explained, we may well ask ourselves who were the first users of fire, traces of which are found only relatively late. But in this case a moment's reflection will provide the correct answer. In all probability man appeared far from the glacial fronts and cold zones. All the present-day primates live in warm regions, and their mode of life requires a mild temperature. There is no reason to suppose that the situation was different in those days. Furthermore, nomadic life required merely temporary shelter, huts made of branches, soon abandoned and rebuilt at the site of the next stopping place. It is therefore not surprising that no traces have been left; if fire was used, the ashes of these temporary hearths were scattered by the wind. Even dead bodies were left behind, with certain exceptions, which we will discuss later; for this reason skeletal human remains are extremely rare. It is all the more interesting to know their significance from a social stand-point. We are now confronted with the problem of the attitude of early man to death, and in a more general manner, to any religious concepts they may have had.

Without doubt the most important discovery for the study of the profound mentality of the first man is the one made at Choukoutien (Weidenreich, 1943). For ten of thousands of years man had been on the march. At the beginning of the Middle Pleistocene he reached the latitude of Peking toward the north, where at that time the prevailing temperature was rather cold. He therefore found refuge in a cave: for the first time we find him in a permanent dwelling, where in that period he remained for a long time. Among the very numerous remnants of stone and bone tools and of hearth implements, in use for a long time, there were bones of *Sinanthropus* (*Pithecanthropus pekinensis*), making up the remains of some forty individuals, with five skulls without faces, and a sixth partly preserved, five adult jaws (one complete to the point of symphysis, the others fragmentary): there was also part of a child's chin. In contrast, few of the other parts of the skeleton were found; there were only three fragmentary femurs and one humerus, all of them without epiphysis, which detracts considerably from their value.

Those skulls that could be reconstructed with the help of fragments show great resemblance to the Javanese *Pithecanthropus*, which would appear to support the theory of a common origin.

No one today disputes the fact that *Sinanthropus* was a man and the maker of tools and fire. The very scanty limb bones found appear to have no significance and must have been taken to the cave by accident. There is no trace of teeth in any of them, although they are often present on broken and scraped animal bones. Skulls and jaws are present in such large numbers that one is led to assume that they were carried there intentionally. Furthermore, in four of these the occipital part was raised by successive fractures, as if there had been an attempt to reach the brain. This suggests funeral rites of the type known as "two stage," which were still observed among the Buginese on the south coast of the Celebes, before their conversion to Islam in the eighteenth century. The body of the deceased was carried far from the dwelling and left out in the open, sheltered from beasts of prey. When the body had dried out, the head could be detached easily, without the need even to cut the cervical vertebrae. (No vertebrae were found at Choukoutien.) The skull was then solemnly carried to the village, carefully washed, and became a kind of protective divinity of the family of the deceased. Sometimes only the jaw was preserved, and it was worn around the neck, suspended from a cord, like a medal. Acts of ritual anthropophagy were associated with this cult; the occipital hole was enlarged with blows from a club on the base of the skull, then the brain was devoured by those who wished to assume the virtues and merits of the dead man. Certain anthropophagous tribes in Central Africa practiced similar rituals for a very long time.

Although we are not able to prove them, the conclusions that can be drawn from such comparisons are striking. Jaws and broken skulls reveal a funerary cult, the importance of which cannot be exaggerated. Will it be possible, aided by these, to penetrate more deeply into the mentality of these ancient men? Obviously, we must guard against making judgments with our Western mentality, yet we must lean, with interest mingled with respect, upon these obviously religious vestiges. What did these men think about before a dead body? The idea of death was spontaneously suggested to their mind. What could be the meaning of this rigidness, this cold, this impressive and final stillness? The dead man is present, there can be no doubt; he does not speak, he appears not to see or to hear; he is all the more formidable. He appears to be jealously guarding a terrible secret, which none can take from him without assuming part of his substance. And thus they believed that the head, the organ of command, so expressive yesterday and today fixed in its fearsome rigidness, must be the object of special veneration. And, in order to cover themselves with its guardian protection, the idea occurred to them to carry a few bones of the deceased about the person, like a talisman.

Any doubts that may be left by such an interpretation will be removed for the most part when the same rites are found to be observed religiously without substantial modification hundreds of thousands of years later (Monte Circeo skull) (Blanc, 1911), which seems to indicate an impressive perenniality of thought. Furthermore, it might be added that for the most part we are acquainted only with the skulls or mandibles of archanthropines, which also seems to indicate that such funerary practices, so suitable for a nomadic way of life, were practiced for a very long time and their use was recognized by all.

We must now return to the behavior of primitive man toward nature, to which he was closely joined, while being at the same time brutally separated from it. Here we encounter great difficulty. Our Western mentality, molded upon Judeo-Christian thought, is disappointed by the pictures that we attempt to make, as accurately as possible, in which we find no trace of the primitive revelation of which the Bible gives us such an excellent description: man entering with both feet upon a world created for him, his assimilation into nature taking place harmoniously. From the outset he is truly the chief and the king of his inferior brothers; it is only when—owing to his vanity—he loses his innocence, that he feels profoundly unhappy, crushed under the weight of an incomprehensible curse, which he tries to appease by holocausts and sacrifices. Father Schmidt (1936) has attempted to justify this point of view by establishing a link between "the primitive character of a culture and the purity of its religion." But this attempt was fruitless: it is plain that we must try to shed all these influences and remain on a phenomenological plane; if reality was different, then we are unable to discover it by scientific means. Perhaps never before did our dramatic powerlessness to depict the integrality of the past appear so clearly. To remedy this, we are forced to make use of observations made on archaic peoples, who seem to us the only ones who kept the thought processes of very early man (Leenhardt, 1953).

In the first stage, bathed, so to speak, in the milieu surrounding him, man was not yet separated from the world: everything was human in some way—the river and the mountain, the dog and the bear, the plant and the tree, are actual personalities; the entire world is impregnated with humanity and is inhabited and driven by the same life; there is no difference between the subject and the object. This is cosmomorphism.

Later, knowledge acquires greater objectivity. The subject and object separate; man becomes the supreme reality to which everything else relates. Objectivity and rationality are beginning to take hold, but the two modes of thought are concurrently used, and this new anthropomorphism continues to be mixed with cosmomorphism.

Mythical ideas then appear; reality seems too complex to be grasped as a whole; it is then circumscribed, and certain aspects are isolated; man grasps it and expresses it by means of pictures, words, and gestures.

When rational knowledge dawns, after long and sometimes disappointing series of observations and experiences, man is not free from his entire past; the two modes of knowledge always remain complementary, since man is not sufficiently released from his first methods to construct his modes of thought rationally.

In these primitive societies it is always difficult to distinguish in practice the "sacred," the realm of religious life, from the "profane," which corresponds to secular life. But it is quite certain that manifestations of inexplicable natural phenomena first of all become objects of religious fear: a storm, a violent wind, a waterspout, volcanic phenomena, reveal mysteries before which human intelligence feels powerless until a rational explanation can be found. It is equally plain that the periodicity of certain events causes them to be attributed to an unknown origin. Thus we are justified in thinking, in accord with Mircea Eliade (1953), that all the elements before which man feels powerless and ignorant, such as water, fire, the sun, the stars, the alternation of the seasons, are like "hierophanies" for primitive man, the supernatural phenomena plunging him into a sacral region, inciting him, despite the anxiety in his heart, to make of them as many spontaneous symbols as occur to his mind. To quote Goetz:

Thus we arrive at the great cosmic rituals, where we find sacrifice and mystery, animism and magic, totems and gods. . . . But always, the transcending God Himself is subjected to the material biological conditions of existence, and life itself is divinified as eternally cyclical and creative: God and the universe blend into a monist unit, sacrificing either the reality of God outside the world, or the reality of the world outside of God [Bergounioux and Goetz, 1958].

The rise that is marked by the substitution of "theophanies" for "hierophanies" was a slow one. In contrast, it is reasonable to suppose that—lost in nature, often crushed by it, at any rate always powerless—man felt himself a supplicating soul, even if only to be delivered from the restraint of the obscure forces that oppressed him or to preserve his humble and precarious happiness. We have already seen him trying to penetrate the mystery of death; that life was no less formidable for him.

Conjectural as they are, these notes on the primitive states of humanity should be received and discussed with attention, for they reveal the importance of the human phenomenon. During this long and painful stagnation a secret psychic activity was ceaselessly exercised: the brain developed, intellectual faculties improved and became more clear cut, social functions began to take place. Heredity also made its appearance, mysteriously enriching the moral substrate of each individual. And in this initially indecisive march upon the roads of time, man learned to dominate his mystery and to find within himself the strength not to abandon the game in which he is engaged in spite of himself, alone and simultaneously joined to his fellows.

BIBLIOGRAPHY

ALIMEN, F.
   1955. *Prehistory of Africa*. Paris: Boubée.

BERGOUNIOUX, F. M.
   1943. *Components of a Civilization*. ("Mém. Ac. Sc. Toulouse," Vol. 5.)
   1958a. *Prehistory and Its Problems*. Paris: Fayard.
   1958b. *The Spirituality of Neanderthal Man*. Utrecht.

BERGOUNIOUX, F. M., and A. GLORY
   1952. *The First Man*. 4th ed. Paris: Didier.

BERGOUNIOUX, F. M., and P. GOETZ
   1958. *The Religion of Prehistoric and Primitive Man*. Paris: Fayard.

BLANC, C. A.
   1911. "Mont Circé Man," *Anthrop.* (Paris).

CHAUCHARD, P.
   1957. *Summary of Human Biology*. Paris: P.U.F.

ELIADE, MIRCEA
   1953. *Treatise on the History of Religion*. Paris: Payot.

HÜRZELER, J.
   1958. "Oreopithecus bambolii," *Verl. Nat. Ges.* (Basel), Vol. 69.

KONIGSWALD, R.
   1956. *The First Men on Earth*. Paris.

LEENHARDT, M.
   1953. "Some Common Elements in the Lower Forms of Religion." In *History of Religion*. Paris: Bloud.

MARTINY, M.
   1956. "Childhood, Maturity, Senility," *Pensée française* (Paris), Vol. 1.

SCHMIDT, R. R.
   1936. *Dawn of the Human Spirit*. Paris: Payot.

TEILHARD DE CHARDIN, P.
   1923. "Paleontology and the Appearance of Man," *Revue Philosophique* (Paris).
   1953. "Notes on the Probability of an Early Bifurcation of the Human Branch," *Ac. des Sciences* (Paris), Vol. 237.
   1955. "The Human Phenomenon," *Le Seuil* (Paris).

VALLOIS, H. V.
  1955. *The Order of the Primates.* ("Tr. de Zool., Grasse," Vol. 17.) Paris: Masson.
VERCORS (JEAN BRULLER)
  1952. *Denatured Animals.* Paris: A. Michel.
WEIDENREICH, F.
  1943. "The Skull of Sinanthropus pekinensis," *Pal. Sin.* (New York).

SOME EVIDENCE FOR THE IDEOLOGIES

OF EARLY MAN

ALBERTO C. BLANC

UMAN behavior in relation to man's ideologies may assume a specific importance and value, possibly more valid than the variations in the shape and size of skull or skeleton. In the following pages some facts will be produced to validate this statement.

Both the extreme complication and precision of psychological functions forming the background of such behavior, and the neurophysiological mechanisms involved, should be kept in mind when examining the available evidence.

I. THE UPPER PALEOLITHIC AND MESOLITHIC

The evidence for a complicated and rich ideological world in the so-called *Homo sapiens* of the Upper Paleolithic and Mesolithic is abundant. The cave engravings and paintings, the burials with their widely varying peculiarities, the evidence for sacrifices (Rust, 1937), and the burials of skulls or the evidence of the use of parts of the skull furnish valuable material for comparison with similar habits (or behavior) not only among the living so-called "primitives" but also in the folklore of the populations that have so-called "higher civilizations." From this it is possible to interpret the ideological motives that determined the apparent behavior and to classify the ideologies involved into the categories in which ethnologists and historians of religion have tried to subdivide the beliefs observable in living *Homo sapiens:* magic, animism, manism, belief in a supreme being, shamanism, fetishism, and so on. I have pointed out (Blanc, 1945) in what measure such tentative classification is inadequate. The main object of ethnologists and historians of religions has often been to resolve the ever apparent complexity of the beliefs into categories that existed only in their own minds, that is, none of the categories they created were, or had been, evidenced anywhere in the pure and simple form in which they had been conceived. They have always appeared associated, in various proportions, with other beliefs, pertaining to different categories; and instead of recognizing and stating the facts, which showed a constant mixture in the orientation of the human mind with regard to the indestructible need (a specifically human trait) to establish relations with the unknown and the uncanny, the authors tried to construct artificial and arbitrary evolutionary series, projecting their categories into the past and assuming that they once had a real existence as pure and isolated ideologies, with exclusion of any other one, and that there had been a development of evolution, which had brought forth other categories derived from the former ones. This inadequate methodology has one of its best examples in Tylor's theory of a transition from a primitive animism to monotheism, through the stages of polydemonism and polytheism. Evolutionism suffered greatly from this obvious error, revealed as such by the studies of Lang on the ideological world of the Australians. But, strangely enough, the dedicated antievolutionistic school, the so-called "School of Vienna" founded by Father W. Schmidt, got entangled in the same methodological error. Assuming as a starting point the positive results reached by Lang, but interpreting them from a theological point of view, Father Schmidt and some of his followers constructed an evolutionary series just as arbitrary as Tylor's: from a primitive monotheism revealed by revelation, man's beliefs were supposed to have degenerated into animism, manism, fetishism, and magic, the last being considered as the extreme consequence of such degeneration.

In reality, if one honestly faces the facts, the evidence proves a constant complexity in human beliefs that is ever present, both in the so-called "primitive" societies and in "civilized" cultures. Only the need for classification, which is inborn in man, was responsible for the creation of the "pure" categories of beliefs, which never and nowhere existed as such (as isolated and pure beliefs in absence of any others) but the main motives of which always existed in a state of mixture together with other motives evidencing other beliefs. The error of Father Schmidt was the same as the one committed by Tylor and other evolutionistic authors: he presumed that the categories born in his mind had had a historically objective existence as such and projected them into the farthest past of human history, considering them as the stages of a series of degenerative phases. This imaginary series is methodologically homologous to the equally imaginary progressive series postulated by Tylor (Blanc, 1945).

My statement on the constant complexity of human beliefs is valid and abundantly proved, at least since the Upper Paleolithic. Magic beliefs, including black magic, are widely evidenced in the Upper Paleolithic. The topographic location of engravings, paintings, and sculptures, often in the deepest and least accessible parts of the caves; the subjects treated; the almost constant alteration of the natural proportions of the human body; the fact that the same rock wall was repeatedly used and covered with successive artistic productions, covering one another and forming a sort of palimpsest, leave little doubt of the magic purpose of most of the Upper Paleolithic art.

It is clear that the purpose has been not to ornament the properly inhabited part of the cave (i.e., the area neighboring the entrance, which is partly accessible to light or at least to half-light) or to represent past events, but to promote the success of a future event that obviously had a major importance for the life of the community (a hunt, the increase of births, etc.). Once the event had taken place, the figures that had been engraved, painted, or sculptured lost any importance and purpose, and the same rock surface was used for new art productions. This was obviously a "sacred" surface, since long stretches of wall just as suitable to be ornamented, and often more easily accessible, were left untouched.

But Paleolithic art does not evidence only magic beliefs.[1] The engraved and painted figure of the so-called "sorcerer" of the Cave of the Trois Frères in Ariège, described originally by Abbé Breuil as the figure of a sorcerer, bearing a sort of costume composed of parts of different animals—the horns of a deer, the paws of a bear, the eyes of an owl, the tail of a wolf or of a horse (Begouen and Breuil, 1920)—obviously the figure of the god or genius of the hunting people. Abbé Breuil was the first to reverse his previous opinion and as early as 1931 clearly pointed out that what he had called a "sorcerer" must rather have represented a mythic supernatural being, furnished with the attributes of the animals that were the object of the hunts of the tribe (Breuil, 1931, 1952, p. 170) (Fig. 1). Other so-called "masked figures" in Upper Paleolithic art are likely to represent similar gods or geniuses. The new interpretation of the "sorcerer" as the mythic god of the hunting people acquires substantial validity by comparison with the god or genius of the fishing tribes of the Solomon Islands: a human figure in a dancing attitude, bearing fishes or parts of fishes' bodies for the head, hands, and feet, and a tuna tail. It is the figure of a supernatural being, regulating by his will the results of the fishing activities upon which the life of the tribe depends, a typically religious belief, following Frazer's definition (Blanc, 1945, pp. 171–72; Pettazzoni, 1957, pp. 202–3) (Fig. 2).

Objects that have been interpreted as "bull roarers" are known from the Upper Paleolithic (La Roche) (Blanc, 1945, 1948) (Fig. 3). They are, in fact, identical in shape and very similar in the ornamental (or more often symbolic) engraved decoration that they bear to the sacred instruments used in the initiation ceremonies by the totemistic tribes in North and Central Australia, which are connected with the belief in a uranic supreme being (Fig. 4). The sacred symbolic meaning of the roar is revealed during the ceremony as representing the voice of the supreme being, the thunder. The "bull roarer" is still used as a toy in Sicily and in other districts of Italy, which might prove to be the evidence for a long survival of an object that originally had a sacred meaning but that had lost its sacred character through the ideological crises undergone by "civilized" Europe, though persisting as a toy in the folk culture.

It has been observed among many modern "primitives" that the belief in a uranic supreme being is intimately related to the belief in a "Master of the

1. We use here the terms "magic" and "religious" following Frazer's definitions, although it is, in our opinion, too schematic: magic being produced by the belief in impersonal forces, which act automatically and obey whoever applies the right formula or magic operation; religion implying the belief in personal forces, and the intervention of supernatural beings, whose capricious will may be influenced by prayer and sacrifices.

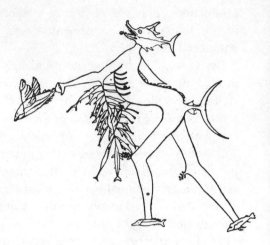

FIGURE 1

The "Master of the Animals" or "God of the Hunters," an engraved and painted figure of the "Grotte des Trois Frères," Montesquieu-Avantès (Ariège, France). (*From H. Breuil.*)

FIGURE 2

The "Genius of the Sea" or "God of the Fishermen," a mythic figure of the present fishing tribes of the Solomon Islands (Melanesia). (*From Codrington.*)

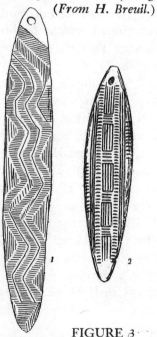

FIGURE 3

"Bull roarers": (1) of the Totemistic Australian tribes from Australia; (2) from the Upper Paleolithic site of "La Roche" (*France*).

FIGURE 4

Australian witch doctor, rotating a bull roarer in an initiation ceremony. The "roar" produced by this sacred instrument symbolizes the voice of the Supreme Being (the Thunder).

Animals," god of the forest and of the hunting (Pettazzoni, 1957). Very often the two myths are coincident in one and the same being. The simultaneous presence of both the figures of a "Master of the Animals" and of the bull roarer (the modern symbol of the uranic supreme being) in the Upper Paleolithic of France suggests that this polyvalence of the supreme being is an archaic feature and that the segregation and differentiation of the specialized myths of the uranic "Father in the Sky," free from any zoömorphic feature, of the "Master of the Animals," deprived of its uranic character, and even of the "Mother Earth" are the product of successive developments. In this process the myth of the "Master of the Animals" seems to have evolved toward the belief in the "Enemy" or "Trickster" (as, for instance, the Coyote in North America), losing its uranic character and acquiring that of a malevolent and clumsy rival of God the Father, living in the sky. There is some evidence pointing to the gradual evolution from the half-beastly, half-human former "Master of the Animals" to the modern myth of the Devil, which has retained a conspicuous portion both of the character of the "Trickster" and of its half-beastly features (Blanc, 1960).

A similar survival that has retained some of the original sacred character likely to have been the background of most Paleolithic customs, is the use for personal ornament of the rudimentary upper canines of the deer. Their use is evidenced in sites and burials of the Upper Paleolithic from England to Spain, France, Germany, Italy, eastern Europe, the Middle and the Far East (Choukoutien's Upper Cave). They are at present the preferred trophy of the deer hunters of Central Europe (*Hirschgrandeln*). The rudimentary canines are often carved out with a knife even before the death of the deer; and in Hungary the hunter kneels down, offering the canines he has collected to the master of the hunt— a probable sign of the former magic or sacred meaning of the trophy. It is obvious that such practice has been traditionally perpetuated from father to son among the deer hunters in the areas where the deer have persisted uninterruptedly since the Upper Paleolithic, as in the forests of Germany, Austria, and Hungary.

The use of red ocher in the burials of the Upper Paleolithic, Mesolithic, and Neolithic (both in laying the cadaver on a bed of ocher and in painting the bones with red ocher in secondary burials) is the oldest evidence for the use of red color for funerary purposes. The practice has survived in Europe in historic times, in Greek, Etruscan, and Roman archeology, as evidenced by numerous burials and sarcophagi bearing traces of red paint in their interior. Homer and other classic authors state that the dead were enveloped in red shrouds, and the same funerary habit was practiced by the noblemen in Florence in the fifteenth century. At present, the dead pope is enveloped in a red shroud. This is a fair example of the almost total loss of a cultural ideological element, surviving only in Europe (as far as I know) in the very conservative funerary ritual of the pontiff.

Burials of skulls in the Upper Paleolithic and Mesolithic sites (Arcy-sur-Curé, Placard, Ofnet, etc.) point to head-hunting or similar practices. In Spain, in

France, and in Moravia, skull cups have been discovered consisting of part of the frontal and the parietals, carefully scalped and cut so as to produce a cup; their position on the floor, resting on their convex part, legitimates such interpretation. The use of strictly similar portions of human skulls as cups for religious ceremonies is well known in present Tibet and occasionally also in the European Middle Ages (King Alboin obliged his wife Rosamunda to drink from the skull of her murdered father).

Sacrifices are clearly evidenced in the Upper Paleolithic (see the seventeen female reindeer buried with stones in their stomachs in the pond near the reindeer hunters' station of Meiendorf (Hamburg) (Rust, 1937; Blanc, 1945, Pl. VI). The engravings discovered in the Upper Paleolithic cave of Addaura (Palermo) point to the existence of human sacrifices of a very peculiar type (Blanc, 1954, 1955; Chiapelli, 1954).

II. EARLY AND LATE NEANDERTHAL MAN

If we try to penetrate the ideological world of Neanderthal man, our tentative analysis is hindered by the lack of any art production. But the burials furnish not only a number of significant hints but also very definite evidence.

The position of the cadaver in burials of Neanderthal man is just as variable as in the Upper Paleolithic, the position varying from an attitude of rest to violently flexed, contracted legs and arms, as if the body had been bound before burial. The interpretation of a similar practice among present "primitives" varies greatly from author to author, the most frequently given being fear of the dead, with the intention of preventing their return.

In the cave Basua (Savona) a vaguely zoömorphic stalagmite has been used by Neanderthal man (evidenced by its footprints, identified by F. Pales) as a target for a presumably magic ceremony consisting of throwing clay pellets at the target. This practice occurred in the innermost chamber of the cave (the cave being a cave bear's den, littered with cave bear bones), 450 meters away from its opening: an extremely uncanny environment. The hypothesis of a game should not be considered, but rather one of a magic ceremony in which it appears for the first time that Neanderthal man used unmodified zoömorphic natural features of the caves for magic purposes, long before the birth of art by the so-called *Homo sapiens*, an art that sometimes consisted of the intentional modification, by the addition of engravings upon vaguely zoömorphic stalagmites or cave walls (Blanc, 1957; Breuil, 1958, p. 88, n. 1).

The most conspicuous evidence for definite ideologies in Neanderthal man consists in the burial of the skull No. 1 of Monte Circeo (Blanc, 1939*a*, *b*, and *c*, 1942, 1958) (Figs. 5-7). The Monte Circeo skull, representing a late or typical Neanderthal of La Chapelle-aux-Saints or Neanderthal form, about the age of forty-five at death, was lying on the floor of a cave surrounded by a circle of stones. The skull bears two mutilations: one caused by one or more violent

FIGURE 5

The Neanderthal skull of Monte Circeo (Circeo I) (*left view*). (*photo A. C. Blanc.*)

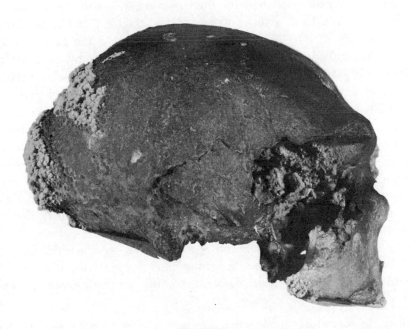

FIGURE 6

The Neanderthal skull of Monte Circeo (Circeo I) (*right view*). (*photo A. C. Blanc.*)

blows on the right temporal region that has caused conspicuous damage to the frontal, the temporal, and the zygoma. This mutilation points to a violent death, more probably a ritual murder. The other mutilation consists of the careful and symmetric incising of the periphery of the *foramen magnum* (which has been completely destroyed) and the consequent artificial production of a subcircular opening about 10–12 centimeters in diameter (Fig. 8). A careful specific study by Sergio Sergi has resulted in a very definite statement on the artificial and intentional nature of the mutilation of the base of the skull; the technical basis for the statement leaves no doubt as to its validity.

Now, this intentional mutilation is *identical* to the one presently produced by head-hunters of Borneo and Melanesia (Blanc, 1945) (Fig. 9) with the object of extracting the brain and eating it for ritual and social purposes, one of which is the necessity for assigning a name to the newborn. In certain tribes of New Guinea a newborn child receives a name only after the killing and beheading of a man whose name is known. The father or a near relative mutilates the base of the skull of the victim, extracts its brain, bakes it with sago, and eats it, after which the infant may bear the name of the dead one. The mutilated skull is kept as a sacred object in the home until the death of the new bearer of the name (Wirz, 1925, p. 59; Volhard, 1939, p. 183). This gruesome custom is practiced by tribes that are not particularly bloodthirsty or aggressive and have rather high morals; the ritual cannibalism is performed as a strict obligation toward the community, on the one hand, and the newborn, on the other. When the Dutch government tried to stop this tradition, the tribes revolted. Their argument was: "We have to give names to our children, and how could we handle it otherwise?" The similarity of the mutilation of the base in Circeo's skull with the mutilation performed by the present head-hunters of Melanesia and Borneo is obvious. As far as I know, such mutilation is at present performed only in relation to ritual cannibalism. Dr. Adolph Schultz has shown me, in Zurich, skulls of gorillas from Africa, mutilated in exactly the same way by natives, for the purpose of extracting and eating the brain. Although no ritual motive is clearly connected with such practice, there is an interesting indication toward an eventual ideological background to it, furnished by Professor H. Vallois during this symposium. Among African tribes that practice this custom, only the male members of the tribe are allowed to eat the brain of the ape, which is strictly forbidden to the women. "If a woman should eat it, she would die; and she does not want to die."

Because of the distance in time and space covered by the evidence so far, I would have hesitated to assume it as strong enough for stating that the Circeo skull mutilation also had a ritual background. But more evidence is available pointing to just such a conclusion:

1. Among the present-day head-hunters, one of the most frequent traditional ways to kill the victim is to strike a blow with a heavy wooden ax on the temporal area of

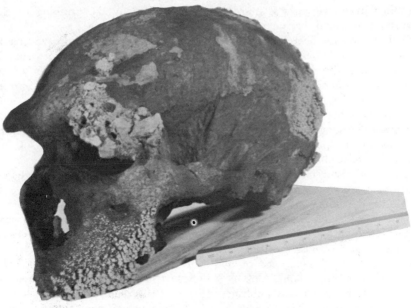

FIGURE 7

The Neanderthal skull of Monte Circeo (Circeo I), showing a lump of the sediment on which it was resting still adhering to its left supraorbital ridge (*photo A. C. Blanc.*)

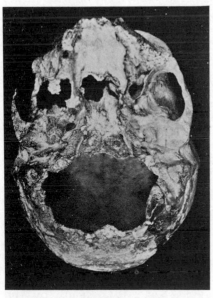

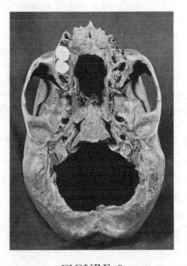

FIGURE 8

The Neanderthal skull of Monte Circeo (Circeo I) (*basal view*); length, 204 mm., width, 155 mm. (*photo S. Sergi.*)

FIGURE 9

Basal view of a modern skull from the Island of D'Entrecasteaux (Melanesia) mutilated by local headhunters with the purpose of extracting the brain and eating it, in a ceremony of ritual cannibalism. The skull is that of an adult male. (Collection Loria, Instituto di Antropologia, University of Rome.) (*Photo S. Sergi.*)

the skull. Circeo's victim was murdered, as is shown by the crushing of the right supraorbital ridge and the fracture of the temporal and zygoma.

2. The victim was beheaded and the skull mutilated outside the cave, inasmuch as no trace of the skeleton or of fragments of the mutilated base have been found inside.

3. The skull, after its mutilation, was laid on the floor in the center of an inner subcircular chamber of the cave and honored by a crown or circle of stones. This is a procedure that has not been used for any of the many animal bones and skulls that litter the other rooms of the cave. The fact that the skull was found *in situ* on the Mousterian floor of the cave, not covered by sediment, is another major reason for excluding the possibility that natural causes, such as the pressure of overlying sediments, produced the mutilations.

4. The skull rested on its forehead and left parietal, with the mutilated base turned upward as if it had been used as a cup (Blanc, 1958, pp. 158–59).

5. While the other chambers of the Circeo cave (Grotta Guattari) are littered with bones, antlers, and skulls, the one in which the Neanderthal skull was lying contained only three groups of a few bones each: one group lying between two big stones resting against the wall near the entrance; another one about two meters away from the skull, composed of bones of *Sus scropha ferus*, *Cervus elaphus*, and *Bos primigenius*. These bones look as if they had been laid there as a ritual offering, and such interpretation was published (Blanc, 1939) before the species of all the bones was determined. The animals to which they belong may confirm this view if consideration is given to the composition of the classical sacrifice of much later archeological times in the Mediterranean area, that is, the *Suovetaurilia* (the sacrifice of the pig, the ram, and the bull). In the Neanderthal cave the deer seems to replace the ram (*Ovis*), and two wild forms, *Bos* and *Sus*, replace the domesticated varieties of the Holocene. If this view is correct, the tradition of the *Suovetaurilia* may have had very deep roots in the past, and the absence of any bone of *Equus* among the bones lying on the floor of the chamber containing the skull may confirm this, *Equus* remains being frequent in the main chamber.

6. While the floor of the main chamber of the cave is covered with a sort of artificial pavement of stones, probably intended to diminish the humidity of the floor and make it more fit for habitation, the small chamber that contained the skull does not show a similar feature. The only stones lying on its floor were the circular group disposed around the skull and only a few others near the walls and the entrance.

These facts all coincide in pointing to a ritual background for the deposition of the Circeo mutilated Neanderthal skull in the chamber that is to be considered as the "sacred" part of the cave (and which was not used for proper habitation but, rather, for ritual meetings and ceremonies). As far as I know from ethnography, this particular mutilation is produced only for the purpose of performing ritual cannibalism. I believe that it is legitimate to assume as highly probable that the significance of Circeo's burial has the same background and significance. This conclusion is strengthened by the previous finds and observations by Weidenreich on the Ehringsdorf skull (Blanc, 1945, 1960), by von Koenigswald on the Ngandong skulls (1937), and by Berckhemer on the Steinheim skull (1934). Weidenreich's conclusion in his very careful study of the Ehringsdorf skull reads as follows:

a) the frontal area bears undoubted signs of having been hit by stone weapons and it can be assumed that this individual had been murdered; b) the absence of the cranial base, no fragment of which was contained in the block of travertine from which the skull has been extracted, indicates that the skull had been opened to extract the brain [Weidenreich, 1928].

Nevertheless, the Ehringsdorf find was so fragmentary that Weidenreich's far-reaching statement may have appeared too definite for the evidence available, and in fact but little notice has been given to it.

In 1931 the eleven mutilated skulls discovered at Ngandong by TerHaar and von Koenigswald brought forth new valuable evidence. The human remains collected amounted to only the eleven skulls and two tibias, whereas the accompanying faunal remains (more than 2,000 specimens) included every part of the skeleton. This obviously points out a selection performed only in reference to the human skulls, as in a present head-hunters' ritual. However, there is more to it. All these skulls show an artificial destruction of the base, together with more extended destruction (some of which may eventually prove not to be artificial) occurring in the occipital area (save in two skulls) and in the facial area. Von Koenigswald had pointed out the similarity of the mutilation of the base with the ritual mutilation performed by the head-hunters from Borneo and had stated that the Ngandong finds evidenced a group of skulls, mutilated for a ritual purpose, collected in a sort of "skull's altar" like the analogous custom observed by ethnographers in present-day Melanesia. Ngandong V clearly shows that this individual had been murdered by a strong blow on the occipital (von Koenigswald, 1937). I have personally examined with the greatest care the specimens from Ngandong, with the kind permission of Ralph von Koenigswald, and have found that the mutilation of the base shows the same shape and features as the mutilation in the Circeo skull, with the destruction of particularly solid and hard portions of the periphery of the *foramen magnum*. The mutilations of the base are certainly artificial. It is very hard to tell whether the facial mutilations are also artificial.

In 1932 the Steinheim skull brought confirmation to Weidenreich's and von Koenigswald's statements (Fig. 10). F. Berckhemer, who carefully collected the skull from the gravels where it was embedded, stated that the absence in the gravels of any fragment of the missing parts of the edge of the *foramen magnum* excluded the possibility that the mutilation had occurred through natural causes (such as the pressure of the sediments after the skull had been deposited into the gravels) and that "it is legitimate to assume that we are facing an extended artificial widening of the foramen performed for the purpose of extracting the brain" (Berckhemer, 1934). The Steinheim skull shows another extensive mutilation on the right temporal area. The features of the mutilation point to a strong blow received before death, just as in the case of the similar mutilation shown on the right temporal in the Circeo skull. As a matter of fact, the mutilations shown by the Steinheim skull are of the same type and shape as in the Circeo skull and in skulls taken by present head-hunters of Melanesia and Borneo.

It is worth noting that these most significant statements, resting on good firm evidence, have encountered a poor reception among interested anthropologists. E. Volhard (1939), in his monograph "Kannibalismus," has stated that no valid evidence for the existence of cannibalism in prehistoric times had yet been observed. Volhard changed his mind only in 1942, when I was able to show him

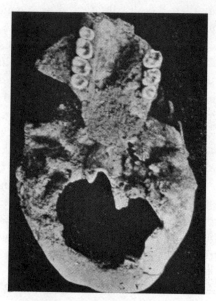

FIGURE 10
The proto-Neanderthal skull of Steinheim (*basal view*) (*from F. Berckhemer*).

the evidence of the Circeo skull. He kindly dedicated his book to me: "To the discoverer of prehistoric cannibalism," an honor that was deserved by Weidenreich, von Koenigswald, and Berckhemer more than by me. There seems to be a widespread reluctance to recognize properly the highly human mental functions in Neanderthal man: the tendency can be traced back in physical anthropology also, and was responsible in this field for serious errors, such as the one by M. Boule in his reconstruction of the base of the La-Chapelle-aux-Saints skull. To this error we owe the well-known reconstruction by Boule of the skeleton of Neanderthal man in an incompletely upright posture—a reconstruction that is still reproduced in recently published books. The evidence of the Saccopastore, Circeo, and La Ferrassie skulls, on the other hand, demonstrates beyond all doubt that Neanderthal man had a fully erect posture, as much so as that of so-called "*Homo sapiens*," and this is as it should be, considering that we now know for certain that a fully erect posture was characteristic of both *Sinanthropus* and *Pithecanthropus*.

The widely different types and chronology of the Neanderthal finds showing the ritual mutilation of the base is highly significant.

Steinheim skull has been dated by W. Soergel to an advanced stage of the Great Interglacial, and, more recently on paleontological grounds, by K. D. Adam to the same Interglacial (Adam, 1954). Its age may therefore be estimated at around 300,000 years. Its type belongs to the so-called "Early Neanderthals" or "Pre-Neanderthals," characterized by a mixture of Neanderthal and *sapiens* features.

The Ehringsdorf skull was included in travertines attributed to the Last Interglacial. Its age may be estimated to be around 150,000–120,000 years. Its type also belongs to the "Early Neanderthals" and bears some more *sapiens*-like features: its occipital is rounded as in the Steinheim, Gibraltar, and Saccopastore skulls.

The dating of the Ngandong skulls in reference to the European finds is not well defined. Their type is a generalized Neanderthal one, probably a Far Eastern representative of the Neanderthal race.

The age of the Circeo skull is very well defined. It was resting on the continental filling of a cave containing a typical Mousterian industry, overlying a *Strombus* beach of the Last Interglacial. Remains of *Elaphus antiquus* and *Rhinoceros merckii* were lying on the same surface. Therefore, its age is definitely later than the Last Interglacial and previous to the extinction in Italy of the above-mentioned pachyderms, all of which points to a late phase of Würm I. A C-14 date of a peat layer in the Pontine plain, comparable in its stratigraphic position and its paleontological and archeological content to the surface of this Circeo Neanderthal cave, has given an age earlier than —55,000 years (Blanc, de Vries, and Follieri, 1957). My previous estimate of the age of the skull had been from —60,000 to —70,000 years (Blanc, 1939).

The conclusion is that the mutilation of the base of the skull has been performed by "early" and "late" Neanderthals for a very long time, estimated to be about 250,000 years. Ritual cannibalism appears to be added to other traditional features of the "Mousterian culture" (*sensu lato*) that have survived for a very long time. The "Mousterian" culture has persisted, practically unchanged, for a long time, while the somatic character of the races that produced it have evolved and changed very definitely during the same period of time. In other words, the cultural features of the "Mousterian" culture appear to have been far more stable than the somatic features of their bearers and some have survived in the present *Homo sapiens* culture (Blanc, 1958). Such stability can be explained only in terms of the power of tradition and of cultural continuity through evolving human races, which in the meanwhile changed somatic type in time and space.

While in the Upper Paleolithic no comparable evidence has ever been found, there is definite evidence of the survival of a ritual cannibalism, having for its object the eating of the brain, in the European late prehistory (Fig. 11). K. Gerhardt's (1951) most valuable discovery of two skulls from Germany's

Bronze Age site of Wansleben and Helfta, Sachsen, bearing the typical mutilation of the *foramen magnum*, is highly significant. The two skulls, both belonging to adult males, show this mutilation, which is undoubtedly intentional and of prehistoric age, following the very careful description by K. Gerhardt and the characters visible on the photos: "Form und Zustand, wie sie eben beschrieben

FIGURE 11
Skull from the Bronze Age site of Wansleben (Sachsen, Germany) belonging to the "Glockenbecker" culture (*basal view*). The base has been intentionally mutilated.
(*From K. Gerhardt.*)

wurden und auch aus den Abbildungen zu ersehen sind, schliessen von vornherein die Möglichkeit aus, dass es sich um organische (pathologische) Veränderungen handeln könnte. Auch eine zufällige Entstehung ist undenkbar. Es bleibt die Deutung einer künstlichen Bewirkung." The Wansleben skull is connected with the "Glockenbecker" culture and belongs to the Mansfelder Seekreis. So does another skull from Helfta, which is connected with the "Frühaunjetitzer" culture, following immediately the "Glockenbecker" culture. In a third skull, from a Neolithic burial of Helfta described by K. Gerhardt, the author inclines to attribute a somewhat smaller mutilation of the foramen to the action of rodents, and effectively this mutilation has a different character, and the traces of the rodent's teeth are visible on its margin. The discovery of the two mutilated skulls from Helfta bridges the Neanderthalian evidence described above, and the custom practiced in the present by the modern head-hunters of Borneo and Melanesia.

III. THE PITHECANTHROPIAN RACES

The evidence for the ideologies of the pithecanthropian races is almost nil. We have, as yet, no sign of the practice of burials or any hint of any belief of any kind, except the most valuable evidence furnished by the *Sinanthropus* site Choukoutien (Peking). There the facts are well known. The site has yielded many thousands of pieces of faunal remains pertaining to every part of the skeleton (just as at Ngandong but on a far larger scale); and, as at Ngandong, the *Sinanthropus* finds, belonging to over forty individuals, are represented by skulls and fragments of skulls but only a very few fragments of limb bones. In this case, as at Ngandong, selection has doubtless been performed so that essentially almost only the skulls of *Sinanthropus* have been brought into the cave, a circumstance that strongly points to the practice of head-hunting.

Moreover, among all the skull fragments available, F. Weidenreich was able to reconstruct an almost complete skull of *Sinanthropus*. Only one area is completely missing (not a single fragment of it having been collected in the cave): the area of the base around the *foramen magnum* (Fig. 12). The reconstructed skull of *Sinanthropus* offers, therefore, an astonishing resemblance to the mutilated skulls of the "early" and "late" Neanderthals and to the skulls mutilated for the purpose of practicing ritual cannibalism in the Bronze Age of Germany and by the present head-hunters from Borneo and New Guinea.

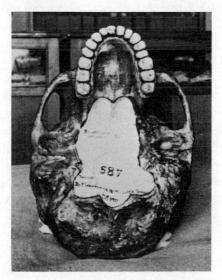

FIGURE 12

Reconstruction of the *Sinanthropus* skull by F. Weidenreich (*basal view*). The reconstruction was made using all the fragments of skulls discovered. No fragment of the white area (the periphery of the *foramen magnum*) has so far been discovered. This fact strongly indicates that the *Sinanthropus* skulls, just as the Circeo I skull, had already been mutilated before their introduction in the cave, probably for ritual purposes.

We may therefore state that the only available objective evidence of an ideology in the pithecanthropian race points definitely to an extremely early birth of a tradition that was to survive major evolutionary events undergone by mankind, through the Neanderthal stages, and that persists in the ethnography of present *"Homo sapiens"*: the ritual mutilation of the base of the skull, very probably for a cannibalistic purpose, since the very first evidence for the tradition.

It may be pointed out that the mental functions and psychical *Einstellung* that form the background of ritual cannibalism may also be traced in the classic Mediterranean world, where the ideological crises undergone, possibly in the late stages of prehistory, may have produced a transition from an archaic effective cannibalism to a symbolic cannibalism. A similar transitional process can be observed in present ethnography, for instance among the Jivaros of Gualaquiza— a valuable evidence for the real existence of such a transitional process under certain cultural circumstances.

In the Dionysiac mysteries of ancient Greece, a goat used to be eaten symbolizing Dionysus. Ritual symbolic theophagy had obviously its origin in former ritual effective cannibalism. The original *Einstellung* was the same, and the mental functions involved were identical: the urgent need (a typically human psychological feature) of establishing a relation with the unknown and a mystic link between life and death. Only a gradual sublimation of the practice, once it had become symbolic, rendered obsolete the continuity of the tradition through the ages.

Finally, it may not be insignificant to note that St. Paul, in his Letter to the Corinthians, stresses with particular strength the motive of the real presence of Christ's blood and flesh in the eucharistic ritual: a powerful means of promoting the penetration and acceptance of Christianity and its major ritual in Greece, where the tradition of the Dionysiac symbolic ritual meal was particularly strong and deeply felt.

We may conclude with the words of Paul Wernert: "The instinctive reactions and the mental functions of primitive mankind are similar in time and in space." And we may, moreover, cut out the word "primitive" when we honestly recognize that some of the primitive "mental folds" that characterize the human mind had their inception in the very early stages of human development, have persisted through the ages (and through the conspicuous changes in the cultural and somatic features of mankind and its racial differentiation), and are undefeatably surviving even in highly "civilized" cultures.

BIBLIOGRAPHY

ADAM, K. A.
  1954. "Die Mittelpleistozänen Fauna von Steinheim an der Murr. (Württemberg),"
  Quaternaria (Rome), Vol. 1.

BEGOUEN, H., and H. BREUL
1920. "Un dessin relevé dans la Grotte des Trois Frères à Montesquieu-Avantès (Ariège)," *C. R. Acad. des Inscriptions* (Paris), pp. 45 and 303, Fig. 2.

BERCKHEMER, F.
1934. "Der Steinheimer Urmensch und die Tierwelt seines Lebensgebietes," *Naturwiss. Monatschr. d. Deutschen Naturkundever. E. V.* (Stuttgart), 47:4.

BLANC, A. C.
1939a. "Il Monte Circeo, le sue grotte paleolitiche ed il suo Uomo fossile," *Boll. Soc. Geogr. It.* (Rome).

1939b. "L'Homme fossile du Mont Circé," *L'Anthropologie* (Paris), Vol. 49, Nos. 3–4.

1939c. "L'Homo fossile del Monte Circeo: Un cranio neandertaliano nella Grotta Guattari a San Felice Circeo," *R. C. Accad. Naz. dei Lincei* (Rome), XXIX, s. 6, I⁰ sem., Fasc. 5.

1942. "I Paleantropi di Saccopastore e del Circeo," *Quartär* (Freiburg), Vol. 4.

1945. *Il Sacro presso i primitivi.* Rome: Partenia.

1954a. "Considerazioni su due figure dell'Addaura," *Quaternaria* (Rome), Vol. 1.

1954b. "Il sacrificio umano dell'Addaura e il nesso ideologico tra morte e generazione nella mentalità primitiva," *Quaternaria* (Rome), Vol. 1.

1955. "Il sacrificio umano dell'Addaura e la messa a morte rituale mediante strangolamento nell'etnologia e nella paletnologia," *Quarternaria* (Rome), Vol. 2.

1957. "A New Paleolithic Cultural Element, Probably of Ideological Significance: The Clay Pellets of the Cave of the Basua (Savona)," *Quaternaria* (Rome), Vol. 4.

1958a. *Dall'astrazione all'organicità,* Figs. 55 and 56. Rome.

1958b. *Torre in Pietra, Saccopastore, Monte Circeo: On the Position of the Mousterian Culture in the Pleistocene Sequence of the Rome Area* ("Hundert Jahre Neanderthaler" [Gedenkbuch, ed. by the Wenner-Gren Foundation for Anthropological Research], pp. 167–74. Utrecht).

1960. "Considerazioni sulla 'preistoria' del dualismo religioso," *Riv. Storica It.* Torino.

BLANC, A. C., H. DE VRIES, and M. FOLLIERI
1957. "A first C14 Date for the Würm I Chronology on the Italian Coast," *Quaternaria* (Rome), Vol. 4.

BREUIL, H.
1931. "Sociologie préhistorique." In *Les Origines de la Societé, Centre International de Synthèse,* Vol. I. Paris.

1952. *Quatre-cents Siècles d'art pariétal.* Paris.

1958. "Quelques notes sur l'origine de l'Art." Appendix to A. C. BLANC, *Dall'Astrazione all'Organicità.* Rome.

CHIAPPELLA, G.
1954. "Altre considerazioni sugli 'acrobati' dell'Addaura," *Quaternaria,* 1:181–83.

GERHARDT, K.
1951. "Künstliche Veränderungen am Hinterhauptloch vorgeschichtlicher Schädel," *Germania,* 29:3–4.

KOENIGSWALD, G. H. R. VON
1937. "A Review of the Stratigraphy of Java and Its Relations to Early Man." In *Early Man.* Philadelphia.

PETTAZZONI, R.
  1957. *L'Essere Supremo nelle religioni primitive*. Torino.
RUST, A.
  1937. *Die altsteinzeitliche Rentierjägerlager Meiendorf*. Neirmünster i.H.
VOLHARD, E.
  1939. *Kannibalismus*. Stuttgart.
WEIDENREICH, F.
  1928. *Der Schädelfund von Weimar-Ehringsdorf*. Jena.
WIRZ, P.
  Die Marind-Anim von Holl. Süd-Neu-Guinea, Vol. 3. Hamburg.

THE SOCIAL LIFE OF EARLY PALEOLITHIC MAN
AS SEEN THROUGH THE WORK OF
THE SOVIET ANTHROPOLOGISTS

G. F. DEBETZ

PRELIMINARY OBSERVATIONS

THE SOCIAL life of Paleolithic man cannot be the object of study through direct observation. The facts dealt with by modern science are not very numerous and have only an indirect relation to the matter under investigation. Therefore, these facts may be understood only in the framework of a system that comprises all knowledge derived from human experience. This means that a philosophical conception of the whole is involved. The role that the philosophical conception plays in certain aspects of scientific research is not always or sufficiently apparent. But the problem to be studied is among those that cannot be dealt with through a simple investigation of facts relating to them directly.[1]

It is the earliest phase of social evolution that is the subject of the present communication. Soviet scholars generally call it the "phase of the primitive human group." The following reasons make us delimit this phase: (*a*) the character of the middle, and especially of the early, Paleolithic implements, which are considerably distinguishable from the implements of the late Paleolithic—proving the existence of a specific phase in the evolution of productive forces, a phase that ethnography does not enable one to study; and (*b*) the notable differences in the physical form of man himself.

Reckoning from the principle that mutual relations exist between phenomena, we should conclude that the social life of early Paleolithic man also had certain characteristics that are not found in even the most primitive societies still in

1. I have based this communication on the research of Soviet scholars and have profited greatly by the advice of my colleagues given on their examination of the manuscript. It is necessary, however, to note that the identical character of the philosophical concepts by no means implies a community of opinion with regard to details. The problems stated in this communication are numerous and are still far from mustering unanimity among Soviet scholars. That is why I wish to stress the fact that I am expressing only my personal opinion on the problems being dealt with.

existence today. It is the import and the role of the facts on the physical type of man in the study of the earliest phase of his social life that is under consideration.

From the start, Soviet scholars will not easily find in the study of the stated problem a common ground with the supporters of the concept that denies the possibility of the existence of man's ancestors in the animal world. However, it would be difficult to meet supporters of such a point of view today. Still, it is necessary to go further. Soviet scholars will not find in the study of this problem a common ground with the supporters of the concept that denies the kinship between modern man and fossil men, that is, with the supporters of the poly-phyletic hypothesis, either.[2]

The problem being dealt with must have as a common base the principle of the evolution of man from lower forms, retaining individual characteristics of the original animal, to higher forms, in which the number of these characteristics is progressively reduced. To go on from this principle, the earliest forms of man should resemble *Pithecanthropus* and the other forms close to *Pithecanthropus*, both morphologically and genetically, according to their geological age and morphological characteristics. The principle of evolution leads us to recognize the existence of an evolutionary phase of the human type that represents a period of transition between the earliest ancestors (*Pithecanthropus* stage) and modern men. This transitional phase is called by the Soviet scholars the Neanderthal stage. At the same time, without contradicting the general principles, different points of view concerning the phylogenetic position of certain particular forms may, and do in fact, exist (for example, the men of La Chapelle aux Saints, of Saccopastore, of Broken-Hill; the men of the Palestine caves, of Swanscombe, and others).

We do not think that it would be useful in this report to stress the differences that exist between Soviet scholars and many Western scholars over the question of "presapiens," although the lack of unity of views on this problem might shrink the base on which the common efforts could be supported.

However, from the morphologic and genetic standpoint, it is not enough to divide the concept of evolution from the *Pithecanthropus* stage to modern man by the intermediate stage. It is necessary to have a precise attitude in regard to the general problems of the evolution of organisms.

There is a belief that this evolution occurs according to inner laws of the organisms. For example, with regard to the problem of human phylogeny, this was the belief of F. Weidenreich (1939). According to this eminent scholar, man evolved by passing through the *Pithecanthropus* stage to the Neanderthal stage and then to the stage of modern man. But, according to him, neither the

2. In order to be fully understood, I note here that the Soviet scholars as citizens of their country do not in principle debar the collaboration in other spheres of social life (for example, in the propaganda of peaceful coexistence) with the opponents of the idea of evolution of the physical type of man from lower forms to higher forms or even with the opponents of the belief in the existence of man's ancestors in the animal world.

level of development of productive forces nor the modifications in the geographic environment played a role in the evolution of the physical type of man. If one shares this belief, the modification of man's physical type clearly cannot then be of importance for the study of his social life. Weidenreich's concept represents a particular case of the application to human phylogeny of the concept of orthogenesis, one of the general doctrines of the evolution of living beings. It is not possible to go into detail about this concept in the framework of the present report. Therefore, I shall limit myself to saying that the Soviet biologists (including anthropologists) do not favor it, and I will cite A. N. Severtzov.

I consider it past belief (but not impossible a priori) to recognize the inner (inherent) principle of evolution as being based on the general law of the adaptation of organisms to the environment. If we recognize this inherent principle of evolution we should acknowledge at the same time that in nature there exists a certain pre-established harmony (in the sense of Leibniz) between the organisms which evolve and the environment which changes. That is to say, it is necessary to assume that a certain and advantageous modification, established before formation of the individual, corresponds to each modification of the environment (and they are innumerable). Such a version of the process of evolution is, to say the least, unlikely, and if we try to understand it we shall see that it explains nothing. To tell the truth, we find there only a statement of the fact of adaptation of organisms and not its explanation [Severtzov, 1912].

CLASSIFICATION OF THE HOMINIDS

The Soviet scholars, in the efforts to study evolution as a process in which the quantitative modifications, in accumulating, bring about the formation of a new characteristic, have expressed their attitude toward the evolution of the physical type of man in the form of the "theory of two jumps." According to this theory, the crucial moments in the evolution of man have been: (a) the separation of man from the animal world, and (b) the appearance of Homo sapiens. It is well understood that none of the Soviet scholars denies the differences that exist between Pithecanthropus and the Neanderthals. But, although these differences are quite substantial, they are not considered as a process of quantitative modification. The transition to Homo sapiens presents a fundamentally new step in hominization. From the time during which man became separated from the animal world up to the appearance of Homo sapiens we have the period of hominization. The period comprising the most remote times of Homo sapiens is marked by the stability of the characteristics of the species.

This picture should also be reflected in the nomenclature. All the fossil species of man should be compared to the modern species. This is why I propose to divide the genus Man into two subgenuses: that of "fossil man" and that of "modern man." According to the rules of nomenclature, the subgenus "fossil man" should be called Pithecanthropus. These landmarks of the system would then take the following form: *Homo (Homo) sapiens, Homo (Pithecanthropus) neadertalensis,* and *Homo (Pithecanthropus) erectus* (Debetz, 1948). The most important boundary lies here between the Neanderthals and modern man, which corresponds to the theoretical conception just stated.

This system, while not meeting any opposition, has, nevertheless, generally failed to receive even the slightest sanction among the Soviet scholars, either through the power of tradition or through indifference toward the problems of nomenclature. Be that as it may, the majority of Soviet scholars, in fact, hold to the conception stated.

THE EVOLUTION OF *HOMO SAPIENS*

It is certainly impossible not to take into consideration the fact that the period of existence of "fossil man"—in other words, the period during which the transformations of the species occurred—is many dozens of times longer than that of the existence of *Homo sapiens.* Therefore, one may assume that the differences exhibited between the modern and the fossil subgenera of the genus *Homo* are not of a quantitative character but are, on the whole, only differences in the duration of existence. Modern man, considered from this viewpoint, has existed so short a time that the characteristics of the species simply have not undergone transformations; with regard to their stability, they are only apparently characteristics. Some Polish anthropologists (Wiercinski, 1956; Wolanski, 1958), in particular, hold fast to the point of view that, in proportion to a unity of time, the transformations that *Homo sapiens* has undergone are much more considerable than are those of fossil species—a point of view that lies incontestably in the framework of formal logic. The logical development of this opinion leads us inevitably to say that the differences that the physical type of future man will show in comparison to that of modern man will not be less important but, on the contrary, more important than those that make modern man different from his fossil forms.

Soviet scholars reject this point of view (Roginskii, 1958). Leaving aside the statement of the practical objections made concerning the method of evaluation of the facts, which would lead us too far afield, we shall limit ourselves to saying that the negation of the theoretical concepts of our Polish colleagues is based upon the theoretical concepts of the development of organisms stated above. Time, taken by itself, cannot be considered as a factor in the development of organisms. On the contrary, these factors are found again in the sphere of relations between the organisms and the environment. The essential environment for man is formed by the sum of the phenomena that are introduced by his industrious activity. All the principal specific marks belonging to man (erect posture, brain, hand) attest the adaptation of man to work.

Comparison of the generally known facts leads, meanwhile, to the conclusion that an inverse relation exists between the transformation of the physical form of man and the modification of the form of work (with all the consequences that derive from this activity). In fossil man relatively insignificant modifications in technique (from which one may therefore assume that the character of his work might undergo, in its entirety, insignificant transformations) was accompanied by a substantial transformation in his morphology. On the contrary, in modern man much more important transformations in technique (and therefore in all the forms of his activity) involved transformations of ever so little importance in his physical form.

These considerations are not in favor of the concepts stated by our Polish colleagues. But would it then be possible that these same considerations are sufficient to deny the role of work in the evolution of man? Formally speaking, such a conclusion is possible, but upon condition of getting away from a general system of scientific conception. In accepting such a conclusion, we would relapse into the theory of the spontaneous evolution of organisms. The Soviet biologists and anthropologists start, as has already been said, from the principle of the direct correlation between the organism and the environment, the latter being a motive power of the evolution of organisms. This conception is based on a considerable number of facts. For one who is of the opinion that there is no correlation between man's activity and his structure, it would have led only to absurdity. That is why Soviet scholars seek another explanation in the facts that exteriorize the contradiction between the rhythms of the evolution of technique and of physical type.

This explanation, like everything that touches on the problem being dealt with, is based on the general principles of scientific research and, in this particular case, on the study of the inconsistencies existing in the substance itself of the phenomenon. Work has brought with it the development of the principal marks of man's physical type. This development has been realized by means of selection, in other words, by biological means. During the first stage of the formation of man, which preceded the development of *Homo sapiens*, selection favored the improvement of work. Yet the predominance of biological laws became at a certain stage an obstacle to the development of work, and this was, without doubt, because selection occurred too slowly and its acceleration brought an increase in the death rate, which threatened the existence of the species itself. This new quality, which appeared when man broke away from the animal world —that is, the form of working—at first made its appearance through the process of selection. But, as a consequence, this same new quality, work, avoided the biological rule that proved to be in complete contradiction to the acceleration of progress of industrial activity. Having played its part, selection became an obstacle to future development; even the act of selection itself created, as a result, conditions preliminary to its radical weakening and practically the cessation of its influence. This was the advent of the era of the unlimited rule of social laws. The physical structure of man had attained such a level that the unlimited development and perfection of all the forms of industrial activity became possible without considerable modification of characteristics of the species that had become an obstacle in the course of progress.

FORMATION OF *HOMO SAPIENS*

At the contemporary stage of science the problem of the development of *Homo sapiens* appears now as the major problem in the evolution of man.

The causes that have induced the formation of the recent species of man have attracted the attention of scholars more than once. There is no need to enumerate here all the opinions presented on this subject. In order to study man's social life, let us limit ourselves to a few of these opinions that are indispensable to an understanding of the importance of the processes and factors that have determined the evolution of the physical type of man.

A. Hrdlička (1927) thought that the formation of *Homo sapiens* was due to the latter's desperate struggle for his life in the conditions of the glacial period. This opinion deserves to be considered and perhaps accepted. But it still does not explain at all why man—who bore characteristics distinctive of *Homo sapiens* that made this species different from the preceding one—triumphed in this struggle for existence.

According to P. P. Efimenko (1934), the development of *Homo sapiens* would have been favored by the disappearance of the isolated nature of human collective groups of the early and middle Paleolithic and by the appearance of exogamy. Efimenko's hypothesis is interesting also from the standpoint of the establishment of immediate ties between the forms of society and the physical type. Neverthe-less, in the light of ethnographical facts, this hypothesis is not very valuable, since exogamy brings with it the shrinking and not the expanding of relations between the sexes. For the rest, just as in Hrdlička's hypothesis, the whole actual complex of distinctive marks remains without explanation.

G. A. Bontch-Osmolovski (1941) deemed that it was the adaptation of the organism of man to the complication of the forms of work and, above all, to the improvement of technique that was the essential factor in evolution. The hand of the precursors of *Homo sapiens* was insufficiently adapted to the cutting of narrow blades, which were at the basis of the late Paleolithic technique and represented an indispensable stage in the evolution of general technique. The common type of structure of the trunk and extremities of the ancestor of modern man, according to Bontch-Osmolovski, were insufficiently adapted to be used for throwing, which is also a condition *sine qua non* for technical progress. What is attractive in the hypothesis of Bontch-Osmolovski is the attempt to explain directly the causes for the appearance of certain characteristics belonging to *Homo sapiens*. Nevertheless, the peculiarities of the structure of the skull, whose importance in the evolution of man is not in any case less important than the peculiarities in the structure of the hand and of the entire body, remain inexplicable. The representation of "clumsy" behavior of the ancestors of *Homo sapiens* has also aroused serious objections.

The most complete and best-founded concept of the origins of *Homo sapiens*, in the author's opinion, is that of Roginskii (1938, 1951). According to this conception, it is exactly the development of social life that was the primary cause of the "second jump" in the formation of *Homo sapiens*.

According to Roginskii, the animal elements of egoism were still very strong in the ancestors of modern man, in other words, in the various forms of fossil man. The evolution of technique in itself not only failed to protect the collective group and its members against this egoism but even made the manifestations of the latter still more dangerous, if the possession of weapons and the evolved practice of killing animals are taken into consideration. Thus even the basis of existence, the integrity and organization of the collective groups of the ancestors of *Homo sapiens*, an indispensable condition for successful development of hunting, was worn away from the inside. This picture of the psyche of fossil men is based in particular on the evident fact that the frontal part of the brain was somewhat less developed in the fossil men than in modern men. Clinical observations that have been made of patients with one or another injury of the frontal lobes reveal that in those cases troubles in the activity of restraint of the brain cortex are produced and fits of overexcitement, fits of rage, sexual laxness, and voracity manifest themselves.

Man of the modern species differs in some measure from his ancestors in traits of pedomorphism. This fact has already been pointed out by L. Bolk. However, the Soviet scholars, for reasons already stated, cannot accept in Bolk's theory the part in which "rejuvenation" is considered apart from the environment. Nevertheless, there is, on the whole, no doubt about there being a preservation of infantile traits in the structure of the skull. The progressive slenderizing of the skeleton may be also noted here. It is very possible that the duration of infancy was shorter in the ancestors of *Homo sapiens*. That is seen both in the comparison of man with the anthropoids and through the observation of the order of tooth eruption in the fossil men. Although the differences that this latter phenomenon shows are not strictly established, it nevertheless cannot be ignored.

In brief, modern man as an individual is weaker than his ancestor. What, then, were his advantages, and why did selection lead to the formation of a species made up of individuals with a more infantile and consequently less robust morphology? Roginskii answers this question by saying that it is just this weakness of the individual that favored the establishment of a more organized and more substantial collective group, in which each of its members, first of all, is seeking protection of the core of this collective group and, in the second place, is capable of submitting to its exigencies, which limit his animal egoism.

These considerations enable us to estimate that the period of development of the physical type of man from his separation from the animal world to the appearance of *Homo sapiens* was also the period of the formation of society. Anthropological research gives us reason to separate and to put into relief the earliest stage of the development of society, in which all the elements of this society were not yet in their final form.

IDEAS REGARDING THE PRIMITIVE HUMAN GROUPS: AN ATTEMPT AT A FACTUAL SURVEY

The formula "Man is an animal that makes tools" is well known. This formula, indeed, makes the essential faculty of man stand out. The Soviet scholars, with one exception,[3] estimate that we can no longer call "animal" a being making tools, but until now it has been a question of convenience of terms. Much more important is the fact that man does not differ from the animals only because he makes tools. All our contemporaries have the gift of speech and art, a systematic conception of the origin and the structure of the universe, of moral and ethical principles regulating the conduct of the members of society, etc. Had all these qualities appeared before man had begun to make tools? Or, strictly speaking, had they appeared at the same time as the making of tools? This conjecture seems unlikely. At least, it is unlikely for those who share the notions of materialism.

After the final jump had been made in the transition from the animal state to the human state, necessary premises had been created for the formation of the enumerated qualities. But these qualities themselves had to pass through a period of evolution before becoming qualities of all men, qualities of *Homo sapiens*.

Thus the primitive human group is the stage of formation of the physical type of man and, also, the stage of the formation of many characteristics of his social life that had appeared as a direct, but not at all immediate, consequence of the transition from the anthropoid—precursor to man—to the maker of tools.

One would not be mistaken in asserting that the differences of the primitive group from all the subsequent forms of social life are essentially of a negative character. The social life of a primitive human group did not have characteristics found in all the subsequent stages of the evolution of society.

It is plausible enough to assume that articulate language, possessed in all its scope by all modern peoples without exception, had not yet taken shape in the primitive human group. The lower forms of language are inseparable from the lower forms of thought. V. V. Bounak (1951, 1958) estimates that, at this stage of the evolution of thought, the interdependence of ideas, which he calls

---

3. B. F. Porshnev, who during these last years has published several studies on primitive society (1955, 1958), estimates that in its first phase manufacture of implements bore an instinctive character. This is why, according to him, *Pithecanthropus* and *Sinanthropus* were not yet men. It is to be noted, however, that in spite of the presence of interesting ideas in his studies, Porchnev's conception has not had repercussions among other Soviet scholars.

"syntagmas," had not yet been created. For lack of space, I shall not pause for a discussion of these assertions stated in the familiar works of Bounak.

According to the belief of Soviet scholars, religion did not exist in primitive groups, even in the simplest forms. No fact exists permitting one to assume the existence of religious beliefs in *Pithecanthropus*. Moreover, having acknowledged the primitive level of language and thought, one could not imagine the possibility of the existence of the complicated system of ideas that any religion, even the most primitive, exhibits. The same considerations are applicable to art.

Relations between the sexes, which play a predominant role in social organization, were also probably at a lower level than all the forms of these relations known through ethnographical data. The Soviet scholars consider the hypothesis of promiscuity as being in closest conformity to the facts and to the theoretical grounds of social order. It is believed that the cases of temporary suspension of sexual restraints at the time of certain festivals, observed by ethnography, may be interpreted as a vestige of the earliest form of relations between the sexes.

Could one consider promiscuity as a heritage from the animal ancestors? Such a point of view does exist, but it runs up against difficulties that are clear when comparison is made with observations of the life of monkeys, which are acquainted with sexual restraints in the form of a "harem." Some Soviet scholars estimate that this question is at present a major one and merits particular attention and detailed and profound study.

The economic basis of the primitive human group has been the object of long debate among Soviet scholars. This discussion had centered on the problem of the role of gathering and hunting. At the beginning of the thirties many Soviet specialists in the history of primitive society believed that gathering was the basis of economic activities in the earliest stages of the evolution of society. The viewpoint is still occasionally expressed today. But, even in 1931, it was opposed in a categorical way by S. P. Tolstov, and justly, in my opinion. These objections were based, in the first place, on theoretical considerations. Gathering is not a characteristically human labor, and it is not accompanied by either the appearance or the development of technique. In the second place, the archeological data give evidence against the hypothesis of the "gathering period." Wherever early Paleolithic tools have been found *in situ* (not only in the geological sense but also in the archeological), tremendous accumulations of bones of large mammals have been observed. The ethnographical information on the tribes for which gathering serves, or was recently serving, as a basis of existence cannot prove the historic reality of the "gathering period." This information is related to a much more advanced stage of social evolution. Once the evolution of a species of modern man is completed, some groups may certainly live on the basis of a gathering economy. It is even very likely that gathering had played an important part at the time of the transition to work on the land. But in the primitive human group of the early Paleolithic, hunting alone was able to give an impetus to the development of tools. It alone was able to support the collective group. Certainly, gathering had always existed, but it did not, and could not, play a predominant role in the first stage of social evolution—that of the primitive group.

Springing from these facts and considerations, opinions have been stated in the specialized Soviet literature (J. I. Semenov, 1956) asserting that it is fitting to divide the history of mankind from the very first into two main periods: (*a*) history of the primitive group (period of the creation, of the formation, of human society), and (*b*) history of human society (period of the evolution of society or of already created society).

Certainly it is not by chance that this principle of dividing the history of mankind into periods coincides with the belief of those Soviet anthropologists who consider the formation of *Homo sapiens* as the most important step in the evolution of man after his separation from the animal world. But one must foresee the inevitable objections coming from the sociologists, who naturally observe that the division into periods of J. I. Semenov reduces the role of a primordial event in the history of mankind and especially the formation of classed society.

But in any case, in the history of primitive society the border between the primitive group and the clan society is much more important than is the border between the blossoming of clan society and the period of disintegration. If the primitive group were not considered outside the framework of primitive clan society, the latter should then be divided into periods in the following manner (Tolstov, 1946, and others):

1. Period of the primitive group
2. Period of clan society
   a) Time of the blossoming of clan society
   b) Time of the disintegration of clan society

THE SEPARATION OF MAN FROM THE ANIMAL WORLD

In order not to be misunderstood, let us remark that the period of existence of the primitive group society, a period between *Australopithecus* and *Homo sapiens*, is not considered by Soviet scholars as a period of domination of biological laws. Important as they may be, biological relations in the primitive group, nevertheless, do not constitute the principal law. The history of society begins at the moment when tools have begun to be made. This turning point, which had manifested itself, from the standpoint of morphology, through the transition of the "cerebral Rubicon," had been of much more importance than the formation of *Homo sapiens*. It is as a result of this turning point that mankind itself was created.

Theoretically, it is necessary to recognize that the period of toolmaking, which set apart the appearance of mankind, had been preceded by a period of tool use (stones, sticks, bones). It is quite probable that the australopithecines might give us an idea of the stage of evolution of the higher animal world to that of the most highly organized present-day animals, but still preceding the transition from the animal state to the human state.

At present the series of problems relating to the transition from the *"Australopithecus* stage" to the *"Pithecanthropus* stage" attracts less attention by Soviet scholars than does the problem of the primitive human group and the formation of *Homo sapiens*.

The most important discussions on this subject took place during the thirties. They concerned the role of the geographical environment and the role of hunting in the process of hominization. P. P. Efimenko (1934) and A. M. Zolotarev (1936) denied the role of these two factors and conceived of the process of hominization as a spontaneous evolution; V. K. Nikolskii (1926) attributed the principal role to the alteration of the geographical environment, while denying the role of hunting; P. I. Boriskovskii (1935), on the contrary, believed that the alterations of the geographical environment could not have great importance and that the principal role came to the way of life based on hunting. In the author's opinion, the most legitimate concept is the concept of S. P. Tolstov (1931) mentioned above. The formation of the primitive human group as a primary form of collective group, which had been at the basis of the process of formation of society, was a necessary condition to the hunting way of life as well as to that of tool-making.

Tools and collective hunting make up the two sides of a single phenomenon of a new quality that had marked the beginning of the transition to the rule of social laws. But the appearance of this new quality had been facilitated by the biological evolution of man's animal ancestors, an evolution, like that of all the animals, necessarily allowing an important place to the geographical environment.

However, the particular characteristics of this environment are still very little known. Determination of these runs up against the problem of the place of origin of mankind. In the Soviet Union, as in the Western countries, many anthropologists declare themselves in favor of Africa. I find the old belief about the Asiatic origins of man better established, but the insufficiency of facts is evident in both cases. Many questions are not clear in the sphere of chronology either. The results of paleography will undoubtedly contribute toward specifying these questions. Unfortunately, it is difficult to determine the major tasks of research in this last branch.

As to the problem of the origins of social life, it appears to be extremely important to study sexual relations among the monkeys. They are undeniably varied. But the quantity of collected facts is still insufficient for the finding of common points in this diversity, characteristic traits whose existence could be attributed, with tolerable assurance, to the direct ancestors of man.

BIBLIOGRAPHY

BONTCH-OSMOLOVSKII, G. A.
  1941. "Kist' iskopaemovo cheloveka iz grota Kiikkoba," *Paleolit Kryma*, vyp. II, L.
BORISKOVSKII, P. I.
  1935. "Istoricheskie predposylki oformleniia tak nazyvaemovo *Homo sapiens*," *Problemy istorii dokapitalisticheskikh obshchestv*, No. 1–2 i 5–6.
BOUNAK, V. V.
  1951. "Proiskhozhdenie rechi po dannym antropologii," *Sbornik Proiskhozhdenie i drevnee rasselenie chelovechestva*. Trudy Instituta etnografii, nov. ser., t. XVI, M.
  1958. "L'origine due langage." In *Les processus de l'humanisation*. Paris: C.N.R.S.
DEBETS, G. F.
  1948. "O sistematike i nomenklature iskopaemykh form cheloveka," *Kratkie soobshcheniia Instituta istorii material'noi kul'tury*, XXIII, M.
EFIMENKO, P. P.
  1934. *Dorodovoe obshchestvo*. L.
HRDLIČKA, A.
  1927. "The Neanderthal Phase of Man," *J. R. Anthrop. Inst. Great Britain and Ireland*, Vol. LVII.
NIKOL'SKII, V. K.
  1926. *Ocherki pervobytnovo chelovechestva*. M.
PORSHNEV, B. F.
  1955. "Materializm i idealizm v voprosakh stanovleniia cheloveka," *Voprosy filosofii*, No. 5.
  1958. "Problema vizniknoveniia chelovecheskovo obshchestva i chelovecheskoi kul'tury," *Vestnik istorii mirovoi kul'tury*, No. 2/8/.
ROGINSKII, IA. IA.
  1938. "Problema proiskhozhdeniia *Homo sapiens*," *Uspekhi sovremennoi biologii*, t. IX, vyp. 2.
  1951. "Osnovnye antropologicheskie voprosy v probleme proiskhozhdeniia sovremennovo cheloveka," *Sbornik Proiskhozhrenie i drevneishee rasselenie chelovechesta*. Trudy Instituta étnografii, nov. ser. t. XVI., M.
  1957. "Ob étapakhi i tempakh évoliutsii gominid," *Sovetskaia étnografiia*, No. 6.
SEMENOV, IU. I.
  1956. "Vozniknovenie i osnovnye étapy razvitiia truda /v sviazi s problemoi stanovleniia chelovecheskovo obshchestva/." *Krasnoiarskii Gosudarstvennyi pedagogicheskii institut. Uchenye zapiski*, t. VI.
SEVERTSOV, A. N.
  1912. *Étiudy po teorii évoliutsii*. M.
TOLSTOV, S. P.
  1931. "Problemy dorodovovo obshchestva." *Sovetskaia étnografiia*, No. 3–4.
  1946. "K voprosu o periodizatsii istorii pervobytnovo obshchestva," *Sovetskaia étnografiia*, No. 1.

WEIDENREICH, F.
1939. "The Phylogenetic Development of Man and the General Theories in Evolution." *Bull. Geol. Soc. China*, Vol. XIX, No. 1.

WIERCINSKI, A.
1956. "Evolutionary Rate of Craniometric Traits in Hominidae," *Acta Palaeontol. Polonica*, Vol. 1, No. 3.

WOLANSKI, N.
1958. "Zagadninie etapowosci w ewolucji form ludzkich," *Przeglad antropologiczny*, 24:1.

ZOLOTAREV, A. M.
1936. "Istoricheskie predposylki formirovaniia *Homo sapiens* v osveshchenii sovetskikh arkheologov," *Antropologicheskii zhurnal*, No. 3.

ACQUISITION OF ANATOMICAL KNOWLEDGE
BY ANCIENT MAN

WILLIAM S. LAUGHLIN

T HE YEAR 1859 has been hailed as the one in which scientists discovered that man was an animal (Eiseley, 1959, p. 225). This may be accepted as a major accomplishment, though the same scientists had some decidedly ambiguous views concerning which animals to include under the rubric of man. Primitive man, and presumably ancient man, had made this discovery some half-million years or more earlier. In fact, we may consider the likelihood that man was always aware of his affinity with other animals and consequently did not need to "discover" this obvious relationship any more than he discovered his stomach or eyeballs, or than the female of our species discovered that she was bearing the young (Fisher, 1958, p. 189). The early apprehension of a working knowledge of anatomy, human and nonhuman, was indispensable to man's survival. This was crucial in an animal form that was liquidating various physical abilities and instincts in exchange for the use of tools, who had both to defend himself from predators and to hunt and utilize other animals and who required assistance for the birth of his young (Washburn and Avis, 1958). Moreover, the early apprehension of anatomical form and function served to configure ancient man's perception of the world. Anatomical form remains a salient organizing system even in cultural categorizations that have little or no apparent connection with anatomy (Kroeber, 1948, p. 300). Many of the kinds of observations recommended in "The Argument from Animals to Men" are habitually made by primitive men and were presumably made by ancient men (Haldane, 1956). I suggest that such observations were essential to survival and constituted a substantial part of the biologically founded culture with which humans conducted their own evolution from the earliest times. Ancient man argued from animals to men and back again with sophistication and success. The evolutionary functions of these arguments and their consequences require at least a prefatory examination.

The acquisition of anatomical knowledge, including treatment of pathology, birth practices, and observations on the effects of close inbreeding, is of interest not only because of its priority in the intellectual history of man and its evolutionary function but also for the light it throws on systems of organization.

The anatomical knowledge of many peoples—here the example provided by the Aleutian Islanders will be used—does not consist merely of an elaboration of words for an area of cultural interest. It is a commonplace fact that people enlarge their lexicon in those areas with which they are concerned, thus the Lapps have a truly enormous number of words for reindeer, the Hottentots and Noer for cattle, and the Arabs for camels. More important is the use of genuinely technical terms, systemization of the observations, discreteness of the observations, their extension beyond the superficial, and verification by actual and intentional dissection for the purpose of learning about the structures.

Much of the detail that can be secured for contemporary groups of man cannot be secured for ancient man. In all probability we shall underestimate the quality of ancient man's intellectual achievements. This area is underestimated in modern primitives. Even though it is possible to infer that an extensive anatomical knowledge was necessary to survival, it is not possible to know in which cases true comparative anatomy was employed, when the dead were dissected to find out why they died, or even whether anatomical terms were contained in the stems used to describe anatomical features. Whether the pericardium was removed from the heart and used as a water container or eaten along with the heart cannot be reconstructed. Related beliefs are similarly beyond recapture. The sacral spot of the newborn Aleut is described as the result of bruising caused by the child's having been kicked out by a spiritual power because of its unwillingness to be born. The general idea of the unwillingness of some infants to be born is found on both sides of the Bering Sea, and some antiquity may therefore be inferred from this distribution. Nevertheless, such beliefs can no more be reconstructed than can the antiquity of the distinction between venous and arterial blood.

The possibility of extending inferences back to the beginning of the Pleistocene is considerably enhanced by the presence of certain elements that have remained relatively constant. First among these must be listed the constancy or uniformity of animal morphology and physiology during the Pleistocene and, by the same token, animal behavior. Second is the indubitable requirement that humans adapt to the behavior of animals, both to secure the animals for food and fabricational purposes and to preserve themselves from the animals. The third constant element is the essentially carnivorous behavior of humans. A fourth consideration is the existence of many retentions in human behavior from prehuman days. Humans did not become human and then learn how to hunt other animals but already were hunters and simply altered their methods of hunting in conjunction with the acquisition of ideas that permitted the use of tools and, later, their manufacture.

All the important categories of animals (genera) remained sufficiently simliar to permit use of the same basic observations. Early mammoths apparently behaved in much the same way as do contemporary elephants, and the difference between a woolly mammoth in Siberia and his more glabrous relative to the south was primarily in size. The anal flap or longer hair would present no problem in killing or utilization. We may assume that a gall bladder was as distasteful to early man in China or Algeria as it is to a modern Eskimo. Musk sacs, similarly, must have been omitted from the diet.

Recognition of blood must surely be numbered among the first conscious thought to flicker across the mind of ancient man. Primary distinctions between liquids and solids are, after all, made by animals because of the simple necessity of drinking one and chewing the other. Ancient man simply rationalized existing behavior toward blood and many other animal substances. Similarly, humans did not discover the difference between marrow and bone, or brain and flesh, but rather they elaborated a variety of new ways of utilizing these substances. Many animals are quite specific in their tastes and select only a particular organ to eat (Washburn, 1957).

Whether a stranded whale discovered on a beach is regarded as a fortunate supply of food or as an embarrassing object to be towed out to sea or buried depends now on cultural systems that provide an interpretation. Diarrhea produced by eating the toothed whale was likely the same intestinal reaction in ancient man as it is in contemporary peoples. Ancient man, like other animals and contemporary peoples in search of food, undoubtedly regarded stranded sea mammals and carcasses of dead animals as the dietary gratuities that they are. With reference to the morphology and related attributes, then, the animals upon which man and his ancestors fed have changed considerably less during the Pleistocene than have the uses to which they have been put.

The archeological record provides many examples of big-game hunting for the earliest of ancient man (Oakley, 1949). Thus, the sites of Acheulian man at Ol Orgesailie contain the broken bones of baboons, wild pigs, and zebra, in association with cleavers, hand-axes, and chipped-stone balls that may have been used as a bolas. Elephants, wild oxen, and horses appear to have been hunted at Torralba, Spain. Choukoutien provides the splendid evidence of *Sinanthropus*, who ate a diversity of things, ranging from rabbits and hackberries to deer and rhinoceros. Somewhere between the rabbits and the rhinoceros the humans themselves must be inventoried, for the evidence of cannibalism seems unequivocable. Bone as well as stone implements are represented. Hunting of large animals may also be attributed to the australopithecines (Oakley, 1957).

From such sites of early man a minimum list of tools can be composed, which must include the bolas, pointed shafts used as spears, hand-axes and cleavers, scrapers, knives, and—in Asia—choppers and chipping tools. Whether sinew or cordage was used for the bolas cannot be reconstructed. If either or both were available for the bolas, they were also available for snares, traps, and lashings in general. This provides quite enough in the way of tools to handle all land animals. Bartholomew and Birdsell (1953, p. 483) observe that large body size, at least in the range of from 50 to 100 pounds, is a virtual necessity for a bipedal tool-using protohominid. Such size would "allow them to utilize without restrictive anatomical specialization and with simple instrumentation, virtually the entire range of food size utilized by all other terrestrial mammals."

A classic example of simple instrumentation is provided by the Koniag Eskimos and Aleuts of southern Alaska. Within the memory of living Eskimos, the brown bear, better known as the Kodiak bear (though this technically applies only to those living on Kodiak Island, which are probably slightly smaller than those on the Alaska Peninsula), was hunted by the simple method of impaling. The Eskimo placed the butt of his spear in the ground, holding it there with one foot, and the bear impaled himself upon the other end. At least some of the Eskimos lashed a cross-piece on the spear to prevent the bear from getting close enough to strike the hunter after he had been impaled. This bear (*Ursus gigas*) is the world's largest carnivore, weighing up to 1,800 pounds, yet it was easily killed by small people who weighed less than 150 pounds. In addition to the efficiency of impaling animals with a pointed shaft, there is another aspect of critical significance to the hunter—his safety. In reviewing hunting of large animals in the Paleolithic, Boas (1938, pp. 253–54) notes: "As soon as a reasonably long shaft allowed an attack from a point beyond the reach of the teeth and paws of the animal, hunting became safer."

The principal advantage of a ground-slate or chipped-stone blade as a spear point lies in the fact that it produces more extensive hemorrhaging than does a pointed stick. It probably offers little or no advantage in piercing the hide of animals. Evidence of the use of pointed sticks is excellent in the archeological record. Among the earliest is the wooden spear from Clacton-on-Sea and associated fling spokeshaves. Another is the wooden spear of Third Interglacial age found between the ribs of an extinct elephant at Lehringen in Saxony (Movius, 1950). A later example is provided by the skeletal remains of the male Skhul IX (McCown and Keith, 1939, pp. 74–75, 373). A pointed spear had pierced the head of the left femur, the floor of the acetabulum, and had entered the pelvic cavity. The authors infer that the weapon had been made of hard wood, for stone or bone would have persisted as did the bone around it.

That man is clearly a carnivore is important to a recognition of the sources of his anatomical information. While it might at first sight appear ludicrous to suggest that every tiger is by preoccupation an anatomist, it should be quite respectable to suggest that if a gorilla were overtaken by culture he would more likely be a botanist, in view of his frugivorous dietary interests. The evidence for considering man a carnivore, with reference to behavior and diet, has been succinctly presented by Washburn and Avis (1958). The archeological evidence in remains of broken bones has already been cited. Hunting as an important activity for recent man is abundantly documented. A further remark of Washburn and Avis requires reiteration: "Unless careful training has hidden the natural drives, men enjoy the chase and the kill. In most cultures torture and suffering are made public spectacles for the enjoyment of all. The victims may be either animal or human" (Washburn and Avis, 1958, p. 433). These authors note three important effects on human behavior and nature: psychological, social, and territorial. The pertinent effect here is the constant concern of man with the morphology of the animals he hunted. In order to hunt effectively, a large amount of information concerning the animals was required. In order to capture and kill the animals and secure maximum use of them, a detailed knowledge of their anatomy was decidedly advantageous. That we should find extensive anatomical knowledge among people who are constantly hunting and butchering mammals is quite understandable. That such knowledge should be as extensive and intensive as it is among the Aleuts and that it should be organized along comparative and experimental lines is understandable in retrospect, but it could have been neither predicted from a knowledge of their economy nor reconstructed from artifactual and osseous remains.

A brief survey of anatomical knowledge among the Aleutian Islanders, and their sources of such knowledge, may provide useful comparative information for projection into the past. The Eskimos and Aleuts have been frequently used as contemporary models of life in the Mesolithic and Upper Paleolithic.

All members of the Eskimo-Aleut linguistic stock are concerned with the hunting of mammals, fish, and birds. The vast majority hunt both sea mammals and land mammals. A small minority are primarily concerned with the hunting of caribou to the exclusion, or virtual exclusion, of sea mammals. These numerically inferior inland variants, found on the Alaska Peninsula and in various places in Alaska and Canada, are not dialectically differentiated and do not represent an earlier stage but are, rather, culturally impoverished groups whose contacts with marine life have been reduced, though never completely eliminated. Occupying as they do the longest linear distribution of any single linguistic and racial stock in the world (some 10,000 miles), there is sufficient ecological diversity to provide variation in their economy and in their culture, but sufficient uniformity to permit rigorous comparative studies in all aspects, biological and cultural. Though the Eskimos of Greenland spent as much time in drawing and quartering mammals as did the Aleuts, they did not develop so sophisticated a knowledge of anatomy. The same basic implement inventory of harpoon, lamp, knives, throwing board, pronged bird spear, fish spears, and skin boats occurs over the entire area, but a considerable difference in the intellectual culture is found in the greater sophistication of the Aleutian Islanders and the Koniag Eskimos of Kodiak Island and the adjacent mainland of the Alaska Peninsula (Laughlin, 1952). Much of this difference can now be explained.

DEVELOPMENT OF HUMAN ANATOMICAL KNOWLEDGE IN THE ALEUTIAN ISLANDS

The Aleutian Islanders are unique among all the preliterate populations of the world for their active interest in and extensive knowledge of human anatomy.

Early observers, such as Count F. P. Lutke (1835–36) and the Reverend I. Veniaminov noted and documented this unusual development. The observation of Veniaminov is especially pertinent:

In the Aleut language there are and formerly were words referring to Anatomy. I do not have in mind such ones as *heart, liver, intestines* and so forth, but those which are of some higher understanding, such as tugix, a large blood-carrying vessel, cugudagil'uk, cunumgudax, sigidaq, and so forth, which I, through downright ignorance of anatomical language, am unable to translate. Such words, apparently, were composed from what the Aleuts before the arrival of the Russians had been studying through the examination of the innards of a person, either of one killed in combat or of a deceased serf, expressly for the science of doctoring [Veniaminov, *Essay of a Grammar of the Aleut-Fox Language*, Foreword, p. v (trans. Gordon H. Marsh from the original Russian)].

It speaks highly of the intellectual candor and honesty of this Russian Orthodox priest that he recognized an important area that he was unable to investigate, and his observation immediately suggests that similar developments among other peoples may suffer from lack of investigation. The successful attempt of the Aleuts at a rational practice of medicine and physical culture and their skilful practice of dry mummification are further supported by the practice of true comparative anatomy—a practice aided by their use of the sea otter, by a generous amount of daily dissection of the mammals on which they lived, and, above all, by a well-developed empiricism, which facilitated the transference of their knowledge of animal anatomy to that of humans.

Our method of studying the Aleut knowledge of anatomy quickly revealed the fact that they could identify an organ or part of an organ as well as provide a name for it. Dr. Victor B. Scheffer of the United States Fish and Wildlife Service kindly placed an abandoned fur seal pup at the disposal of an Aleut, who dissected it for us, picking up each part, ureter or pancreas, with forceps and giving us the appropriate name at the same time. We attended the butchering of several animals. When we provided the Aleuts with a human skeleton, they obliged us with lectures in basic osteology, noting that the human mandible was composed of two parts in the immature person and that, unlike the seal's, it fused into a single bone. Aleut and Eskimo are ideal languages for mammalian anatomy because they have a dual ending. Thus, when one-half of the mandible is under discussion, the singular ending is employed; and when the entire mandible or both *os coxae* are under discussion, the dual ending is employed.

METHOD OF DESCRIPTION

It is of major interest that all the terms in their anatomical description are contained within a single language. In contrast, our anatomical vocabularies are based extensively on Latin and Greek words and on terms fabricated from combinations of them. Many of the terms that we consider technical are considered so because of the foreign linguistic elements of which they are composed; they are often merely descriptive rather than specific.

Within the Aleut language are many specific terms for external and internal topography. These may be classed into monosyllabic, disyllabic, and poly-syllabic words. Many terms have a derived origin. Such words are "tooth" (literally "biter"), "nose" (literally "breather"), and "ear" (literally "hearer"), "trachea" (literally "place of sound"). Diminutive suffixes appear in the words for the uvula, little finger, little toe, whorl of hair/dermatoglyph. The word for the uvula is, interestingly, initiated with a uvular sound in all three dialects of Aleut.

Descriptive expressions of two or more words represent a large part of the vocabulary: the socket for the eye is, literally "customary hole/bed of the eye"; the two mental foramina (literally "both customary holes of the blood vessels of the jaw"), the bicipital tendon (literally, "tendon on the inside of the bend of the arm").

The detail of their anatomical classification is demonstrated by their nomen-clature for musculature. Muscles fall into three categories: muscles with large bunched bellies, such as the *biceps brachii;* flat muscles, such as the pectorals; and long stringy muscles, such as the sartorii.

It is of interest that the Aleut frequently use anatomical analogies to describe anatomical features. Thus the first posterior sacral foramina are termed the "eyes" of the sacrum. These were important sites for acupuncture. The septum of the nose is also known as the "little man of the nose," the tragus is the "post" or "little man of the ear," and the root of a molar tooth is, naturally, a "leg."

Concerned with bone, they distinguish "bone in general," "soft, cancel-lous or interior bone," "hard bone or ivory." Marrow is, of course, distinguished from brain and spinal cord. Nerves are distinguished from tendons, and blood flowing from the heart is distinguished from blood returning to the heart. It is within the realm of possibility, though no longer capable of demonstration, that the Aleuts had discovered the principle of circulation of the blood. Until the seventeenth century in England a majority of medical scientists believed in the existence of perforations in the septum of the heart (Galen's septum perfora-tions), which permitted blood to flow from one side to the other. The Aleuts had such frequent recourse to dissection that we may safely say that they would never have believed in the existence of holes in a septum that they could see was intact.

The Aleuts and the Eskimos are able to state position very precisely. This is done by means of demonstratives and postpositions, so that position, relative position, relative level, invisible position (invisible to the speaker), down on the water, upward on the land and toward the interior, and enclosure or house position (the one farthest back or nearest the entrance, etc.) can be deftly depicted. This habitual concern with position is expressed in internal anatomy as easily as in external geography.

SAMPLE GLOSSARY OF HUMAN ANATOMICAL TERMS
(From Marsh and Laughlin, 1956, pp. 58–76)

English	*Literal Translation*
Tragus	Post/little man of the ear
Root of molar	Leg of the tooth
Pericardium	Sac of the heart
Pyloric end of stomach	Umbilicus of the stomach the stomach its curl
Spleen	Backpack of the stomach
First posterior sacral foramina	Both eyes of the sacrum
Thenar eminence	Place of stoneflaking
Moon of the thumb	Moon of the thumb
Pulse/artery	None
Vein	Blue thing (on back of hand, etc.)
Sesamoid bone	The muscle-itself-its having kinked
Caul	Kamleyka (waterproof parka) of the baby

SOURCES OF ALEUT ANATOMICAL KNOWLEDGE

The sources of Aleut anatomical knowledge may be partitioned into categories that are also suitable for comparative purposes. Consequently, they are arranged in descending order of ubiquity: (1) study of anatomical structures, (2) rational medicine and physical culture, (3) dissection of human bodies, (4) true comparative anatomy, employing especially the sea otter, and (5) making of dried mummies.

First, subsisting almost exclusively on fish, meat, and fowl, they acquired from the butchering of these animals the kind of familiarity with animal structures that all hunting peoples achieve. And this may be extended back to ancient man. However, here as elsewhere in their culture, they practiced their disciplined art of observation more extensively than did most preliterate people. This much is shared with Eskimos. "However, as a branch of the Eskimo-Aleut stock—a stock whose culture emphasizes a pragmatic orientation to its environment and a concentration on structural details of practical importance—they extended more minutely their observation and utilization of animals' tissues than, for example, most of the Indian tribes of North America" (Marsh and Laughlin, 1956, p. 40). Even an abbreviated list of the uses of internal tissues indicates the great fabricational use that they made of tissues that in many or most parts of the world are discarded:

1. Pericardium . . Water bags, containers
2. Intestines . . . Shirt (kamleyka) rain parkas, pouches, bags, insulation on harpoon and spear lashings, etc.
3. Oesophagus . . Leggings of boots, parka, and pants and leggings of water boots
4. Stomach . . . . Floats, food storage containers
5. Tongue (whale) . Rain parka, using skin of whale's tongue
6. Caul (of humans) Carried as protective charm
7. Bladder . . . . Floats

A large glossary would be required to itemize the medical, magical, and religious uses of internal organs and tissues. Marrow was used for paint base, eyeballs and blood for glue, ink sac of octopus for black pigment.

Second, they generalized from animal morphology and behavior to human, making use of their habits of observation and experimentation, and used these observed similarities in their practice of medicine, hygiene, and physical culture. They note that the blood of the hair seal is much darker than that of other sea mammals and they infer that this is because he "sleeps too much." They appear to be aware of the effects of oxygenating blood and have, further, the opportunity to observe this in themselves in their recourse to annual blood-letting. Sick animals eat and drink very little, and so the Aleuts emulate them. A vast majority of medical treatments include resting and fasting for several days. A former headman of a village on Kagamil Island was famous for the training he gave his boys. They ran up and down the steep hill by the village carrying large stones. He would listen to their heartbeat to see whether they remained in sufficiently good condition to perform these exercises without undue exertion. Contemporary evidence is provided by Dr. Fred Alexander, "I have seen hypertension suspected because the pulse in a small temporal artery seemed much stronger than normal" (Alexander, 1949, p. 4). They justify the use of boiled foods as the result of an experiment in which the umiak crew of one village, where food was steamed, raced the crew of a village where food was boiled. Delivery of offspring was an area of considerable skill.

Third, the Aleuts dissected the dead to find out why they died and also to become more familiar with the internal anatomy of humans. A number of early Russian observers call attention to this practice, as recorded by Veniaminov in *Notes on the Islands of the Unalaska Division.*

The Aleut medicine men in former times were famed for their knowledge. In order to more properly learn the internal parts of man, and especially those parts on which they used to perform operations, they used to open dead serfs, or killed enemies. Even I had the chance to see several old Russians who had been treated by Aleut doctors who had lauded them to the limit [Veniaminov (trans.), in Hrdlička, 1945, p. 176].

The last person to witness such a dissection was an old woman, over ninety, who died at Nikolski, Umnak, in the 1930's. As a woman doctor she was permitted to attend post mortems but not to dissect.

Fourth, comparative anatomy was deliberately practiced on the sea otter. This animal was chosen because of his morphological and behavioral similarities to humans. The behavioral similarities are fairly well described in the literature, though not as accurately as is known to the Aleuts. Their use of rocks has been frequently referred to and their human-like behavior has been noted by a wide variety of observers. The sea otter has succeeded in freeing his hands by supporting his body in water and swimming on his back, an interesting evolutionary substitute for erect posture in terrestrial mammals. It is in this position that he uses a rock for an anvil, upon which he crushes shellfish. It is this characteristic that is represented by the cleft bow of the Aleutian kayak.

In addition to its behavioral characteristics, the sea otter has a number of points of morphological similarity to man, and, compared with other sea mammals, it is the most similar. The retention of a pronating and supinating forearm in contrast to the flippers of seals; flat grinding molars; femur, tibia, and fibula of marked similarity to man's; and the tendency toward white hair in the aged further provide a logical basis for use of the sea otter in the study of anatomy and for the conception that it is descended from man. The comparative dissection of sea otters survived beyond the dissection of humans. The last dissection was made in 1911, at which time the killing of sea otters was outlawed by the United States government.

Fifth, the manufacture of dry mummies of selected individuals and families, especially in the Eastern Aleutians, was a notable source of information as well as an application of knowledge. Often the viscera were removed through an incision in the perineal region or in the abdomen or upper thorax. The interior was then stuffed with dried grass or moss and the exterior was wiped and dried at intervals. After some months the body was flexed and encased in grass mats and sealskin bags, bound, and then placed in a case or under a rock overhang. The bodies might be disposed on wood racks, suspended in cradles, or simply placed on the floor of the cave, where they were preserved from moisture. The distribution of mummification, the associated artifacts, and the condition of the mummies indicate that this practice was a comparatively recent development, perhaps of only a few hundred years' antiquity prior to the eighteenth-century arrival of the Russians. It was probably introduced by the Neo-Aleuts.

Even a brief reference to mummification is incomplete without noting the close relationships of dismemberment and joint binding. A slain enemy was dismembered at the joints of the arms and legs, and the head was removed. The purpose was primarily protection of the slayer, chiefly from joint diseases, which would otherwise befall him later in life. This practice was required of both women and men. Attention to the joints of the body, and the anticipation of joint disease from failure to dismember, also characterize the menarcheal treatment of girls, all of whose joints are bound as part of this observance. Joint binding also extends to the surviving spouse and the rationale is explicit. The widow or widower would otherwise go to pieces, just as the skeleton of a deceased person falls apart and disarticulates in the ground. The dismembered body is like the disintegrated body, from which the breath soul will depart and be less likely to injure the slayer. Mummification is the opposite of dismemberment and retains the soul in the body with the preservation of the intact body. Consequently, mummies were of considerable utility. They could be visited in their caves and could provide various kinds of help to the living. Furthermore, "a piece of dead man" constituted the most powerful charm known to the Aleuts. A finger or some other piece removed from a mummy protected its bearer in many circumstances, though it eventually led to premature death. Mummy grease smeared on the surface of ivory, for example, would serve as a preservative against pitting and erosion.

APPLICATION OF ANATOMICAL INFORMATION

Acupuncture, blood-letting, and massage are the three most common applications of anatomical knowledge, in addition to the various skills employed in delivering babies. Acupuncture was performed both at fixed sites on the body, such as "the two eyes of the sacrum" previously cited, and at various places indicated by the particular illness. The Aleut practice of acupuncture differs from the Chinese in being less elaborate and less rigidly prescribed. Two techniques are distinguishable. In the first, two dots are marked on the skin, a fold of skin between the two dots is raised, and the lancet is then run through the fold of skin from one dot to the other. Even the scalp was raised in this fashion for piercing. The second technique was more hazardous, for it consisted of thrusting the lancet straight into the body.

Closely related to acupuncture is the regular blood-letting, employed once a year on many men, seldom on women. The blood may be let either at the ankles from the long saphenous vein (*kitam namii*), where it passes in front of the medial malleolous, or at the elbow from the cubital or basilic vein. The blood is let in the same month of each year but never from the same vein in two successive years. Some persons let their own blood. Sucking was also employed.

Massage is extensively employed and is a specialty of female practitioners; it is used especially during pregnancy and childbirth, being given at regular monthly intervals during pregnancy and after the delivery to place the organs back in their proper positions. One objective was to prevent the baby from getting too large. The last female doctor to witness a human dissection was noted for the effectiveness of her massage and of her palpation in locating disorders. Though her fingers had become crooked and flexed with arthritis, she straightened them by binding them to wood sticks and thus continued her practice until her death.

Surgery was employed, but few references remain. Suturing with sinew was apparently common. More serious operations were performed while the patient was kept warm in the sweat bath. Application of herbal hot packs to sore points was also done in the sweat bath.

The Aleuts are aware that a sharp blow on the brachiordialis muscle on the outside of the forearm will temporarily paralyze the arm. They note that sea lions and dogs attempt to bite each other in this spot when fighting. The spot is termed "daylight of the hand/forearm" and was utilized in formal wrestling and mortal combat. The temporal artery was given attention in wrestling and in diagnosis. In wrestling, an attempt might also be made to squeeze a man's head at the temples, to cut off the blood supply or to crush the temples. The medical practitioner watched and felt the frontal artery. Aleuts favored the side of the head in clubbing both humans and seals. The practice of cutting out a seal's heart to be eaten before the animal had died might also be listed as a source of knowledge.

PROJECTIONS OF ANATOMICAL ORIENTATION

Generically there are two principal kinds of projection of anatomical orientation: conceiving inanimate objects in anatomical form and applying the same basic stem to diverse objects, which are thus viewed as sharing a common attribute and as representing characteristics similar to those of animals.

In their material culture many objects receive anatomical designations. The parts of the throwing board are so named: the little ivory pin that engages the butt of the harpoon or spear is termed the "ziphisternum"; the flat surface above the pin is the "forehead of the throwing board"; the ridge along the underside of the back is the "hump of the throwing board"; and the concavity, also on the underside, that is hollowed to accommodate the thenar eminence is named the "thenar of the throwing board." This side of the throwing board is painted black to represent the fur of an animal, and the other side is painted red to represent blood.

The bow of the skin boat, either single, double, or triple-hatch, represents a sea otter in his characteristic pose of swimming on his back and eating from his chest. A cleft in the double-curved bow represents the space between the head and shoulders and the arms and hands of the sea otter. The deck ridge is called the "sternum." Ballast stones were carried inside the kayak in simulation of those found inside the sea lion's stomach.

The small island of Anangula was clearly envisaged by the Aleuts as a whale swimming north through the sea. Their name for the northeast end, with its hill separated by a slight saddle from the body of the island means, "the bust of Anangula," with the word for "bust" being a term that designates the head and shoulders of a sea mammal. The long, low, southwestern tip of the island is termed "The tail of Anangula," the word for "tail" being their word that can apply to the tail of only a whale or a fish and to no other mammal. When we assemble these two pieces of information, it is clear that the sea mammal conceptualized is a whale. They see in a permanent snow bank on the side of Mount Vsevidof the shape of a sea-lion stomach. The northern lights represent a bucket of blood that is being spilled; the term for the Milky Way is the same as for the *linea alba*.

Occasional anatomical terms appear with high frequency. The name for the funnel-shaped entrance to the impounding pool of the fish weir is "penis of the creek/fish-weir." The bifurcated base of the single-piece harpoon socket is known as the "legs" of the socket, using, of course, a dual ending. The small hole in the parka for the ends of the drawstring, also that at the waist of the pants, is termed "its biters." These are the places where the drawstrings are secured, and the analogy with teeth is of a very common type.

Personal names, traditional tales and games and riddles are lavishly endowed with anatomical themes. A man with short arms and long trunk is named "hair seal" for his external resemblance to the seal. Dismemberment is extended to hawks and owls and occurs frequently in stories. Cannibalism is very common in the stories, taking on clever forms—a man, for example, brings home animal entrails for his wife, and she later discovers that she has been eating her relatives.

Of considerable interest for comparative purposes is the attitude toward menarche. The pubescent girl must be isolated and all her exuvia must be disposed of in such a way that they cannot affect the winds, the sun, or the sea, for any contact would drive the fish, animals, and birds away. However, her repulsive qualities are made use of for securing stranded whales. The Aleuts first noted that, if such a girl came down to the beach where a stranded whale was being cut up, it would go back to the sea, even if it were only a skeleton. Drawing upon this extremely repulsive power, the Aleuts will employ such a girl to circumambulate the whale, using a boat or raft to get around the seaward side if necessary. The logic is impeccable, granting the premise that she can repulse in any direction.

If we take those words that share a common stem, we find a cogent relation for seemingly diverse things. The words for (1) blowhole of the whale, (2) intestines, (3) daylight, (4) brachioradialis muscle of the forearm, (5) breath, and (6) holy spirit (a word constructed since the arrival of Christianity) all share a common stem. If we bear in mind the Aleut belief in a breath soul and the identification of breath soul and daylight, the blowhole of the whale is the place where the breath can be seen to emanate; the intestines are the seat of the soul; the arm loses its life when it is paralyzed in fighting by a blow on brachioradialis; and the holy spirit is an especially large light.

In retrospect, it is seen that the Aleutian Islanders have elaborated a culture saturated with anatomical themes and concepts. There is no segment of the culture that is not so structured. It is pertinent to ask two questions: How much of this orientation and elaboration could be inferred from the material remains available in an archeological record? and What led to this development among the Aleuts (the Koniags of Kodiak Islands probably had much the same development) but not among other Eskimo groups, even those with much the same ecological base and material culture?

SOURCES OF ANATOMICAL INFORMATION AMONG THE MANO AND THE TUNGUS

Mummification involving evisceration and the use of a particular animal for comparative anatomical dissection are two distinctive features of the Aleuts in contrast to other Eskimo groups. Either autopsy of the dead or mummification is not uncommon in the Bering Sea region and, of course, in other areas around the world.

The Chukchee practiced a form of autopsy in which one man, the "fortifier," exposed the internal organs and announced the "probable reason" of death on the appearance of the liver and heart (Bogoras, 1909, pp. 527–28). Similarly, "The Reindeer Koryak of the Palpal Ridge dissect bodies before burning them, in order to find out what ailed them" (Jochelson, 1908, p. 113). The Yukaghir cut the flesh from the bones of the deceased shamans, dried them in the sun, and distributed them to the relatives of the shaman. The skull was placed on a manikin, which was used for divination and other purposes. The likelihood that a more typical autopsy was also practiced is indicated in an account of a traditional tale in which, following the death of an older brother: "according to custom, his body was dissected to learn the cause of death, and, according to the tradition, his heart was found to be torn in two" (Jochelson, 1910, pp. 221, 79). The Ainu are credited with a rather ingenious system of evisceration for mummification, namely, removal of the intestines through the anus (Montandon, 1937, p. 150). Mortuary customs involving the use of parts of the dead, skull cults, etc., have been reported for every major area of the world (MacLeod, 1925; Kroeber, 1948, pp. 300–304) as well as for the Bering Sea and North Pacific area, and they obviously constitute a rather ubiquitous source of information.

If we proceed to a culture in which the hunting of wild animals is relatively less important than among these northern groups, we see that the same sources of information are present. In discussing the "Native Knowledge of Anatomy," Harley notes for the Mano of Liberia:

The leech's knowledge of anatomy is naturally limited, but it is probably more exact than would be expected of primitive people. The tribesmen are accustomed to cutting up wild, as well as domestic animals. As cannibals, they used to cut up human beings. On occasion they did the same for other purposes, as, for example, those noted above under "Medicine" and under "Witchcraft." There is also a practice closely parallel to our custom of performing an autopsy on cases in which the cause of death is obscure. The native leech will open up a cadaver and remove a diseased organ, especially if this organ was the seat of a tumor which was recognizable before death and supposed to be witch-substance. The diseased organ will be removed and buried separately from the rest of the body so that the spirit of the deceased will not pass the disease on to some other member of the family [Harley, 1941, p. 41].

Cutting up wild and domestic animals, and cannibalism, stand out as general sources, and, with the exception of domestic animals, these may be attributed to early man as evidenced from the archeological remains.

One of the richest sources, based on direct observations made over a long period of time under eminently suitable conditions, is that of the anatomical knowledge of the Tungus, by Shirokogoroff (1935, pp. 73–76 *et passim*). Here, as with the Aleuts, we may see the part played by anatomy in the daily life of these hunters and reindeer-breeders. At least five major points stand out in clear relief: (1) the Tungus are anatomists and not simply butchers; (2) variations, similarities and dissimilarities, and homologies and analogies are carefully studied; (3) animals are caught and kept for the purpose of study; (4) surgery involving tissue transplantation is conducted; (5) sophisticated observations permitting the recognition of microörganisms are made; and (6) (the basic point) these practices are all part of a necessary method of adaptation for survival.

Shirokogoroff speaks directly to the point in documenting the anatomical preoccupations of the Tungus:

> When killing a new animal a Tungus is first of all interested in finding the anatomical peculiarities of this animal. Indeed, it is very essential, for he must skin and sometimes dissect the animal without breaking the skin and bones. Here the Tungus appears before us as an anatomist. As a matter of fact, the skinning and dressing of the animals is one of the essential elements of the Tungus education. The man who does not know how to do it, will not be able to carry out this industry. A fact may help us to understand the Tungus attitude in this matter. A man amongst the Birarcen did not know that the articulation of ribs of the bear is not like that in some cervines with which he was familiar. In fact, when the breast bone is taken off the ribs in cervines must be turned outside, while in the bear they must be pressed inside. He did try to dissect the animal and he could not do it. Then he tried to break the chest with a heavy piece of wood. This did not solve the problem, but the meat was reduced to pieces, and thus could not be transported and used. This man's name was always repeated as an instance which must not be followed. Everybody laughed at him. However, the Tungus is not only a butcher, he is an anatomist. He is interested in the comparative study of bones and soft parts of the body and he comes to form a good idea as to the anatomical similarities and dissimilarities in animals and even man. Let us remark that the occasions of studying human anatomy present themselves rather often, especially, in former days, for the Tungus at least those of Manchuria did interfere in the traumatic cases and they did practise the cleaning of bones after a certain period after death and thus could and must know the skeleton, also soft parts of the body [Shirokogoroff, 1935, p. 73].

The Tungus compare the analogous and homologous bones of different animals and may use the same word for the same articulation even though it occurs in a different position. They have noted that the bat has long arms, like man, and is not a bird.

Of considerable importance is the practice of capturing animals for observation of their behavior and anatomy. One example is cited of a group of Tungus who searched for a bird that was reported to dive into holes in the ice and to emerge from other holes. Finally catching such a bird, they attached a string to it in order to facilitate their observations of how it dived, what it ate, etc. Finally, they killed and anatomized it, examining the skin especially for insects.

Closely related is the practice of keeping the young of various animals, especially those with which they want more familiarity, though they may rationalize this by explaining that the animals are kept for the amusement of children. The adults spend their time observing them, and it is clear that here lies a possible preliminary step in the domestication of animals.

Sinew from the leg of a partridge is used to splice the severed sinews in the hand of a man, and the separated ends are joined with a long hair (Shirokogoroff, p. 95).

They infer the idea of microörganisms from the observation of worms in wounds, as they gradually grow large enough to be visible to the naked eye. They infer that there are very small worms that cannot be seen and that various diseases may be caused by these.

Throughout their observations is the recurring argument to men. Hair and skin are subject to change. Though taking a long time in man, it occurs most rapidly in snakes. Going beyond the changes within an individual in his life span, they infer that man was formerly hairy but lost his hair as a consequence of using salt and must therefore use clothing. Interestingly, they credit salt and hot food for the loss of formerly good olfactory functions in man. Like the Aleuts, they are not in the least hostile to the idea of evolution.

Their ideas concerning coitus, castration, and inheritance vary from absolute accuracy concerning the first two, to the general acceptance of the last, with failure to distinguish "moral" qualities from those that are purely physical.

In this respect, the intrusion of another example from people who hunt and who breed animals, the Nez Percé, may illustrate what might have been done many times over with reindeer or other animals but escaped detection. The Nez Percé succeeded in developing a purebred line of horses, the Apaloosa. Since they did not receive the horse until sometime after A.D. 1700 and were known to have developed the line by the middle of the nineteenth century, it seems evident that it did not develop by chance. We know, of course, that they paid careful attention to the breeding of these horses for their unusual coat color and pattern.

Shirokogoroff itemized four conditions that affect the relative familiarity of man with the various animals: (1) they may pay more attention to animals on which they are living (and within this we should note that, as with the Aleuts, where certain tissues are used for fabricational purposes, they are well known, thus the Tungus have names for some of the most important tendons because they are used for thread); (2) not all animals allow man to approach them closely; (3) the number of animals is different for different species; and (4) the animals behave differently toward man, and those that are dangerous attract more attention.

The ideas of the Tungus, like those of the Aleuts, are well elaborated in the general area of functional and gross anatomy and in behavior. They admit that these animals have certain territories. Recognizing the ownership of territory, then, requires various specialized behavior on the part of the human. Depending on whether the animal is considered very intelligent and whether he can understand human speech, they placate or frighten him upon entering his territory. "Yet, when a Tungus speaks to the tiger, he leaves his gun down, etc. and does not believe the tiger to be a being endowed with supernatural power. He hopes to be understood but if he fails he has to fight. . . . It is different with the bear which cannot understand speech" (Shirokogoroff, p. 79).

A final observation consists in a similarity between European and Tungus anatomists. The Tungus seem to have imported a number of terms from Mongol, sometimes preserving their own as well. This is analogous to the substitution or addition of Latin anatomical terms for Anglo-Saxon terms.

FACTORS IN THE UNDERESTIMATION OF
PRIMITIVE KNOWLEDGE

The consistent underestimation of primitives' knowledge is a notorious and unfortunate fact, though the reasons are not difficult to assay. Apparently without exception, every fieldworker who has included such an investigation in his schedule has remarked that he was unable to exhaust the native's knowledge because of too little time or because he himself lacked the necessary knowledge to record those things that the native informant wished to tell or show him. We have already seen Veniaminov's candid admission that he did not possess sufficient anatomical information to record what the Aleuts knew. Shirokogoroff notes: "I have carried this experiment with many Tungus in order to find how far they are familiar with the small bones and for gathering data for my dictionary. Indeed, I was unable to exhaust this branch of their knowledge as it was impossible to do with all the plants and animals, known to the Tungus" (p. 74). Dr. Cooper notes that after a Cree hunter explained to him in considerable detail the shape, position, and functions of the four parts of the caribou stomach, "I had to look up the point when I got back home to my books. He was right" (Cooper, 1945, p. 361). Dr. Steggerda recorded the names of 441 plants and animals known to one Maya Indian and observed that the Indian could doubtless have enumerated at least one-third more animals and plants had time permitted working longer (Steggerda, *Proc. Eighth Amer. Sci. Cong.*, p. 91). Such statements can be multiplied many times over by recourse to reports of field investigators. They are notoriously absent in secondary works.

Failure to speak the language, or at least to record in the native's language, is a serious barrier. This failure leads to inaccuracy and often blunts the interest of the native. It precludes any chance of examining the system of organization in detail and omits a practical test of what the native actually does know. It may also lead to obscure discussions of whether the native was "aware" of the true meaning of physiological paternity and so dissolve into semasiological ambiguities. Additionally, the interesting speculations and discussions concerning the identification of parts and their functions, which so often form a part of the conversation of natives, are lost. In this respect it is interesting to see how

Chamisso overcame the linguistic problem in his study of the Aleut knowledge of whales. He asked the Aleuts to carve wooden models of each of the whales known to them. As a consequence he was able to place on record a study of whales that has never been duplicated (Chamisso, 1824). The disposition of this study (published in Latin) provides an example of intellectual embalming, and the author will probably continue to remain better known for his authorship of *Peter Schlemihl*.

Lack of training in the natural sciences not only may disqualify an observer but also may lead to imputations of magic where none in fact exists. Even the use of divination may have a very valuable function in randomizing the choice of hunting routes selected by the hunter and thus maximizing the likelihood of meeting game that has come to know the hunter's habits over a period of time. Arctic Eskimos avoid eating the liver of polar bear for the very good reason that it makes them sick. Whether this is called hypervitaminosis or magic will depend upon the knowledge of the investigator. After all, few Europeans have seen a vitamin, much less a hypervitamin. Most investigators have not hunted for a living, and many have not dressed out anything larger than a rabbit or pheasant. As Shirokogoroff points out, "hunting stories" have become synonymous with imagination of not ill-natured liars in our society. "It shows only one thing, that the life of cities does not impose knowledge and accuracy regarding wild animals" (p. 77).

Another source of underestimation lies in the fact that much knowledge is secret. It may be confined to members of a guild or union and transmitted only in schools and between members, as in the Poro (Harley, 1941, p. 123). In addition, the complex of practices that involves such knowledge may have been suppressed for political or religious reasons. Suppression of shamanism in the Aleutian Islands and in Greenland has undoubtedly removed much information from the reach of even assiduous investigators.

Where an important animal, such as the sea otter used for comparative anatomy by the Aleuts, is protected by federal law, the practice of comparative anatomy must suffer accordingly. Thus conservation measures have affected the continuation of anatomical knowledge in many places in the world. Removal of Indians to reservations, where they can no longer practice their traditional economy effectively, eliminates maintenance and transmission of the anatomical knowledge previously essential to their survival. The discouragement of cannibalism and head-hunting similarly interferes with a basic source of information.

The supply of informed observers, anthropologists, zoölogists, botanists, etc., was unfortunately in short supply at the time Europeans first made contact with many remote people. At present there is a more ample supply of observers, but the supply of subjects has diminished. In addition, there are many current fads of research that place more stress on feelings and attitudes of natives and less on their abilities, achievements, and adaptations to local circumstances (Linne, 1957; Kroeber, 1957).

Other factors that have led to the underestimation of the knowledge of primitive peoples are the short periods of time that are spent in the field with the people and a belief in the inability of natives to accumulate knowledge in the same way Europeans do. Harley's expression of this fact, phrased for studies of native medical practice, is precisely to the point.

The best accounts of native medical practice are from men who have spent years of actual residence among the natives, either as missionaries or as government officials. This is especially true where anthropological training was part of their equipment for life among people of so different a culture. Those who have gone to Africa primarily as anthropologists have either lacked medical training or failed to stay long enough to penetrate the secrets of the native leech [Harley, 1941, p. xiii].

UNRECONSTRUCTABLE ASPECTS

Two categories of information that are unreconstructable deserve mention, for in themselves they are important and also indicate other things that are beyond recall. The first of these, consisting of the words, meanings, relations, and intellectual organization thereof, is largely if not totally beyond apprehension. The second of these categories consists of those artifacts or devices that depend upon transformation states. One of these, the baleen or bone blade used to puncture the intestines of the polar bear, is an item that cannot be appreciated from any archeological record. Arctic Eskimos place a blade of baleen or thin bone into a ball of blubber or fat, having folded the blade into an S shape, and freeze the blade and fat. After being swallowed by the bear, the fat thaws out and the blade unfolds, thus piercing the intestines and other internal tissues. Other examples of the use of transformation states consist of the manufacture of whole sleds of frozen flesh, and runners of frozen mud and water. A change in temperature may eliminate an entire trait—disastrous for the archeologist and for the traveling Eskimo.

An interesting variation of the manufacture of artifacts by utilization of transformation states is provided by the excavations of Sir Aurel Stein at the settlement of Niya, Khotan. He found two tree trunks side by side, half-buried in the floor of an outhouse, with layers of poplar leaves in the sand below them. Local informants recognized this assemblage as a refrigerator. The ice was placed between the trunks and covered with poplar leaves (Clark, 1947, pp. 167–68). Without the ethnographic information of living peoples this reconstruction would have been impossible. It is likely that a great many early hunting methods that presuppose and contribute to a knowledge of anatomy are beyond recall, and these may have been critical in the early history of man. Many of those things that depended upon temperature changes for their manufacture or use, as well as all those things that may have decomposed in the intervening years— cordage, poisons, wood tools—were important in mammal hunting, as in the case of the Eskimo intestinal blade.

One more category, that of diseases and fractures, was undoubtedly crucial in the life of early man, as it still is for both modern man and his primate relatives. Attention to parasites, diseases with visible manifestations, and fractures constitute a source of anatomical information. Unfortunately, as Schultz has demonstrated, it is not possible to ascertain with certainty when man elaborated the art of setting and holding broken bones. Well-healed fractures are found in abundant numbers among the nonhuman primates (Schultz, 1949).

PROTOHOMINID CONTINUITIES

A number of researchers, employing divergent kinds of materials, have adumbrated the point that there is no vast intellectual gap in the line leading to hominids, or from ancient to recent man (Harlow, 1958; Simpson, 1958; Washburn and Avis, 1958; Count, 1958; Fisher, 1958). This is not to note that human behavior is not now unique in many respects and that a considerable number of differences may not be found between points widely separated on the continuum leading to man. As Simpson has phrased it, *"Something about our abilities and behaviors is different and was once, even if not suddenly, new"* (Simpson, 1958, p. 519).

Much if not most of ancient man's behavior was partially modified from that of his predecessors. Normal eating, as Washburn has noted, is a selective process among living carnivores (Washburn, 1957, p. 612). Food preferences of this sort require an elementary distinction between the different parts of the animal's body. The pertinence to my argument is that this constitutes a basis for anatomical knowledge. Conferring a name on a heart or liver necessarily came after recognition of the organs. As to the problem of knowing whether the earliest forms of man were hunters or were hunted, there may be no suitable evidence among the bones of associated animals, for man's habits may have been quite similar to those of his contemporaries.

The sites of hunters and hunted must have been remarkably similar for thousands of years. If the inventory of animals found with *Australopithecus* resembles that of carnivores, it can be assumed that it is because he had similar hunting and dietary habits. If we further accept the likelihood that *Australopithecus* selected the stones most suitable for tools, while retaining his older carnivorous habits, we should expect the kind of inventory of associated bones that is currently reported (Washburn, 1957). Man's knowledge of animal morphology, physiology, and behavior could be well in advance of technical adaptations. In fact, it would appear most likely that tools were made for specific purposes and that procurement of meat was among such purposes.

THE ARGUMENT FROM CONTEMPORARY DISTRIBUTION

Acceptance of the general proposition that traits with wide distribution are older than those with a more limited distribution permits us to infer great antiquity for practices connected with childbirth and menstruation. Equally or more interesting is the similarity of attitudes and beliefs concerning these found in widely separated and unrelated areas around the world. In his study of "Primitive Obstetrics" Professor Spencer called attention to similarity of such beliefs: "But since the human frame is everywhere subject to the same laws, it follows that many widely scattered and culturally divergent groups may arrive at similar conclusions with respect to birth and so develop quite similar ceremonial attitudes" (Spencer, 1950, pp. 1158–59).

The fact that trephining is found in widely separated areas (Peru, Denmark, Algeria, and Oceania) constitutes good evidence that some independent invention is involved (Popham, 1954; Stewart, 1958). The same problem and the same morphology have been combined with a similar conclusion and technique. Thus it is not simply the ubiquity of anatomical practices among primitive peoples but the development of analogous attitudes, beliefs, and practices, based on a demonstrably similar morphology, that suggests the likelihood that such practices occurred very early in human history. The basic ways of eviscerating a mammal are considerably more limited than are the grammars that are used to describe such an activity.

Caesarean operations are comparatively rare in their distribution, but the idea of assisting women at childbirth is universal. Autopsy of the dead is comparatively rare, but attention of some sort to the dead is universal.

Referring to the use of contemporary distributions I would suggest that Boas overlooks anatomical knowledge in claiming that astronomical observations are most widely distributed. His remarks are pertinent:

Man has not only utilized his experience in handling materials but has also, at an early time, learned to observe nature in such a manner as to utilize his experiences in regulating his activities. Astronomical and meteorological observations and those relating to the tides are probably most widely found [Boas, 1938, p. 274].

Since the occurrence of animals with the seasons, and their morphological variations are carefully noted, these two bodies of observations have an equally long history and widespread distribution.

We may approach the contemporary distribution of anatomical interest in still another way. In attempting to find objective criteria for evaluating progress, Kroeber lists the "decline of infantile obsession with the outstanding physiological events of human life" (Kroeber, 1948, p. 304). Some of these practices that characterize backward, as against advanced, cultures are: blood or animal sacrifice; segregation of women at parturition and menstruation; contamination by death or corpses; puberty-crisis rites; preoccupation with the dead body—including mummification, skull preservation, and skull cult, wearing of skull or jaw by widows, disinterment and reburial, eating of bits of the body or of cremation ashes, human sacrifice, head-hunting, and cannibalism. Though Kroeber's estimate of their significance for progress may be debated, this list does indicate the extent to which such matters provide foci for intellectual and cultural organization. These constitute sources of information as well as projections of anatomical interest.

Like many other authors, Kroeber refers to the Eskimo as though they constituted a monolithic entity with reference to their beliefs and practices. In point of fact, the greater use of magic and of shamans occurs in the culturally impoverished central and Arctic Eskimo area. The greater use of public ceremonials, with less dependence on individual shamans, occurs in the western and southern areas of greater ecological abundance and larger population size and antiquity (Marsh, 1954). It is in this latter area, the Aleutians and the Alaska Peninsula, that human anatomical knowledge was carried to its furthest development. Mummies do occur in Greenland, but they have not been eviscerated and there is no corresponding development of autopsy or comparative anatomy (J. Meldgaard, 1953).

SUMMARY

Contemporary evidence and inferences from archeological and paleontological evidence all indicate that man recognized his affinity with other animals from earliest times. Ancient man appears to have been a hunter, and a big-game hunter where big game was available. *Zinjanthropus boisei* appears to have eaten not only small mammals, birds, and reptiles but also the immature specimens of giant pigs (Leakey, 1959). The extent to which he was carnivorous must be inferred from the broken bones in his living sites and, later, from the presence of tools. It is likely that his protohominid forebears were carnivorous in many of their habits and that many of man's habits were retained from this kind of ancestry and then elaborated. Ancient man was a carnivore who had to hunt in order to eat and in order to utilize animal products for fabricational purposes as well as for food. Knowledge of anatomy has thus been of immediate value in making a living.

The body size of the protohominids, together with simple instrumentation, and pack hunting, is sufficient to enable them to kill all terrestrial animals, including man. The simplicity of implements that can be used to kill large herbivores and carnivores is remarkable. Selection of suitable stones, superseded by worked stone tools, clubs, and pointed shafts, is quite adequate to secure all kinds of animals by an animal who makes relatively acute observations. The elaboration of his knowledge of anatomy was facilitated by the constancy of animal morphology, physiology, and behavior during the Pleistocene. In addition, man had the advantage of being able to transfer observations based on his own structure to that of most of the animals he hunted and, similarly, to argue from the animals back to his own condition. Universal situations, such as childbirth, pathologies, growth, and death, in addition to the same kind of sensory apparatus, provided sources of information that were applicable to both the observers and the observed.

The extent and the system of organization of such knowledge, revealed in such contemporary groups as the Aleutian Islanders and contiguous Eskimos, cannot be reconstructed from archeological evidence. Though varying greatly around the world, the anatomical information possessed by most peoples has probably been consistently underestimated. Rational medicine and physical culture, true comparative anatomy, dissection of the deceased for information, and mummification have appeared in many places and have collectively occurred with a single grouping of people whose life bears many similarities to that of Paleolithic man, that is, the Aleutian Islanders. The ubiquity of such occurrences, separately and collectively, plus the immediate practical value of such practices, permit us to infer the value and likelihood of such underlying anatomical knowledge with the first appearance of hunting. Further, it can be inferred that anatomical knowledge was prior to other categories of learning in humans and that such observations provided the basis for the design of tools, beginning with the first club, knife, and spear. The organization of the mammalian body provides a basis for intellectual organization, and anatomical analogies and reasoning are found in all cultures. The ancient Greek maxim that "man is the measure of all things" is literally true. Units of measurement based on dimensions of the body (cubit, ell, fistmele, fathom, hand) are universally distributed. It is suggested that while learning to learn, ancient man was learning anatomy.

BIBLIOGRAPHY

ACKERKNECHT, E. H.
   1943. "Primitive Autopsies and the History of Anatomy," *Bull. Hist. Med.*, 13:334–39.
   1947. "Primitive Surgery," *Amer. Anthrop.*, 49:25–45.

ALEXANDER, FRED
   1949. "A Medical Survey of the Aleutian Islands," *New England J. Med.*, 240:1035–40.

BARTHOLOMEW, GEORGE A., JR., and JOSEPH B. BIRDSELL
   1953. "Ecology and the Protohominids," *Amer. Anthrop.*, 55:481–98.

BOAS, FRANZ
   1938. "Invention." In Boas *et al.*, *General Anhropology*, Chap. 6, pp. 238–81.

BOGORAS, WALDEMAR
   1909. *The Chukchee.* ("Publs. of the Jesup North Pacific Expedition," Vol. 7, Part 2.)

CHAMISSO, ADELBERTUS DE
   1824. "Cetaceorum maris Kamtschatici imagines, ab Aleutis e ligno fictas, adumbravit recensuitque," *Verhandlungen der kaiserlichen Leopoldinisch-Carolinischen Akademie der Naturforscher*, 12, Part 1, 249–63. Bonn.

CLARK, GRAHAME
1947. *Archaeology and Society*. 2d rev. ed. London: Methuen.

COOPER, JOHN M.
1935. "Magic and Science," *Thought*, 10:357–73.

COUNT, EARL W.
1958. "The Biological Basis of Human Society," *Amer. Anthrop.*, 60:1049–85.

DART, RAYMOND A.
1949. "The Predatory Implemental Technique of *Australopithecus*," *Amer. J. Phys. Anthrop.*, 7:1–38.

1958. "The Minimal Bone-Breccia Content of Makapansgat and the Australopithecine Predatory Habit," *Amer. Anthrop.*, 60:923–31.

FISHER, RONALD A.
1958. *The Genetical Theory of Natural Selection*. 2d rev. ed. New York: Dover.

HALDANE, J. B. S.
1956. "The Argument from Animals to Men: An Examination of Its Validity for Anthropology," *J. Roy. Anthrop. Inst.*, 86, Part II, 1–14.

HARLEY, GEORGE WAY
1941. "Native African Medicine, with Special Reference to Its Practice in the Mano Tribe of Liberia." Cambridge: Harvard University Press.

HARLOW, HARRY F.
1958. "The Evolution of Learning." In A. ROE and G. G. SIMPSON (eds.), *Behavior and Evolution*. New Haven: Yale University Press, pp. 269–90.

HOWELL, F. CLARK
1954. "Hominids, Pebble Tools and the African Villafranchian." *Amer. Anthrop.*, 56:378–86.

HRDLIČKA, ALEŠ
1944. *The Anthropology of Kodiak Island*. Philadelphia: Wistar Institute of Anatomy and Biology.

1945. *The Aleutian and Commander Islands*. Philadelphia: Wistar Institute of Anatomy and Biology.

JOCHELSON, WALDEMAR
1905–8. *The Koryak*. ("Publs. of the Jesup North Pacific Expedition," Vol. 6, Part 1.)
1910. *The Yukaghir and the Yukaghirized Tungus*. ("Publs. of the Jesup North Pacific Expedition," Vol. 9.)

KIRKPATRICK, CHARLES M., DONALD E. STULLKEN, and ROBERT D. JONES, JR.
1955. "Notes on Captive Sea Otters," *Arctic*, 8:46–59.

KROEBER, A. L.
1948. *Anthropology*. New rev. ed. New York: Harcourt, Brace.

1957. *Ethnographic Interpretations*. ("Univ. Calif. Publs. Amer. Archaeol. and Ethnol.," Vol. 47, No. 2, pp. 191–204.)

LAUGHLIN, W. S.
1950. "Blood Groups, Morphology and Population Size of the Eskimos," *Cold Spring Harbor Symp. Quant. Biol.*, 15:164–73.

LAUGHLIN, W. S., and G. H. MARSH
1951. "A New View of the History of the Aleutians," *Arctic*, 4:75–88.
1952. "The Aleut-Eskimo Community," *Anthrop. Papers Univ. Alaska*, 1:25–46.

LEAKEY, L. S. B.

1959. "A New Fossil Skull from Olduvai," *Nature*, 184:491–93.

LINNE, S.

1957. "Technical Secrets of American Indians," *J. Roy. Anthrop. Inst.*, 87:149–64.

MacLEOD, WILLIAM CHRISTIE

1925. "Certain Mortuary Aspects of Northwest Coast Culture," *Amer. Anthrop.*, 27:122–48.

MARSH, GORDON H.

1954. "A Comparative Survey of Eskimo-Aleut Religion," *Anthrop. Papers Univ. Alaska*, 3:21–36.

MARSH, GORDON H., and WILLIAM S. LAUGHLIN

1956. "Human Anatomical Knowledge among the Aleutian Islanders," *Southwestern J. Anthrop.*, 12:38–78.

McCOWN, THEODORE D., and ARTHUR KEITH

1939. *The Stone Age of Mount Carmel: The Fossil Human Remains from the Levalloiso-Mousterian.* Oxford.

MELDGAARD, JORGEN

1953. "Fra En Grønlansk Mumiehule," *Nationalmuseets Arbejdsmark*, pp. 14–20.

MONTANDON, GEORGE

1937. *La Civilization Ainou et les cultures Arctiques.* Paris: Payot.

MOVIUS, H. L.

1950. "A Wooden Spear of Third Interglacial Age from Lower Saxony," *Southwestern J. Anthrop.*, 6:139–42.

OAKLEY, KENNETH P.

1949. *Man the Tool-maker.* London: British Museum (Natural History).

POPHAM, ROBERT E.

1954. "Trepanation as a Rational Procedure in Primitive Surgery," *Univ. Toronto Med. Jour.*, 31:204–11.

ROBINSON, J. T.

1957. "Occurrence of Stone Artifacts with *Australopithecus* at Sterkfontein," *Nature*, 180:521–24.

ROE, ANNE, and G. G. SIMPSON (eds.)

1958. *Behavior and Evolution.* New Haven: Yale University Press.

SCHULTZ, ADOLPH H.

1949a. "Notes on Diseases and Healed Fractures of Wild Apes," *Bull. Hist. Med.*, 7:571–82.

1949b. "Sex Differences in the Pelves of Primates," *Amer. J. Phys. Anthrop.*, 7:401–23.

1955. "Primatology in Its Relation to Anthropology," *Year-Book of Anthropol.*, pp. 47–60.

SHIROKOGOROFF, S. M.

1935. *Psychomental Complex of the Tungus.* London: Kegan Paul.

SPENCER, ROBERT F.

1949–50. "Primitive Obstetrics." In *CIBA Symposia*, 11:1158–88.

STEWART, T. D.

1958. "Stone Age Skull Surgery: A General Review, with Emphasis on the New World." In *Smithsonian Report for 1957*, pp. 469–91. Washington.

Washburn, S. L.
1957. "Australopithecines: The Hunters or the Hunted?" *Amer. Anthrop.*, 59:612–14.

Washburn, S. L., and Virginia Avis
1958. "Evolution of Human Behavior." In Anne Roe and G. G. Simpson (eds.), *Behavior and Evolution*, pp. 421–36. New Haven: Yale University Press.
1959. "Speculations on the Interrelations of the History of Tools and Biological Evolution," *Human Biol.*, 31:21–31.

Watson, William
1956. *Flint Implements*. London: British Museum.

ON MAN'S USE OF FIRE, WITH COMMENTS
ON TOOL-MAKING AND HUNTING

KENNETH P. OAKLEY

USE OF FIRE

THE earliest hominids were probably pygmoid-size creatures (e.g., *Australopithecus* of Sterkfontein) living in warm temperate and subtropical environments. Extension of their range into cooler regions may have been accompanied by some increases in bulk (cf. Bergman's rule),[1] but, in any case the use of fire would have enormously helped survival beyond the winter frost line. The earliest known use of fire was during the time of the Second Glaciation (Mindel), a horizon not far removed from the time of the *Australopithecus/Pithecanthropus* displacement. The production of artificial environments, including the manifold uses of fire, may also have had some part in the *neanderthalensis/sapiens* displacement. This occurred at the peak of the Fourth (or Würm) Glaciation, which, although less extensive than the Third, was responsible for a higher percentage of the fauna's becoming extinct, possibly on account of the great intensity of the cold.

I have already reviewed elsewhere the evidence regarding man's early use of fire (Oakley, 1956, pp. 36–48; 1958, pp. 135–45), but I believe that, in view of its importance in relation to man's social evolution, no apology is needed for repeating the review—brought up to date—in the present symposium.

EARLIEST EVIDENCE OF THE USE OF FIRE

The claim has been advanced that *Australopithecus* was a fire-user, but this has not been substantiated. I believe it is worth recording the facts that lay behind this claim. In 1925 Professor Raymond Dart received pieces of bone breccia collected by Mr. W. I. Eitzman of Pietersburg at limeworks in the Makapansgat Valley near Potgietersrus in the Transvaal. Since some of the fragments of bone had a charred appearance, Professor Dart suspected that this was a cave deposit containing hearths of early man (Dart, 1925). Some

1. Professor W. F. Laughlin drew my attention to the possibly significant fact that many Arctic peoples, although of stocky build, have exceptionally large heads.

of the blackened fragments were submitted for analysis to Dr. James Moir of the Government Chemical Laboratories and to Dr. F. W. Fox of the South African Institute for Medical Research. Acid residues of the bones contained matter that, by means of transformation into carbon dioxide, was proved to be carbon. This was taken to be confirmation that the blackness of the bone fragments was due to charring.

Some twenty years later, fossil bones of *Australopithecus* were discovered in blocks of breccia at the Makapan Limeworks, and Professor Dart recognized that they were identical with the deposit in which the carbon had been identified. He concluded that *Australopithecus* had been a fire-user, and he accordingly described the specimens under the new name *Australopithecus prometheus* (Dart, 1925). Examination of blocks of the breccia had also revealed patches of glasslike material that appeared to support the idea that fires had burned in the cave (1952, p. 97), but subsequently this material proved to be collophane (amorphous calcium phosphate) having no connection with burning. Through the courtesy of Professor Dart, and with the aid of a grant from the Wenner Gren Foundation, I had an opportunity in 1953 to visit the Makapansgat Valley and to collect a series of samples of the fossil bones in the Limeworks Cave for further analysis. Analysis of samples of the bones in the australopithecine breccia failed to confirm the presence of free carbon. The blackness of the bone fragments in all the specimens that I collected proved to be due to oxides of iron and manganese.

One could not doubt the correctness of the determinations made by Moir and Fox, but the fact remained that the blackness of the bones could be entirely accounted for by the mineral staining. The true explanation of the apparent discrepancy between the results obtained in 1925 and in 1953 became obvious when Mr. Eitzman (1958) published a record of the percentage of carbon that had been found in the black Makapan bones: 0.16 per cent! The presence of traces of acid-insoluble carbonaceous matter in fossil bone is no proof of burning. As a result of the extensive analytical studies of fossil bones undertaken at the British Museum (Natural History) and elsewhere during the last ten years, it has been established that carbon in the form of residual protein or amino acids survives in bones for hundreds of thousands of years. Many early Pleistocene bones, quite unburned and without any trace of blackness, contain as much as 0.2 per cent carbon in the form of degraded protein. Analyses of charred bones, on the other hand, show percentages of carbon ranging from 1 to 10 per cent and more.

I think we can now be quite sure that there is no valid evidence that any of the bones associated with *Australopithecus* are charred.

It has been suggested that some of the crackled and distorted bones in the Makapan gray breccia owe their condition to calcination (i.e., being burned to the extent of losing their free carbon). However, analyses have shown that calcined bones have a lower fluorine content than do uncalcined bones from the same bed, whereas the crackled bones from the Makapan breccias have the same fluorine content as do uncrackled bones in the same layer. The pattern of crackling in the Makapan bones is evidently due to calcite mineralization.

Recently more than fifty pebble tools were found in breccia at the Sterkfontein Caves, southwest of Pretoria, associated with teeth of *Australopithecus* and fragmentary animal remains (Robinson and Mason, 1957). So far, no traces of fire have been noticed in this layer. It is still regarded by some authorities as doubtful whether the tools were made by *Australopithecus* or by some other allied type of hominid[2] who hunted the latter; but the circumstances in which the tools occurred make it quite certain that they were left by hominids who spent at least some daylight hours *in* the cave. Until this discovery was made, no evidence was known of hominids' occupying caves in Africa before Upper Pleistocene times.

There appears to be a complete lack of evidence of man's use of fire in Africa in earlier and Middle Pleistocene times. No charred bones or fire-reddened or fire-crackled stones have been reported from Oldowan, Chellean, or Lower or Middle Acheulian occupation sites in Africa. If fire had been in regular use, one would have expected such evidence to have been noticed in the Chellean butchering site in Bed II at Olduvai, for example, or in the Lower Acheulian butchering site at Ternifine (Palikao), where remains of *Atlanthropus* were discovered. Dr. L. S. B. Leakey made a special point of searching for evidence of fire on the late Middle Acheulian occupation surfaces[3] at Olorgesailie in Kenya; and he reported that none was found.

In marked contrast to the negative indications in the earlier Paleolithic horizons in Africa, there is positive evidence of the use of fire at the Final Acheulian levels in Cape Province, Transvaal, and Northern Rhodesia and on all succeeding cultural horizons, at innumerable sites in the open and in caves.

The late Professor van Riet Lowe (1954) discovered hand-axes of the Final Acheulian stage in the top few inches of a thick bed of ashes in the Cave of Hearths at 4,950 feet above sea level in the Makapansgat Valley, Transvaal. The greater part of this "Basal Hearth" was found to consist of phosphatic ash representing a thick deposit of bat guano that had been set alight, presumably by the fires of the Acheulian hunters who were the first men to occupy the mouth of the cave (Oakley, 1954). In overlying deposits, the ashes of human hearths were found at nine levels, representing cultures ranging from Fauresmith (equivalent to Middle Paleolithic in Europe), through Middle Stone Age (equivalent to Upper Paleolithic), and Late Stone Age (Microlithic) to the Iron Age.

Professor A. J. H. Goodwin (1929) found signs of the use of fire by the Late Acheulian occupants of the Montagu Cave at about 1,300 feet above sea level

---

2. *Paranthropus* and the variant known as "Telanthropus" were approximately contemporary.

3. Stage 8 of the eleven stages of Acheulian culture described in East Africa.

in the Cape Province; and unmistakable evidence, in the form of charcoal and
charred wooden artifacts, has recently been revealed by Dr. Desmond Clark
on the Final Acheulian "floor" at the open site near Kalambo Falls in Northern
Rhodesia. Radiocarbon dating of wood from this site indicates an antiquity of
more than 53,000 years (*fide* Professor H. de Vries).

In Asia and Europe there is evidence that fire was used earlier than in Africa.
The oldest undoubted hearths are those recorded in the Choukoutien caves,
occupied by Peking man during a phase of the Second (or Mindel) Glaciation.[4]
The first indication of fire found at this site was a piece of burned antler
collected by Father Teilhard de Chardin in 1930 and shown to Abbé H. Breuil,
who recognized its immense significance (Black, 1931; Breuil, 1932). Evidence of
fires in the form of charred bone and antler, fragments of charcoal, seams of
finely divided charcoal, and red and yellow baked clay floors were eventually
found at many levels throughout the "Sinanthropus"-occupation deposits at
Locality 1 of Choukoutien.

The oldest known pieces of charcoal and burned bones due to human agency
are recorded from a gully deposit at Locality 13, which is older than the "Sinanthropus" cave deposits. The charred fragments were associated with lumps of
rock foreign to the site, a chert chopping tool of Soan type, and associated faunal
remains indicating an appreciably earlier stratigraphic horizon, but probably
within the period of the Second (or Mindel) Glaciation (Movius, 1949).

Charred wood was found in the river gravels that yielded the remains of
Java man, *Pithecanthropus erectus* (Carthaus, 1911), but it is doubtful whether
they represent fires of human origin, for volcanic activity in that region no doubt
caused forest fires quite frequently during the accumulation of the deposits.

"Heat-crackled" flints in Tertiary gravels in Europe were the subject of much
controversy during the last century, but these are no longer regarded seriously
as having any bearing on the beginnings of hominid culture. Some, such as those
in the Lower Miocene (or Upper Oligocene) deposits at Thenay, probably owed
the "crackling" to the action of thermal springs or geysers (Sollas, 1924, p. 275;
Breuil, 1958, p. 145). Grass and forest fires caused by lightning and other natural
agencies have no doubt been responsible for occasionally cracking and reddening
stones in soils of all ages.

The oldest acceptable indications of the use of fire by man in Europe and
Western Asia are associated with Acheulian hand-axe culture. Charred wood has
been recorded by M. Saint Périer (1932, p. 16) in the Middle Acheulian lakeside
occupation site at Torralba in the Soria Province of Spain; charcoal was reported
by Dr. Richard West (1954) from the (Middle) Acheulian horizon in the lake
beds at Hoxne in Suffolk; while carbonized vegetable matter and fire-crazed
flints were closely associated with the Middle Acheulian workshop debris of

4. Unpublished palynological evidence indicates, according to Dr. B. Kurtén, that the
Choukoutien occupation deposits at Locality 1 were formed when the climate was cooler
than at the present day.

Swanscombe man (Wymer, 1955). Professor F. Bordes (1958) has also reported burned flints from the Middle Acheulian *atelier* at Cagny-la-Garenne.

There is a conspicuous absence of evidence of fire with the Early Clactonian industries in Britain. Hazzledine Warren found only one partly burned flint among the many hundreds that he collected from the Elephant Bed at Clacton-on-Sea, Essex, and none of the wood in that bed was charred. Yet in the later "Acheulio-Clactonian" industry at Stoke Newington in the same county "more than one per cent of the artifacts are slightly burnt" (Warren, 1951, p. 129). The Stoke Newington gravels may represent an interstadial of the Third Glaciation, whereas the Early Clactonian levels date from the Second Interglacial. However, Torralba, Hoxne, and Swanscombe all provide indications that fire was probably being used in Europe to some extent before the Third Glaciation.

At Pech de l'Azé II in the Dordogne, Bordes has found evidence of fire at a level that he correlates with the Third Glaciation (the cultural horizon is either debased Acheulian or Clactonian). He is inclined to impute similar dating (Bordes, 1958) to the hearths discovered by Mlle G. Henri-Martin at Fonté-chevade with a Tayacian industry, and to those found by Father C. Burdo at La Cotte de St.-Brelade with an Upper Acheulian industry.

Fire was certainly being used by some groups living in Europe under the warmer conditions of the Last Interglacial period, for example at Lehringen (Saxony) and at Ehringsdorf near Weimar; but a number of occupation sites with hearths that were until recently referred to this Interglacial are now considered to date from the time of onset of the Last Glaciation, for example, the Early Mousterian at Krapina in Yugoslavia and the Final Acheulian or Micoquian sites in Palestine and Syria. In Southwest Asia there is a remarkable absence of evidence of fire in the immediately preceding levels.

Hearths are of common occurrence in the cave occupation layers of the neanderthalers who lived during the earlier stages of the Last Glaciation and who were responsible for various Mousterian industries grouped as Middle Paleolithic. There are, however, a few Mousterian sites at which evidence of fire is lacking. At High Cave in Tangier, Professor C. S. Coon (1954, p. 60) found no burned bones or other signs of fire with the Levalloiso-Mousterian, yet charred bones were abundant in the contemporary levels at Haua Fteah in Cyrenaica excavated by Dr. Charles McBurney. M. Arambourou and Dr. Jude (1955) have pointed out that while hearths occur in the Mousterian layer in the Bourgeois-Delaunay grotto, Charente, they are absent from the same level in the neighboring Suard grotto. Are there soil conditions, they ask, under which traces of fire are obliterated? If uncharred bones have survived, it seems most unlikely that carbon would have disappeared; but the matter requires fuller investigation. At any rate, all the Upper Paleolithic peoples were regular fire-users.

It is probable that the earliest Paleolithic fire-*users* were not fire-*makers* but collected this precious commodity from natural conflagrations and conserved

it. Before man could utilize the accidental discovery that this or that action led
to fire, he would have required some experience of handling it, and this he could
have gained only through having isolated and controlled fire of natural origin.
Early man could have repeatedly captured fire without much difficulty in some
volcanic areas. Elsewhere he would have depended on accidental fires, either
such fires as those that are started by lightning in dry forest or grassland or
where there are seepages of mineral oil and gas, or those that originate
occasionally in humid regions through spontaneous combustion. A cliff of oil
shale in Dorset (England) was ignited in 1846 through the heat of oxidation
of pyrites nodules near the surface, and it burned for four years (Davies, 1956,
p. 66). Some types of coal are liable to spontaneous combustion through contact
with air. Since Choukoutien is situated not far from outcrops of a coal-bearing
formation, it is possible that "Sinanthropus" obtained fire through cliff falls
exposing such coals.

Those early human groups who used fire without knowing how to make it
would have conserved it desperately after capturing it. Means of making fire
may have been discovered many times during the long prehistory of mankind,
and in some regions the art may have been lost for long periods. Even in recent
times some of the Andamanese Islanders are said to be ignorant of fire-making
and have had to rely on the preservation of fire caches, relighted when necessary
by brands collected from neighboring peoples who have the knowledge. Many
myths and customs show that even among people who know how to make
fire there is a strong tradition of the virtue of the undying flames. One
Northumbrian family a few years ago boasted that the peat fire in their cottage
had not been allowed to go out for two centuries (Low, 1941, p. 11).

It is possible that the few Lower Paleolithic groups who used fire were still
at the stage of *fire-collecting*, but the regularity with which hearths accompany
Middle and Upper Paleolithic industries leaves no doubt that most of the
neanderthalers and all the Cro-Magnon and related peoples were *fire-producers*,
with fire-making devices as part of their regular equipment.

Discoveries of how to make fire probably occurred through the use and
manufacture of tools. The sparks produced by striking stones together must
have been very evident to early men working in a dim light. The sparks made
by striking flint on flint have only slight incendiary properties. Professor
B. F. Porshnev (1955) has reported experiments showing that fire can be
started by such sparks, but only under ideal conditions and with elaborately
prepared tinder. The *percussion method* of making fire was probably discovered through the chance use of a nodule of iron pyrites as a hammerstone
for striking flint. Whereas "flint sparks" have only the heat generated by the
percussive friction, and lose it rapidly, pyritic sparks (like iron sparks) develop
additional heat through combustion in the air. The striking of pyrites by flint
or quartz was probably the first regular method of making fire and is still
used by the Canoe Indians of Tierra del Fuego and by the Greenland Eskimos.

Nodular iron pyrites has been found in at least one Mousterian occupation deposit (Layer 15 in Cave of the Hyena at Arcy-sur-Cure) (Leroi-Gourhan, 1956). Abraded nodules of pyrites, evidently used for fire-making, have been found at Upper Paleolithic and Mesolithic sites.

It is probable that Paleolithic and Mesolithic peoples commonly used dried fungi as tinder (*amadou*) when making fire by percussion. Fragments of the fungus *Fomes fomentarius* were found amidst the occupation debris at the Mousterian site at Salzgitter-Lebenstedt, in Germany (Grahmann, 1956, Fig. 15), and also on the Mesolithic site of Star Carr in Yorkshire, where they were associated with nodules of iron pyrites (Clark, 1954, p. 167).

It seems rather improbable that the frictional methods of making fire were invented before technology had reached the stage at which bone, antler, ivory, and wood were sawed and shaped by grinding and when holes were bored in such materials by the rapid rotation of a drill. Thus the devices known as the fire saw, the fire plough and the fire twirl may not have been invented before the end of Paleolithic times.[5] (Indeed, it is unlikely that the true fire drill, which is operated by a bow, was introduced before Neolithic times.) All these methods of fire-making require friction on wood sufficiently sustained to rub off fine particles that are hot enough to smolder.

A charred rod of beechwood found with Mousterian industry at Krapina has been claimed as a fire twirl (Gorjanovic-Kramberger, 1909), but it may be only a kind of peg that was accidentally charred.

Largely on the basis of the lack of unquestionable evidence of cave-dwelling or the use of fire in Africa before the time of the Final Acheulian culture, I have suggested in some previous publications on this subject (Oakley, 1956, 1957) that it was only when man had fire regularly at his disposal that he occupied caves, for fire alone would enable him to drive out dangerous carnivores. However, the discovery of pebble tools in one of the cave deposits at Sterkfontein has shown that caves were, at least in daytime,[6] occasionally frequented by the early hominids in Africa. There is, nevertheless, probably some correlation between the use of fire and occupation of caves, as the evidence from Choukoutien shows. The excavators reported on their findings at Locality 1 as follows:

. . . evidence of the dominance of human occupation became increasingly numerous above layer 6, while on the contrary, below layer 7 traces of the contemporary occupancy by hyaenas and bears became increasingly obvious. . . . *Sinanthropus* remains occur . . . in especial association with the cultural ashy layers. [Black, Teilhard de Chardin, Young, and Pei, 1934, p. 22].

5. Unexplained grooves have been observed in humanly cut charred wood from the late Acheulian "floors" at Kalambo Falls in Northern Rhodesia. The possibility that these represent a frictional fire-making device should be borne in mind.

6. It may well be that caves were never used for shelter at night until man had the protection of fire, for the habit of snoring, which characterizes the hominoids, would have continually attracted night-prowling carnivores.

In other words, it would appear that at one stage man's hold on these caves was precarious but that, as time went on, he occupied them more or less continuously —a development that may perhaps have reflected the acquisition of knowledge of how the fires could be renewed if they went out.

It is possible that the connection between cave-dwelling and use of fire arises from the fact that both are means of adaptation to colder or wetter environments. In this context it is perhaps significant that in Western Asia fire-using commenced (or recommenced?) dramatically at precisely the same archeological horizon as in Africa. In the Final Acheulian levels at et-Tabun (Mount Carmel) (Garrod and Bate, 1937, p. 66) and Oumn Qatafa (Neuville, 1931) in Palestine, and in the corresponding "Jabrudian" level 14 at Jabrud in Syria (Rust, 1951, pp. 34–35), there are abundant traces of fire; yet none occurs in the long series of underlying occupation layers. As the Final Acheulian in Southwest Asia was close in time to the onset of the Last Glaciation further north, it appears likely that increasing cold was the spur to man's mastering the art of fire-making, perhaps after a long period during which the art had been lost.

The occurrence of evidence of fire-using at the equivalent cultural horizon so far away in South Africa could indicate the rapid diffusion from the north of information regarding reliable means of making fire; but it may also be a reflection of the unpleasantly damp conditions associated with the beginning of the Last Pluvial period.

In addition to serving man for warmth and protection, fire also served Paleolithic man as a hunting weapon, for driving game into pitfalls and corrals. Fire is still used in America as a means of driving bears out of caves. One is reminded that the stubs of burned-out brands that were found on the clay floor of Tana della Basua near Toirano are considered by Professor A. C. Blanc (1958, pp. 167–74, 267–69) to represent the ritualized activity of Neanderthal bear-hunters. Not least important was fire's usefulness as a tool, for example in tempering wood. The yew-wood spear found with Levalloisian flint flakes amidst bones of *Elephas antiquus* at Lehringen had a "fire-hardened tip" (Movius, 1950). At sites where the only available stone for making tools consisted of large blocks, unworkable by percussion owing to their rounded form (e.g., at Fontmaure, according to Bordes, and at Hangklip in South Africa), Paleolithic man apparently flaked the material in the first place by the method of fire-setting.

The use of fire greatly extended man's horizons, not only physically, in the sense of environment, but emotionally, for hearth is almost synonymous with home. Arambourou and Jude (1955, p. 17) have shown that the successive Upper Paleolithic inhabitants of an *abri* at Bourdeilles took the greatest care in the disposition of their fires, and these authors infer that "ces feux protégeaient les occupants contre les animaux, les moustiques et peut-être contre les puissances mystérieuses de la nuit."

Before man had fire, his cultural activities must have terminated at sundown.

Indeed, the lighting aspect of fire[7] was probably almost as important as its heating aspect in extending man's range. It is often assumed that man could not have lived in the cold regions without fire for warmth. In the initial stages of conquest of the northern lands, before full adaptation had occurred, this may well have been so; but Thomas Simpson (1843, p. 346), writing of the seal-hunting Eskimo, has recorded: "They never seem to think of fire as a means of imparting warmth—their lamps are used for cooking, light, melting snow and drying clothes rather than to warm the air." Their use of blubber as both fuel and food reminds us that its heating value is theoretically the same whether burned or digested. The mammoth-hunters of Moravia apparently fed their fires with marrow dripping from mammoth leg bones, broken in half for the purpose, but there is little doubt that the same material would have been equally valued as food.

Like the Eskimos, the Upper Paleolithic hunters in loess country were probably short of wood: it is interesting to find that they sometimes used coal as fuel (Klima, 1955).

Professor Coon (1955, p. 62) has suggested that the Neanderthalers used fire only for warmth and protection and not for cooking. He points out that in Mousterian layers the long bones of animals have invariably been split for marrow, whereas in later Paleolithic deposits they have been mostly broken in half for sucking out the marrow. He says that experiment shows how difficult it is to extract marrow from raw bones unless they are split open longitudinally, but that after being cooked the marrow can be sucked out when the bone is cut or broken in half. However, in European sites the proportion of burned to unburned bones is just as high in Mousterian occupation layers as in Upper Paleolithic levels, so it is difficult to believe that no cooking of meat occurred in the former time but was practiced in the latter time. Nevertheless, Professor Coon has raised an important question, which should engage the attention of all excavators of Paleolithic occupation deposits. Until recently, few excavators have reported in sufficient detail the condition of animal bones or given statistics of the various kinds represented. One point worth noting in this connection is that a number of the fragments of human bone found at Krapina had been charred, but apparently this was not the case in the Choukoutien deposits, where only animal bones were in a charred or calcined condition.

At the Sirgenstein cave in Württemberg charred bones that had been split and broken up for marrow were the main feature of the Mousterian hearths. As wood charcoal was lacking in the ashes of these hearths, it has been suggested that fat-laden bones served as fuel (Sollas, 1924, p. 233) but it is doubtful whether they would have been of much value for that purpose after the

---

7. The oldest known lamps date from Upper Paleolithic times.

marrow had been removed. In other words, the evidence from Sirgenstein supports the view that Neanderthal man cooked his meat.

We have already noted that at some Mousterian cave sites no burned bones or other evidence of fire have been found (e.g., High Cave in Tangier, Bisitun in Iran, and Grotte Suard in Charente), whereas abundant evidence of fire occurs in contemporaneous Mousterian sites in the same regions. No satisfactory explanation of the difference has yet been suggested.

Domestication of fire probably reacted on man's physical development as well as on his culture, for it would have reduced some selective pressures and increased others. As cooked food replaced a diet consisting entirely of raw meat and fresh vegetable matter, the whole pattern of mastication, digestion, and nutrition was altered. Cooking breaks down the tough fibers of meat and roots releasing amino acids and sugars (Coon, 1955, pp. 62–63), and by softening the food and making it in some ways more nutritious, it reduces the time and energy consumed in eating.

Sir James Frazer (1931, p. 203) was impressed by the number of myths on the origin of fire in which there is insistence that the greatest hardship for man to bear in an age without fire would be having to depend on the sun to warm his food. Frazer thought that this craving for hot food was a natural instinct of the human organism for which a physical cause may be assigned by science. More recently Dr. H. Hediger (1950, p. 134), in his observations on animals in captivity, has noted that warm food is natural for all predatory animals. Is there not a good case for regarding man as a predator?

ADDENDUM

One aspect of the significance of fire to man has perhaps been overlooked. There are indications that fire not only appeals to man's rational mind but that it also has deep subconscious or sensual appeal. Fire obsession has been observed among primitive peoples,[8] as well as in some psychopaths.

8. "The darkness fell quickly because of the rising storm, and the dance of the Eland naturally made way for the greatest of all the Bushman dances: The Fire Dance. Here the women, without a pause, grouped themselves singing in the centre of the clearing. Quickly they piled a fire there, lit it the classical way, and then an uncle of Nxou's led the men in a ring dancing around the fire. They danced the first Bushman soul setting out in the darkness, before mind or matter, to look for substance for fire. They looked in vain for its spoor in the sand as if fire were some subtle animal. Hour after hour they went round and round in the same circle without finding it. They called on the sun, moon and stars to give them fire. Then we saw them leading the blind companions who, in some prehistoric period of the quest, had gone too near the searching flames. Because it was a sacred dance we noticed how in the progress of his search the seeker now acquired the power of healing. Suddenly he would break off his dancing to stand behind a moaning woman and, with trembling hands draw out of her the spirit that was causing her unrest, emitting in the process the cry of the animal with which the alien invader was identified. That done, he

The fact, mentioned in discussion by Professor Schultz, that the Philippine tarsier has been named *Tarsier carbonarius* (Heude, 1898), on account of its propensity for picking up hot embers from campfire sites, suggests than man's ancestors far below hominid level of evolution may have been attracted to natural fires and toyed with burning matter just as rooks and some other birds exhibiting "anting behavior" seek fire and smoke (Burton, 1959, pp. 99–109). After all, is not tobacco-smoking—addiction to which apes and men are equally liable—a form of "anting behavior"?

These considerations lead one to bear in mind that man's ancestors may have become familiar with burning matter plucked from natural conflagrations long before such activity became *purposive* fire-using.

MAN AS TOOL-MAKER

The ancestral stock of apes and man was probably not highly adapted to forest life. Some of the monkey-like apes, such as *Proconsul*, lived in woodlands and could brachiate but could also probably run short distances bipedally on the ground. During Miocene times in East Africa they inhabited a mixed environment of corridor forests along streams and lakes, separated by bushy grassland. It has been suggested that members of the group were sometimes forced to move through the tall grass between forest areas and that, since this necessitated raising their level of vision, bipedal abilities would have had selective advantages. Supposedly, some members of the group moved into permanent forest and became solely arboreal, with hands specialized for hooking onto or hanging from boughs, while other members became adapted to more open country and evolved into bipeds.

In these latter—one might call them protohominids—the feet became rigid supporting organs, with pelvic changes accompanying bipedalism. The hands were freed as manipulative organs. It seems a mistake to think that tool-making depended upon any evolution of the hand; probably a generalized pongid hand could make tools if enough brain capacity were present. As Wood-Jones has

would return to join the magic circle still dancing in search of fire. How the dancers found the power to go on ever faster and faster, hour after hour, seemed beyond explanation or belief. They danced so hard and long that the circle in the sand became a groove, then the groove a ditch high up to their calves. Long before the end they seemed to pass over into a dimension of reality far out of reach of my understanding, and to a moment and a place which belonged only technically to the desert in which we were all gathered. Indeed, so obsessed did the men become by this search for fire that they were drawn nearer and nearer to the flames beside which the woman sat. Then, suddenly, they halved the circle and went dancing with their bare feet through the middle of the flames. But even that was not the end of the quest. Now, the longing became so intense that two of the older women were kept constantly busy preventing some fire-obsessed man from breaking out of the circle and hurling himself head first straight into the flames, like a moth overcome by excess of longing for the light. Indeed one man did break through, and before he could be stopped had scooped up a handful of burning coals and attempted to swallow them whole" [van der Post, 1958, p. 244].

indicated, manual skill depends upon initiation and co-ordination in the cerebral system. Men have developed manual skill even when their hands and limbs were maimed. Refined stereoscopic-color vision and erect posture with a vertical position of the skull are probably important. These allow close visual concentration over a wide field. The earliest hominids would have been anatomically equipped to use tools. It is a question of when they did, and why.

Tools are additions to the body that supplement the hands and teeth. In the arboreal prosimians, hands are climbing and feeding organs. These hands could have been used for other activities whenever such animals became ground-dwellers. Even baboons, partly ground-dwelling but adapted for quadrupedal progression, occasionally use a pebble to kill a scorpion needed as food (observation by Professor D. M. S. Watson). Chimpanzees are rarely known to use tools in the wild but will do so in capitivity when they are forced to live on the ground.

When did tool-using begin? If the protohominids inhabiting the edge of the forest spent much time on the open ground, it is conceivable that they began picking up things to use. Life in the open is more precarious than life in the trees, and tool-using would offer a selective advantage. An increased period of learning would also be an important factor; the mother would assist and teach the child for a protracted period if adult status was retarded (as it may well have been) through the acquisition of bipedal habit and through continuing operation of the principle of pedomorphism.

Tool-making requires a higher order of intelligence than does tool-using. Chimpanzees are the only reported animals that *make* tools, and then only in captivity. Sultan, the chimpanzee observed by Kohler, was capable of improvising tools in certain situations. Tool-making occurred only in the presence of a visible reward, and never without it. In the chimpanzee the mental range seems to be limited to present situations, with little conception of past or future. The power of conceptual thought is basic to tool-making but is only "incipient" in apes. For instance, a chimpanzee can learn to make fine discriminations in color shading but retains the learning for only a short time; a chimpanzee, through constant exploratory activity, will see possible single sticks to use as tools in a broken box but not in a whole box. Man can see a tool in a formless lump of stone. This ability of conceptual thought may have been present in a few individuals in a group, becoming extended by selection when conditions demanded. The range of tool types already present in the oldest industries includes *tools for making other tools* (e.g., hammerstones), illustrating that what we regard as the unique foresight of man was present at a very early stage in his evolution.

By the end of Lower Pleistocene times, the human level of cerebral development had certainly been reached, and stone artifacts of crudely standardized types were being made (e.g., Oldowan pebble tools). The incipient standardization shows that the manufacture of such tools (e.g., at Sterkfontein) was not an isolated occurrence but was already a tradition that served certain permanent needs of the earliest human beings. What were these needs? The use of tools and weapons was surely the means whereby the Hominidae kept themselves alive after they had abandoned the protection and sustenance provided by forests.

The tree-climbing primates had no use for tools. Tool-using arose in connection with adaptation to life on open ground away from forests. In the evolution of the primates the forelimbs have continually showed a tendency to take on functions performed in their ancestors by the teeth. The use of tools is evidently an extension of this trend, and we may suppose that tools were largely substitutes for teeth.

The apes of today are forest creatures, subsisting almost exclusively on fruits, leaves, shoots, and insects. All known races of man, on the other hand, include a substantial proportion of mammalian flesh in their diet. We have ample evidence that Peking man, Neanderthal man, and Late Paleolithic races of *Homo sapiens* were meat-eaters. I suggest that meat-eating is as old as man the tool-maker, that with adaptation to partly open forest margins the diet of proto-men inevitably became more varied, and that they changed from being eaters largely of plants and the fruits of plants to being in part meat-eaters.

It seems probable, on the important analogy of the baboons, that early Hominidae living in such country (savanna) may have become increasingly addicted to flesh-eating as a result of the intensification of the struggle for existence by excessive drought. It may be recalled that baboons, which in daytime range into grassland away from trees, occasionally prey on lambs and other animals of similar size, using their powerful canine teeth as offensive weapons, and, moreover, that this habit is likely to become more prevalent when conditions of existence are hard. Owing to the extensive folklore associated with baboons, reports of the carnivorous habits of those in South Africa have been discounted by some zoologists, but information from many different observers, collected by my friend Mr. F. E. Hiley in 1950, leaves no doubt that such reports are substantially true. A report from Captain H. B. Potter, with long experience as a game conservator in Zululand, is typical of those received:

The following are my personal observations over a period of twenty years' wardenship in the Hluhluwe Game Reserve: I have seen full-grown poultry killed and actually eaten by baboons, mostly however by aged individuals. Eggs and chickens are taken by the dozen, by old and young baboons. I have on many occasions actually witnessed apparently organized hunts which often result in the death of the intended victim. The baboons, usually led by a veteran of the troop, surround an unsuspecting three-parts-grown Mountain Reedbuck, or Duiker, as the case may be, and on one occasion a young Reedbuck doe was the victim. It would appear that on a given signal the baboons close in on their quarry, catch it and tear it asunder. As a matter of interest I have refrained from interference in these grim encounters so that I would be in a position authentically to record the results. In nine cases out of ten the game animal is devoured limb by limb and after the affair is over all that is to be found are the skull and leg bones.

Baboons, like some other monkeys, and apes too, have powerful canine teeth, serving mainly for defense against carnivores and, in males, for gaining dominance. It has been suggested that the reduction in the size of the canine teeth in hominids was an outcome of functional replacement by hand weapons. The canine teeth may have been reduced in the Hominidae at an evolutionary stage below that of systematic tool-making. That australopithecines, with small canines, must surely have been at least tool-*users*. Certainly the protohominids would have needed some means of defending themselves in the open and, having their hands free, may well have used stones as missiles and sticks or animal long bones as clubs.

In dry, open country the protohominids, like baboons, might readily have taken to eating flesh, particularly in times of drought or scarcity of food.[9] Although they lacked teeth suited to carnivorous habits, they could easily have killed small mammals. Life in the open set a premium on co-operation. Drawing on our knowledge of the mentality and social life of other primates, particularly baboons, it seems not unreasonable to suppose that, hunting in groups, the protohominids could have killed medium-sized mammals, say, by cornering them and using improvised hand weapons such as they might earlier have *learned to improvise in the first instance for their own defense*. The protohominids could certainly have killed small mammals.

It should not be forgotten that in the wild, after a kill by one of the larger carnivores, there is a scavenging food queue; when the lions, for instance, have had their fill, the hyenas and then the vultures enter the scene of slaughter. The protohominids may have first obtained the meat of larger mammals by entering this queue at an early stage. It has been reported that African children have been known to drive lions from their kill by beating tins. It is certainly conceivable that the protohominids used tactics of intimidation to facilitate their scavenging and that this preceded the hunting of larger wild game.

This is frankly speculation, for there is still no direct evidence that the earliest Hominidae were semicarnivorous or that they passed through a tool-using stage before becoming tool-makers. It is true that Dart has claimed that the quantities of broken animal bones found at Makapan in association with *Australopithecus* represent the food refuse of this creature and that some of the bones had been *used* as weapons, but other authorities are unconvinced and consider that the Makapan "bone statistics" can be satisfactorily explained as representing the product of *several* selective agencies, notably hyenas. The few pieces of mammalian bone found in the tool-bearing layer at Sterkfontein may yield some important clues bearing on this problem. Although there is a strong probability that all

9. Dr. C. B. Goodhart (Cambridge University Museum of Zoölogy) has suggested that meat-eating may have begun through cannibalism at this stage. He pointed out (*in lit.*) that the practice of eating the placenta is widespread among baboons and other mammals: "When food is short a still-born or sickly new-born baby might well be eaten as well as the placenta."

australopithecines were tool-users, and that some at least were tool-makers, the evidence remains *sub judice*.[10]

By the time that the Hominidae had evolved into tool-makers, they were evidently largely carnivorous—quantities of meat bones were associated with the remains of *Pithecanthropus pekinensis*. It is easy to see how the one habit led to the other. Although the killing of game may have been accomplished easily enough in some such way as that suggested above, the early hominids must often have encountered difficulty in removing skin and fur and in dividing the flesh. In the absence of strong canine teeth, the solution would have been overcome most readily by using sharp pieces of stone. Here, surely, was the origin of the tradition of tool-making. Where no naturally sharp pieces of stone lay readily to hand, some of the more intelligent individuals saw that pebbles, which broke on the ground when thrown, provided the solution. By breaking pebbles, fresh sharp edges were produced. Once the tradition of tool-making had begun, the manifold uses of chipped stones became obvious. They were useful for sharpening sticks for digging out burrowing mammals; for making spears sharp enough to be effective weapons in hunting larger game; for scraping meat from bones, splitting them to get at the marrow; and for chopping the meat into convenient mouthfuls. All the main uses of stone tools were, I suggest, connected in the first place with adoption of semicarnivorous habits.

From the endowment of nature we should be vegetarians. We lack the teeth evolved by true carnivores, and we have the long gut associated with a herbivorous diet. Furthermore, we are the only members of the Hominoidea accustomed to eating meat on any considerable scale. It is true that anthropoid apes, like most herbivores, consume small quantities of animal protein; some of them occasionally rob birds' nests of eggs and fledglings, but by and large they are fruit and plant eaters.

One can well imagine that a changing environment, for instance during a period of desiccation, may have produced an abnormal appetite in the early hominids. Gorillas in captivity quickly develop a liking for meat, and this appears to be due to a change in the flora and fauna of their intestines. Normally, their intestines are richly supplied with ciliate protozoa (Infusoria), which serve to digest cellulose. According to Reichenow (1920), under the abnormal conditions of captivity the Infusoria are ingested, and, with their disappearance from the intestines, the animal develops an abnormal appetite and readily takes to eating meat—and may even prefer meat to its normal fare.

By widening his diet and becoming a tool-maker, man became the most adaptable of all primates. The change from herbivorous to semicarnivorous habits was important from the point of view of the use of energy. To obtain a given

10. The discovery by Dr. and Mrs. Leakey, announced while this was in the press, of an australopithecine skull on an Oldowan occupation site at Olduvai has confirmed that the advanced members of this group were tool-makers.

amount of energy, a carnivore subsists on a smaller quantity of food than does a herbivore. Instead of eating almost continually, like their ancestors, the Hominidae spent much of their time hunting. This led to increased interdependence. New skills and aptitudes were developed through this new way of life, and with increasing control of environment through the use of manufactured tools, man became the most adaptable of all creatures, free to spread into every climatic zone.

An important step in the control of environment in northern climes was the making of fire. This could have been discovered only as an outcome of tool-making.

To sum up: I think it may fairly be claimed that tool-making is one of man's fundamental characteristics from a biological point of view. But the definition of man as the tool-*making* primate carries the implication that the term "human" should be applied only to the later members of the family Hominidae.

BIBLIOGRAPHY

ARAMBOUROU, M., and P.-E. JUDE
1955. *Soc. d'Etude et de Recherches prehist. de l'Inst. Pratique de Prehistoire, Les Eyzies*, Bull. 5, pp. 16–19.

BLACK, DAVIDSON
1931. "Evidence of the Use of Fire by *Sinanthropus*," *Bull. Geol. Soc. China*, 11: 107–8.

BLACK, DAVIDSON, R. TEILHARD DE CHARDIN, C. C. YOUNG, and W. C. PEI
1934. *Fossil Man in China: The Choukoutien Cave Deposits, with a Synopsis of Our Present Knowledge.* ("Mem. Geol. Surv. China," Ser. A, No. 11.)

BLANC, ALBERTO CARLO
1958. "Torre in Pietra, Saccopastore, Monte Circeo: On the Position of the Mousterian Culture in the Pleistocene Sequences of the Rome Area," pp. 167–74. In *Hundert Jahre Neandertaler: 1856-1956: Gedenkbuch der Internationalen Neandertal Feier, Dusseldorf, 26–30 August, 1956.* Utrecht: Kemenk en Zoon N.V.

BORDES, FRANCOIS H.
1958. Review of K. P. Oakley's "Fire as a Paleolithic Tool and Weapon," *L'Anthropologie*, 41:316, nn. 1, 2.

BREUIL, (L'ABBE) HENRI
1932. "Le feu et l'industrie de pierre et d'os dans gisement du *Siananthropus* à Choukoutien," *L'Anthropologie*, 42:1-17.
1958. In *Les processus de l'humanisation.* Paris: C.N.R.S.

BURTON, M.
1959. *Phoenix Re-born.* London: Hutchinson & Co.

CARTHAUS, E.
1911. "Spuren von möglicherweise menschlicher Tätigket in der Trinil-Schichten." in M. L. SELENKA and MAX BLANCKENHORN, *Die Pithecanthropus-Schichten in Java*, pp. 231-34. Leipzig: Engelmann.

CLARK, J. G. D.
 1954. *Excavations at Starr Carr*. Cambridge, England: Cambridge University Press.

COON, CARLETON S.
 1954. *The Story of Man*. New York: Knopf.

DART, RAYMOND A.
 1925. "A Note on Makapansgat: A Site of Early Human Occupation," *S. Afr. J. Sci.*, 22:371–81.

 1948. "The Makapansgat Protohuman *Australopithecus prometheus*," *Amer. J. Phys. Anthrop.*, n.s., 6:259–83.

 1952. "Faunal and Climatic Fluctuations in Makapansgat Valley," *Proc. 1st Pan-African Cong. Prehist., 1947*, pp. 96–106.

DAVIES, GEORGE McDONALD
 1956. *The Dorset Coast*. 2d ed. London: Black.

EITZMAN, W. I.
 1958. "Reminiscences of Makapansgat Limeworks and Its Bones-Breccial Layers," *S. Afr. J. Sci.*, 54:177.

FRAZER, SIR JAMES G.
 1931. *Myths of the Origin of Fire: An Essay*. New York: Macmillan.

GARROD, D. A. E., and D. M. A. BATE
 1937. *Stone Age of Mt. Carmel. I. Excavations in the Wady el Mughara*. Oxford: Clarendon Press.

GOODWIN, A. J. H.
 1929. "The Montagu Cave," *Annals S. Afr. Mus.*, 24:1–16.

GORJANOVIC-KRAMBERGER, K.
 1909. "Uber ein vermutliches Feuerholz des *Homo primigenius* aus Krapina," *Verh. Ges. Deutsch. Naturw. und Aerzte*, 81:211–13.

GRAHMANN, RUDOLF
 1956. *Urgeschichte der Menschheit*. 2d ed. Stuttgart: Kohlhammer.

HEDIGER, H. P.
 1950. *Wild Animals in Captivity*. London: Butterworth.

HEUDE, PIERRE MARIE
 1898. "Memoires concernant l'histoire naturelle de l'Empire Chinois, par des pères de la compagnie de Jesus: Etudes Odontologiques, Lemuriens, Tarsiens, Galeopitheciens, et Cebiens," *Mém. Hist. nat. chinois*, 4:155–81.

KLIMA, BOHUSLAV
 1955. "Fouilles de la station paleolithiques d'Ostravo-Petrkovice (Ostrova-Petrjko-vitse) en 1953," *Arch. rozh.*, 7:28.

LEROI-GOURHAN, ANDRÉ
 1952. "Among the Most Ancient Human Remains Yet Discovered; Early Mousterian Jaw Bones Found at Arcy-sur-Cure on an Unique Site Continuously Occupied for 140,000 Years," *Illustrated London News*, November 29, pp. 902–5.

LOW, A. M.
 1941. *The Romance of Fire*. London: Gifford.

LOWE, C. VAN RIET
 1954. "The Cave Hearths," *S. Afr. Archeol. Bull.*, No. 33, pp. 25–29.

MOVIUS, H. L.
 1949. "The Lower Paleolithic Cultures of Southern and Eastern Asia," *Trans. Amer. Phil. Soc.*, n.s., 38:329–420.

1950. "A Wooden Spear of Third Interglacial Age from Lower Saxony," *Southwest J. Anthrop.*, 6:140.

NEUVILLE, R.
1931. "L'Acheuléen supérieur de La Grotte d'Oumn-Qatafa," *L'Anthropologie*, 41:13-51.

OAKLEY, K. P.
1954. "Evidence of Fire in South African Cave Deposits," *Nature*, 174:261.
1956. "Fire as Paleolithic Tool and Weapon," *Proc. Prehist. Soc.*, 1955, XXI:36-48.
1957. "The Dating of the Broken Hill, Florisbad, and Saldanha Skulls," *Proc. Pan-Afr. Congr. Prehist.*, 1955, pp. 385-86.
1958. "Utilisation du feu par l'homme." In *Les processus de l'humanisation*. Paris: C.N.R.S.

PORSHNEV, B. F.
1955. "O drevneishem sposobe polucheniia ognia," *Sovetskaya etnografiya*, 1:7-28, esp. p. 15.

REICHENOW, E.
1920. "Den Wiederkäuer-Infusarien verwandte Formen aus Gorilla und Schimpanse," *Arch. f. Protistenkunde*, 41:1-33.

ROBINSON, J. T., and R. J. MASON
1957. "Occurrence of Stone Artifacts with Australopithecines at Sterkfontein," *Nature*, 180:521-24.

RUST, ALFRED
1951. *Die Höhlenfunde von Jabrud (Syrien)* Neumünster: Wachholtz.

SAINT-PÉRIER, M.
1933. *L'Art préhistorique (époque paléolithique)*. Paris: Rieder.

SIMPSON, THOMAS
1843. *Narrative of the Discoveries on the North Coast of America Effected by the Officers of the Hudson's Bay Company, 1836-39*. London: Bentley.

SOLLAS, W. H.
1924. *Ancient Hunters.* 3d ed. New York: Macmillan.

VAN DER POST, L.
1958. *The Lost World of the Kalahari.* New York: Morrow.

WARREN, S. H.
1951. "The Clactonian Flint Industry: A New Interpretation," *Proc. Geol. Assoc. London*, 62:107-35.

WEST, RICHARD G., and C. M. B. McBURNEY
1954. "The Quaternary Deposits at Hoxne, Suffolk," *Proc. Prehist. Soc.*, 20:135.

WYMER, B. O.
1955. "The Discovery of the Right Parietal Bone at Swanscombe, Kent," *Man*, 55:133.

THE SOCIAL LIFE OF SPANISH PALEOLITHIC HUNTERS AS SHOWN BY LEVANTINE ART

LUIS PERICOT

I. THE DIFFICULTY OF COMING TO SOCIOECONOMIC CONCLUSIONS FROM ARCHAEOLOGICAL DATA

IT IS a commonplace to say that archeology ought not to be a mere accumulation of inert facts, an oft-reiterated typological enumeration in which the force of the scientist is devitalized in an endless series of minute classifications with many contradictions. We are all trying to avoid the denomination of "reliquarians," which Russian authors sometimes employ disparagingly, or the not-less-disparaging term of *pucherólogos*, which some Spanish colleagues have directed toward us on occasion. But it is not easy to avoid the epithets that the study of the cultural material may impose upon an archeologist. On the one hand, prehistory is a science that is still young and has not yet been able to assemble a sufficient amount of material to give us a satisfactory scheme of the cultural evolution in the earliest times in the life of mankind. On the other hand, a socioeconomic interpretation of archeological data is much more difficult than would appear at first sight.

It is not easy to draw exact conclusions from a few implements and ornaments that form the most part of what is at our disposal. Habitation sites, even tombs, do not often offer us clear detail. Especially in the oldest periods, where it is the most difficult even to imagine the forms of the social and spiritual life, reconstructions from archeological data often result in excessive fantasy. With respect to the comparison with present-day primitive peoples, it is a truism that comparison is dangerous because of the fact that, although many archaic forms may have been preserved among present-day primitives, we are never certain that there have not been numerous changes during thousands of years through contacts and borrowings.

II. WHAT WE MAY LEARN FROM THE ART

Fortunately, we have at our disposal something more than merely a few implements and ceramics. The Upper Paleolithic hunters in western Europe

194

succeeded in creating the first art in history, and, thus forging the first great culture of mankind, they transmitted a message to us in which is included something of their spiritual life. It is not to be doubted that through their art we can understand something of the mentality of Quaternary man and even guess in what phase of his social evolution it may have occurred. We are presented with a great amount of material—sculpture, reliefs, paintings, and engravings on cave walls, on the one hand, and manifestations of *art mobilier,* on the other.

The most important art of this kind is the art of the caves, which, in relief, paintings, and engravings, fills the walls of caves and rock shelters in certain regions of the world, although in this paper I am limiting myself to a consideration of the sites of western Europe, which can be established securely as belonging to the Upper Paleolithic or to the early Mesolithic.

Since the discovery of the wall paintings in Altamira in 1879 and especially since the beginning of this century, we have been constantly adding to our knowledge of this art, and there are surely still great treasures of this kind to be discovered. Today, cave art is known in the most widely separated regions of the earth and forms a great arch, extending from Patagonia to the extreme south of Africa. And in spite of the great differences in the peoples who created it and the different periods of time involved, the art always shows something that may be said to have been held in common.

The classic art of the hunting peoples of the Upper Paleolithic of the west is the cave art that has been called "Franco-Cantabrian" and for which Spanish scholars have proposed the name *hispano-francés* because the Cantabrian zone cannot be considered as if it were simply a province of an extended French area.

At the same time, an impressive quantity of *art mobilier* exists, including engravings and, in exceptional circumstances, paintings, duplicating the art on the walls of the caves.

The area of the Spanish-French art extends from the region of Aquitaine, that is, the southwest of France, with its center in the Dordogne and neighboring regions, to the zone of the French Pyrenees and the Spanish Cantabrian Mountains, with an extension toward the Spanish Meseta and Andalucia (province of Malaga), reaching the Levant in the well-known site of Parpalló, which posesses an extraordinary number of engraved and painted plaques. Another extension exists in Italy and Sicily, but these sites present problems of chronology and evaluation related to the great enigma of African cave art, which cannot be discussed in this paper.

The study of Spanish-French cave art has been undertaken principally by that great master, Abbé Henri Breuil. His chronological system (1912), based upon the most minute observation and careful method, no one would dispute at the present time. Nevertheless, basing my arguments on my own discoveries in the cave of Parpalló, I think that there are some points in the system of this great French scholar that might be clarified. However, the problem is too great for discussion here. Leaving aside, then, the chronological and interpretative

problems, as well as the purely aesthetic values of this art, we may devote ourselves to the implications that clarify the social life of the hunters who executed it.

On the whole, almost all the authors are agreed that the Spanish-French cave
art reflects the ideology and organization of peoples dedicated to the hunting of
large animals. The art appears to have a magical-totemistic character. In
fact, there are many and undisputable examples (not only in the cave art but
especially in the statuettes and reliefs of wounded animals pierced with darts)
that assure us that sympathetic magic was used normally among those peoples.
The hunting magic of those Paleolithic peoples is apparently connected with
well-known present-day primitives, among whom similar rites appear to be
practiced. The human figure occurs very rarely, a fact that may be interpreted
as a means of defense from magic directed against the individual. On the other
hand, anthropomorphic representations occur frequently, especially figures of
men disguised as animals, a fact that appears to indicate the conjuring-up of
witches and sorcerers. It is not impossible that, in some cases, they may have
wished to represent a true "Spirit of the Chase," that is, a true divinity presiding
over the ceremonies or rites, which were probably celebrated in the secret hiding
places of small caves. By comparing these with the rites of present-day peoples,
we are led to think of secret societies' wearing of animal disguises, shamans
dressed in the same manner, spirit devils that must be combatted, etc. We find
human and animal figures with characteristics indicating a cult of fertility and
rites intended to increase it, thereby increasing the game, which would be
supremely important in the life of these peoples. Nor ought we to lose sight of
the fact that there may have been animals that were consumed in great quantities,
as, for example, the rabbit (in Spain), and that nevertheless do not appear in the
art. Without doubt, this fact may be interpreted as indicating that not so much
effort was required for the capture of the smaller animals. The larger animals
required greater efforts, which were exerted by the larger social group, since it
probably hunted its food in common.

From parallels between Spanish-French cave art and that of certain present-
day primitive hunting groups, it is logical to deduce that the Upper Paleolithic
hunters were probably organized on a basis of totemism, and there are many
traces of totemism in cave paintings that may be pointed out. Nevertheless, there
have been authors who have denied the existence of totemism among the Quaternary painters. We have today a definite indication of the existence of totemism
in that period, in the cave of Lascaux, in the scene of the bison attacking a
hunter who has previously wounded it. In this scene there appears a pole termi-
nating in the figure of a totemistic symbol.

Other motifs also occur—motifs that for the moment are impossible to analyze.
The so-called "tectiform" signs may indicate huts or traps. They may be traps
with which to hunt spirits. Diverse motifs, such as rectangles, may also be traps.
The so-called "escutiformes," "escaleriformes," "claviformes" (in the shape of

shields, ladders, maces), rows of dots, rectangles in color, all resist analysis at the present time.

If we take into account the many overpaintings, the quality of the precious and of the efficacious "fetiche" that is involved in many of the objects of the *art mobilier*, and the sacred character of the caves in which such works of art are found (the art is found in a small proportion of the inhabited caves, mostly in isolated corners and inaccessible places), it is evident that we are face to face with a world of magic, in which the mysterious, the sacred, and the action of man upon nature by means of predetermined rites occupied a predominant and permanent place in the social life of the people. At the same time, in my point of view, we see the western painter, from the beginning of this art, as a true artist, proud of his function, learning from his teacher, and enjoying in his own way the beauty that for the first time man learned to create. That is to say, for the first time a symbiosis occurs, in which values, at once magical and surely aesthetic, having the force of social and religious compulsion, exist side by side with full liberty of artistic creation. The same symbiosis and the same contrast has occurred in the late periods. This fact, for me, is the most important conclusion of a historical nature that may be derived from the study of the cave art of the Quaternary.

III. THE CAVE ART OF THE SPANISH LEVANT

The discovery of the cave art of the Spanish Levant, an outstanding phase of prehistoric art, took place in 1903, very shortly after the authenticity of Spanish-French cave art had been accepted, when Juan Cabré discovered the painted deers in the ravine of Calapatá. But it was not until 1907, with the find of Roca del Moros in Cogul, which contains the famous scene of women dancing before a satyr, that our prehistorians found themselves in the presence of a kind of art previously unsuspected in the Quaternary, an art containing an abundance of human figures and complicated scenes. After this there was a steady flow of sensational discoveries: Alpera in 1910, Albarracín in 1910 and 1948, Alcañiz in 1913, Minateda in 1914, Valltorta in 1918, Bicorp in 1919, Ares in 1934, Alacón in 1947, to cite only a few of the most important. Today we possess large numbers of these paintings, which are constantly increasing and which include some thirty-two sites, some of which contain several small caves or rock shelters.

Their distribution is well known. They extend through the limestone *sierras* of the Spanish Levant, from the south of Cataluña to the province of Almería, penetrating the interior through Lower Aragón and the province of Teruel. In the northern part of this territory, in the south of the province of Lérida, one of the most notable of these friezes is found—that of Cogul. Toward the coast, in the region between Castellón and Tarragona, the rock shelter of La Cenia, one of those most recently discovered, contains some interesting figures. There are several rock shelters in the zone of Morella, and in Lower Aragón the rock shelters of Calapatá and of Secans (in Cretas and Mazaleón) are found. Near Alcañiz there is the rock shelter of Val del Charco del Agua Amarga. More toward the interior of the province of Teruel there are the rock shelters of Alacón, and in the extreme west are the important complexes of the region of Albarracin and of Tormén. In the coastal zone the province of Castellón is the richest in the Levant, and in it occur the complex near Morella, already mentioned, and the important sites in the ravines of Valltorta and Ares del Maestre, as well as several other less important groups. A number of rock shelters are found in Valltorta, among which some are very well known, particularly Civil and Saltadora; in Ares there are still greater numbers of rock shelters. Cingle de la Mola Remigia, Les Dogues, and Recó den Moleró are especially outstanding. Moving from this region to the mountainous part of Valencia, we find Dos Aguas and, most important, the Cueva de la Araña in Bicorp. Toward the interior we find the rock shelter of Tortosillas (Ayora, Valencia) and that of Villar del Humo in the province of Cuenca. The province of Albacete contains two of the richest complexes, that of Alpera (Cueva de la Vieja and Cueva del Queso) and that of Minateda. Entering the province of Murcia, we find the two rock shelters, Cantos de la Visera, near Yecla, and Peliciego (Jumilla). In the province of Almeria, Breuil has pointed out some less important sites: Cueva de las Grajas (Topares), Lavaderos de Tello and Estrecho de Santonje in Velez Blanco, and the cave Chiquita de los Treinta (Chirivel). All these sites have figures of the type previously mentioned, and they are found also in the province of Jaen in the rock shelters of Tabla del Pochico in Aldeaquemada and the Cueva del Santo (near Santa Elena), as well as in sites farther away, like the province of Cadiz, the Batuecas (province of Salamanca), and the surroundings of Arronches in Portugal. But to include all these in the same chronological group may be a doubtful procedure, since some of them may be assigned to the Neolithic. The only one of these that we must probably include among the naturalistic paintings of the Levant is the Cueva Chiquita de los Treinta, where Breuil found a probable Solutrean point.

It is evident that as we move to the south, even in the Levant, the style changes from the naturalism of the older eastern paintings and becomes increasingly schematic. This transition is often difficult to delineate, since the exact limits of the styles have not yet been established.

All the sites that have been mentioned have certain characteristics in common. All are rock shelters in the open air in which the paintings are easily seen, contrary to the situation in the caves. The figures are of small size, having always a certain simplification or stylization, and are grouped in scenes accompanied by figures of animals. The human figures are represented in action sometimes violent. The styles of north and south are sufficiently different to be contrasted. Another difference is in the patina, which has been acquired by sites in the open air. Nevertheless, the colors and techniques are not very different. The red color predominates, while black, ocher, and, occasionally, white are much less used.

IV. CHRONOLOGY

There is an important point that ought to be made clear here, and that is that, if we are to utilize the data supplied by the Levantine rock paintings to help us in understanding the life of the hunters of the Quaternary, it is necessary that the paintings be of this date. It is well known that this question has been much debated.

The traditional orthodox opinion, according to which the art of the Levant was contemporaneous with Spanish-French art, with parallel phases, has undergone severe attacks recently. For my part, I defended this opinion for a certain time, until I was convinced that there was sufficient proof to the contrary. Nevertheless, the contrary opinion is open to certain doubts and has not succeeded in creating a theory that covers every aspect of the problem.

Breuil, after studying the paintings of Minateda and their superimpositions, established six fundamental periods in the art of the Levant; two of these, with linear figures, are assigned to the Aurignacian, and another three are assigned to the Solutrean or Magdalenian. The technique evolves, beginning with monochrome and ending in semipolichrome, paralleling the north (in some figures of Cogul, Albarracín, and Lavaderos de Tello); Breuil's sixth period, decadent and schematic, would correspond to the Epipaleolithic and extend even over the Neolithic. The arguments of Breuil and his school in favor of a Quaternary age for these paintings may be summed up in the following manner: There is a similarity in the evolution, as we have seen. Although the fauna is modern for the most part, or indifferent to climate, examples of typical Quaternary animals are not lacking—a rhinoceros in Alpera and Gasulla, a chamois in Tortosillas and Gasulla, and perhaps bisons in Tormon, Minateda, Cogul, and Gasulla, among others. The abundance of wild animals, although of species that have continued to the present time, would indicate the Paleolithic. The environment is Paleolithic, recalling present-day hunting peoples, and indicates the magical and totemistic atmosphere of the latter as well.

The same may be said of the armaments and adornments. Discoveries in France of painted plaques of undeniable Aurignacian age (Pechialet, Labatut) and of the notable paintings of Lascaux, which show traces of the Levantine style, advance this argument. The finds of Parpalló have proved also that from the Aurignacian to the Magdalenian these peoples were painting and that the fauna represented was that of the present time. It would appear, therefore, that there was a connection between the two styles during the Aurignacian, which were later isolated by a recurrence of cold, and that the art of the Levant later evolved in its own way. It must not be forgotten that the cave of Casares in the province of Guadalajara (approximately one hundred kilometers distant from the paintings of the Albarracín group), whose Paleolithic age no one would dispute, shows numerous engravings of human figures, although these may not be in the same style as those of the rock shelters of the Levant. Also of importance is the fact that in some rock shelters (Cueva Chiquita de los Treinta, Cantos de la Visera) arrows, which may be classified as Solutrean, are found. If we accept the fact that painted pebbles with motifs already schematized exist in the Azilian and recall that a similar stage in the Cueva de la Cocina yields plaques engraved with purely geometric motifs, we may conclude that the whole evolution of naturalistic art was probably accomplished before the end of the Quaternary. To all this may be added a new argument, derived from the presence of a cave art in Sicily, which Italian authors attribute to the Paleolithic. It is clear that, if the hypothesis that a part of African art is Paleolithic could be proved, the Paleolithic age of the art of the Levant would be demonstrated.

In spite of the fact that so many arguments of this kind can be assembled, some Spanish archeologists have defended the arguments for a later age. This is the "heterodox thesis" defended now by the generation of younger investigators and those who have been working for the last twenty years. To these may be added a good number of foreign specialists, among whom today it is common to agree that the cave art of the Levant is at least Epipaleolithic.

Cabré, Durán y Sanpere, and Hernández Pacheco were the first to cast doubt on the Paleolithic age of these paintings, having noticed the obvious differences with respect to the northern art and rejecting dubious interpretations of Quaternary animals, i.e., animals that were indeterminable because of their bad state of preservation. They also noted that there was an apparent similarity between the climate indicated and the post-Quaternary climate. Their position was reinforced by the absence, at Parpalló, of figures similar to the cave art of the region, and above all by the fact that remains of microlithic implements clearly Epipaleolithic, were very often found in the sites, below the figures. Professors Martínez Santa-Olalla and Almagro were the heralds of these new ideas and accented the idea of the modernity of these frescos, which they moved up in time, toward the Neolithic. Professor Almagro has given particular attention to the problem, carrying on excavations at the base of the sites, with detailed study of some of the paintings and their superimpositions. The material encountered in some of the sites includes half-moon-shaped mycroliths, a type that lasted until the beginning of the Age of Metal. Among the new arguments adduced by Professor Almagro are the following: in general, the extremely reduced size of the figures, sometimes only a few centimeters high; the poor technique and execution; the supposed polychromes being the result of superposition at different times; the development of the use of basketry shown by numerous paintings, as well as the use of rope, which according to this author suggests the proximity of Neolithic stages; the scenes of gathering, which in Alacón apparently show women gathering fruits along a row, or furrow, which would appear to indicate a climate and environment already very advanced in those heights where the paintings are found. In the rock shelter of Cogul, a study of the graffiti shows Iberian and archaic Latin inscriptions of votive character, which seem to be proof of the fact that these places continued to be considered sacred until relatively late times, which, according to Almagro, would seem to fit better with the idea of a post-Paleolithic origin for such a sanctuary. Finally, in some cases we have representations of domestic animals (a horse with reins at Villar del Humo, a rider wearing a plume at Gasulla, a possible rider at Alacón—to all of which another author has recently added the bovines of Alpera). All these would take the paintings into the full Neolithic.

A few years ago I adopted a position that is based on the following fundamental facts: The Paleolithic atmosphere of hunting peoples, without agriculture but practicing gathering in certain places that shortly took on a favorable climate (as recent climatic studies have insistently shown) lasted at least until the fourth millennium B.C. in the mountains of the Spanish Levant, when Neolithic contributions gradually modified the culture. The environment reflected by the paintings is then fundamentally Paleolithic, but the chronology of the paintings does not necessarily fall within the Paleolithic. In the last analysis, "Paleolithic" and "Epipaleolithic" are terms that we have invented, mere labels whose value ought not to be exaggerated in this Levantine region of moderate climate. Nor can it be denied that there are technical similarities between the art of the Levant and some aspects of the Spanish-French animal art (including the Solutrean plaques of Parpalló). As has been shown at Parpalló, painting existed in the Levant during the Upper Paleolithic. At the same time, we learn, on the one hand, that the Magdalenian abandoned the practice and, on the other, that the naturalistic and abstract styles existed side by side, in the same environment. That the rock shelters of the Spanish Levant were in some manner sanctuaries, sacred places for many millennia, can hardly be doubted and cannot be used as an argument against their great age. Nor ought we to lose sight of the fact that we know a great deal about the seminaturalistic paintings from the early Neolithic of Andalucia. These styles are all schematic from the beginning of the Bronze Age. These end the cycle of naturalistic paintings, and the latter must therefore logically be anterior and antecedent to the former.

We have delimited a long stage in the Spanish Levant that, at a broad estimate, may have lasted as much as ten millennia, during which the pictorial art was developing. Such a long duration must have been accompanied by an evolution of taste, techniques, and motifs, reckoning even with the conservatism of primitives. Now remains the task of analyzing the paintings minutely in order to describe the distinct phases through which the art of these Levantine hunters was developed. The first step, the beginning, may be contemporaneous with the northern Magdalenian, during which the hunters of the Spanish Levant employed implements derived from the Gravettian, a period I have termed "Epigravettian," and which has a tendency toward microlithism. This technique may perhaps have been augmented by contributions from the south. If this hypothesis is valid, we ought

to be able to show which painted friezes already existed at the end of the Paleolithic. Unfortunately, we have no other criteria than the doubtful one of suppos-
ing that the oldest are representations of animals in an attitude of repose, of good
size and of a style in every way similar to the northern figures and often, like
them, with finely engraved silhouettes. Examples of this stage would be the
bovines of Cocinilla del Obispo and Prado del Navazo in Abarracín and
similar figures in Cogul, Calapatá, Alpera, Val del Charco del Agua Amarga,
Ladruñan, etc. At a somewhat later period, which we may provisionally place
in the Epipaleolithic, human figures are incorporated into the relatively static
hunting scenes, as in Barranco del Gascons, the hunter of chamois in Tormón, the
archers among the bovines of Prado del Navazo. We do not know the reason for
this innovation, although the human figure had been represented earlier in a certain schematic manner even at Parpalló. Perhaps this may be due to an outside
influence (African?), or it may be the work of an artistic genius. In any case,
it reflects a decisive change of mentality.

Indeed, by way of the representation of human figures, the Levantine art begins
to take on the quality of minute description. And thus we arrive at a third phase,
a period of smaller figures, of more definite movement, with scenes of battle and
hunting, of violent attitudes, the *carrera en vuelo*. The descriptive scenes reach
their apogee in this period, and we shall discuss this more fully later on.

As a derivation from the preceding type, a much more stylized figure appears
(the fighting or dancing warriors of Morella), the use of figures of very small
size, true miniatures in calligraphic style (combat from Les Dogues) or in strange
attitudes (the fallen man of La Cenia; the dancer of Dos Aguas). Finally, we have
the fifth and ultimate phase, of degeneration, including scenes of a domestic nature,
which may indicate the beginning of domestication (a possible dog accompanying
a hunter, in Alpera; the riders of Gasulla and Alacón, etc.), just before this art
is totally transformed into a schematic style. To this phase would belong, also,
the last style of Minateda, the man leading a horse of Boniches, and other similar
figures.

It cannot be denied that the chronological reconstruction that has just been
attempted is purely theoretical. In addition, it bears no relation to the succession
of styles recognized by Breuil at Minateda. I give it as a working hypothesis without forgetting that the differences I have indicated either have chronological
significance or may perhaps be due to regional differences (a position preferred
by Professor Almagro) or to other reasons that elude us at the present time.

Let us now discuss the character of this art, which evidently cannot be the
same as that of the northern one. We are dealing with an expressionistic art that
appears to have a commemorative or historical quality and that we might call
"memorialistic." Nevertheless, although we recognize a greater awareness in the
Levantine paintings, which explains why things are represented as they are—
horns being shown from the front, for example—there are many reasons for sup-
posing also that we are dealing with an art of primitive magic. The majority of

the scenes we have described—hunting, for example—do not appear to be of such importance as to merit the honor of commemoration and graphic recording, and many figures are dispersed, without forming groups. The scenes of a warlike character lack sufficient detail to personalize the figures and would appear to indicate magical use, a preservative magic of protection to insure that no harm comes to the person represented. The detail of the ornament appears to have the same significance. The robustness of the legs of the hunters and their agility and rapidity in the chase probably had the same magical end, to involve these qualities in reality. The figure in the cave of Saltadora that represents a fallen warrior pierced with arrows, his diadem in the act of falling, has been interpreted as an attempt to incapacitate a chief, to compel him to lose the force and authority symbolized in the diadem or crown. An analogous end might be attributed to the representations of combat, some of which might better be classed as war dances, and to the scenes of execution in the rock shelters of Ares. Certain figures may well be heroes; in the face of failure in the hunt, or of danger of attack by other groups, the artists may have tried to evoke the memory of famous hunters or warriors, the remembrance of whose successes may have been maintained in the oral tradition; in painting these heroes, they were exaggerating the characteristics, both their movements and their successes.

As far as the representation of animals is concerned, the parallel with the northern art is more evident. We find hundreds of animals, pierced by arrows or fallen, like the beautiful chamois of Tormón. At other times we see the hunter following the track of the animal. Many times also one animal has been transformed into another, or has been repainted, sure proof that magical rites were repeated in the same sacred place. Animals are represented not only to insure their capture but also to increase their reproduction. In all these interpretations we are aided by ethnological comparison, since the practices of present-day primitive groups facilitate analogy to those practices we have assumed for our ancestor painters. A great number of paintings in Africa have a style similar to that of the Spanish Levant, although the animals represented are not always the same. In Africa we see human figures interpreted in the same manner, women with shirts, an identical artistic vision, and even the same patina on the paintings. But in Africa the hunting people and their art have continued until recent time.

The discovery of anthropomorphic figures in the Levantine art, especially the two from Barranco de la Gasulla, supplies another element in favor of this magic thesis. The figures may represent masked hunters or members of a secret society. What is apparent here is that our Levantine painters possessed an animal mythology similar to the totemistic beliefs of present-day primitives and to those of Franco-Cantabrians of the Paleolithic. It has been said also that the representation of spiders in the friezes of Ares might be explained by the fact that these creatures were believed to belong to the mythical world and were honored because of their ability to capture their prey in a trap.

The superposition of paintings would appear to indicate also that esthetic or documentary considerations were not primary. The paintings were always made on the same sites, consecrated by tradition. Magnificent rock shelters, where we eagerly seek rock paintings, contain nothing, while others that we consider much less adequate have been preferred, for reasons we do not know. They mounted their scenes and repainted the figures repeatedly, to renew their magical rites, and even transformed one animal into another, generally by adding the appropriate horns. All this indicates with incontestable force that magic was one of the roots of Levantine rock painting.

Nevertheless, I believe that in the last phases of this art the artist was composing his scenes without a transcendent aim—for example, the woman leading a child by the hand in Minateda, or the man leading a horse in Boniches. But, above all, I wish to emphasize my conviction that in the post-Paleolithic phases of this art, and more emphatically in each progressive phase, we find a commemorative or memorialistic aspect, which exists also among various present-day primitives. And I wish to emphasize, as I have done for the northern art, that it not be denied that there is artistic value, an esthetic sense, and great technical ability transmitted through true schools of painter-magicians. Without these and without the greatest spiritual devotion, the idea of magic alone cannot explain the display of hundreds of frescos in the rock shelters of our mountainous Levant.

After this discussion of the purposes and the chronology, we may utilize what we have learned in order to understand the atmosphere in which the hunters of the end of the Quaternary lived. But whatever the absolute chronology of these paintings may be (its apogee could be placed between the eighth and the fifth millennia B.C.), the paintings reflect the activities of groups of hunters and gatherers that continued the traditions of those who lived in the same mountains during the end of the Paleolithic.

V. CLOTHES, ADORNMENT, AND ARMS

There is nothing in this art by which we can know the type of habitation. From the archeological data obtained up to the present time, and taking into account the favorable climate of the region during these millennia, we may feel sure that the people lived in the open air, seeking refuge in the many rock shelters of the region when necessary. In the floor of many of these shelters, including those that contain paintings, or in nearby caves (as in Cueva de la Cocina, in Dos Aguas) remains of occupation have been found.

The greater number of the human figures represented are masculine and, in general, appear to be archers or warriors. The details of the face are rarely shown, but in some instances the protuberance of a nose or a beard may be seen. They always appear in the nude, although, as we shall see, with abundant body ornaments. There are a few examples, two of them quite clear in the rock shelter of Secans, in Mazaleon, and in the Cova Remigia (Ares), in which is clearly shown the use of a kind of short breeches. The really curious fact is how often there appears an article of clothing called *zaragüelles*, a kind of breeches that is still in use by the country people of the Levant Aragón region, although its use is rapidly disappearing.

The adornments that we see on the figures of archers are extremely varied. In the headdresses we may observe ornaments in the forms of horns, of animal ears, of feathers, and some even more elaborate, with strings of beads or shell, perhaps used as hair nets; there may be one or several feathers, well apparent, and in some cases a true crest similar to an American Indian headdress appears to cover the head of a chief. There are also some true diadems, like a hoop with hanging plumes, which has a parallel in the headdress of present-day primitives. We see this in the figure of the fallen chief from Valltorta. Many times the hair is simply knotted, forming a bunch or a tuft. Ribbons or strips, either divided into fringes or not, hang from the neck, from the arms or forearms, from the knee or from the leg, and form a sort of belt from which they hang, the ribbons or strips seeming to float in motion. At times these ornaments may be very complex, as in the case of the personage of Cerro Felio (Alacón).

The hangings of the belt are often so complex that they sometimes appear like true aprons, but they may be observed sometimes on the back part of the body (in the same way as in the Venus of Lespugue, whose Aurignacian age cannot be doubted).

Arm bands, often very bulky, and rings or simple bracelets may be seen on arms, wrists, legs, and ankles. We can often guess at the representation of crude footwear. There are many examples and great variation in the caps and head coverings. There are also cylindrical bonnets and tall-crowned hats, as in the case of the solitary hunter of chamois of Tormón and in one of the battle scenes in Val del Charco del Agua Amarga; and we can even guess at a kind of irregular fur cap in the outstanding personage of Gasulla.

In the representations of women, much rarer than those of men, the women were almost never in the nude, an evident contrast to the representations of women in the Quaternary art of France. On the other hand, they are usually shown with the breasts exposed but with a bell-shaped skirt reaching to the knee, a design so often repeated that we may assume it to have been the common article of clothing. Such representations are well known in the feminine figures of Cogul but may be seen also in Alpera, Tormón, Minateda, Alacón, Dos Aguas, La Cenia, and Alcañiz. In the rock shelter of Cinto de las Letras in Dos Aguas there are figures of women whose skirts are depicted in another way, although they are not fundamentally different, and in one case we may assume an article of clothing similar to a tunic. One of the figures climbing a rope ladder (Alacón), and the well-known scene of honey-gathering (Bicorp) represent women in the opinion of some authors. The figures show certain feminine characteristics, and the bunch of hair appears to be dressed with elegance. At Alacón the figure wears a short skirt in back. Outstanding, also, is one of the women who appears in Minateda who wears a short skirt made in two or three pieces, separated front and back.

Implements and armaments are also very interesting. We see painted canes or poles, baskets, bows and their accessories, and snares. The baskets are of several kinds, and we must assume that they were braided of vegetable fibers. Sometimes we see them hanging from the arm of an individual, as in the gatherer of the Cueva de la Araña and the archer of de Cueva del Civil. In the rock shelter of Ares there are bags or baskets of several kinds; in one case we are led to think of a double sack or saddlebag.

The bow is the only weapon we see in use by these hunters, even though other representations appear to be of spears and darts, which were thrown by other means not shown. The bows may be small and simple or large and composite. The latter may perhaps have certain implications for the chronology. Sometimes we can see the string of the bow very well, and in certain cases the bow is extended beyond the string. The archers are seen in various positions, raising or swinging the bows above their heads (Gasulla). The arrows appear with certain detail, in the hand of the archer, struck into the ground near him, in bundles, or in the quiver. The point may be straight or oblique. Sometimes notches, as on a harpoon, appear below the triangular tip of the point (Cueva Remigia). The end of the arrow often shows a protrusion that we assume to indicate feathering. A number of quivers are represented, sometimes drawn to perfection to show the arrows in the interior.

The construction of the rope ladders, which appear in several of the complexes, allows us to assume great craftsmanship.

VI. THE CHASE

The principal motif of the Levantine paintings is the chase, as we have seen. The animals hunted are primarily goats and deer; the boar also is shown with relative frequency; other species like bovines and chamois are shown more rarely; other animals are doubtful.

The hunt was carried on either by individual hunters, by small groups, or by large groups surrounding the animals, doubtless in a true *caza al ojeo*, driving them toward places from which they could not escape, like the cliffs near the rock shelters, or into stockades. The scenes of archers are very vivid. We see them in many positions, shooting at adult deer and their young in frescos like those of Araña and Valltorta. We have some of the most vivid scenes in the small groups, especially the hunt of the boar (Val del Charco, Gasulla) with its appearance of flying, reflecting the fine skill as hunters possessed by those men to whom it was a question of life or death to capture the prey, which could only be obtained by endurance and ability. We see also the individual hunter, or what is represented as such, who is sometimes shown following the trail of an animal whose traces are clearly seen. We may cite as another example the man approaching the chamois he has just killed in Tormón, and the beautiful figure of the archer aiming at a mountain goat, in Gasulla. In the same site there is a scene showing the opposite action, a wounded bovine attacking an archer who is fleeing. In certain cases we may guess at hunting by means of lassos, but this and other techniques, like the use of traps, cannot be clearly defined in the pictures preserved in the Levant.

VII. BATTLES AND DANCING WARRIORS

Another kind of scene of great interest to us is the battle scene in which groups of armed warriors are deployed against one another. Through these scenes we may catch a glimpse of the practices of war employed by the peoples of that time. As in the case of similar scenes, occurring thousands of years later on Iberian ceramics, many times we do not know whether we are witnessing a real battle or only the simulation of a kind of game of war.

Among the scenes of the Levantine rock paintings we sometimes see one clearly defined as a war dance. This is the case in the scene of the rock shelters of Morella, in which we see seven warriors, in opposed positions, holding bows; one of them, at least, is wounded.

Other groups of archers who are engaging in quiet or solemn activity (the group in the cave of Civil, the group surrounding a chief in Alpera, the group of Alacón, the groups of Minateda) may be included in a similar class. But I should like to call attention primarily to the scenes of real combat, in which we see the pursuit of one or another group at a frenzied pace, although the artist has avoided the representation of warriors defeated in battle, even though the wounded or dead individuals who appear singly may be the consequence of the battle. Let us look at the scene of the frieze of the Val del Charco del Agua Amarga in Alcañiz. Seven archers who wear plumes upon their heads (perhaps three to six more can be assigned to this fleeing group) are in full flight from a group of eight archers, who are pursuing them. The latter group have robust legs, and some of them appear to be wearing a kind of cylindrical hat upon their heads. Open combat is shown in the rock shelter of Les Dogues in Ares, where two groups of archers are deployed, composed, respectively, of eleven and sixteen individuals; at least one is wounded, with a leg pierced by an arrow.

In Minateda the battle is engaged. Eight warriors with striped bodies are attacking five others, painted in uniform color, one of whom appears to be wounded by several arrows. Lesser scenes of battle may be seen in Alpera and Alacón.

VIII. MILITARY LIFE AND HIERARCHY

We are examining the very substance of the social life of the Paleolithic hunter when we try to discover which representations indicate a hierarchy in the group or a definite status. It is generally assumed that some outstanding figures, of larger size, represented important personages, the great departed chiefs of the tribe, distinguished warriors or powerful shamans. Such is the case with the important personage with the crest of plumes on his head who is the center of the Alpera frieze. Another great personage is the center of a group of twenty-five archers in the rock shelter of Civil. In some rare instances the hierarchy is seen to be clearly indicated. Outstanding is a scene in the Cueva Remigia in which four warriors appear to be walking briskly, brandishing their bows, following a personage armed with the same weapon—but carried in a distinct manner. This personage appears to be painted more carefully, as if it showed greater seriousness; and, moreover, he wears on his head a tall cap or hat apparently made of fur. Of all the scenes in the rock paintings, this one is the most suggestive from the point of view of the military organization. Various other groups represented in the rock shelters of Gasulla are outstanding in reflecting this ability to express the idea of rank and discipline skilfully with rudimentary means. In Gasulla the artist has succeeded in giving the impression of life and movement in a scene in which rows of archers raise their bows over their heads at the same time as if in a cheer. More static, but very lively, nevertheless, is the scene in the rock shelter of Mortero de Alacón in which seven individuals with triangular torsos and linear legs raise their arms, which hold bows or canes as if to initiate a ritual dance. Finally, it was Obermaier who pointed out the special character of the figures on the rock shelter of Saltadora, in the ravine of Valltorta, where we see a warrior, wounded by several darts, falling forward, while at the same time his very elaborate diadem, probably a symbol of authority, falls from his head.

IX. SCENES OF PUNISHMENT

It was Obermaier, also, who realized the importance of the scenes represented in the cave Remigia, in which we see groups of archers (with five individuals in one case, and ten in another) raising their bows, while at a certain distance in front of them appears a man who has fallen, pierced with arrows. There is every indication that we are witnessing scenes of execution, which we may call the first pages of a penal code. In another place in the same locality we see a man who has fallen, pierced with arrows.

X. SCENES OF GATHERING AND HOME LIFE

No matter how solemn or enigmatic we may consider the Levantine art, we find also a certain air of intimacy and the representation of daily life because of the great number of figures that do not appear to have an especial importance or that show the more simple aspects of the daily life, particularly gathering and domestic scenes. The seated woman and the woman in the art of gathering in the rock shelter of Mortero in Alacón; the donkeys being tamed and subdued by men, one of whom is riding, and the pair of women in Alpera; the men climbing with ropes, the rope ladders or perhaps a tree, in Alacón, Alpera, and Gasulla; the woman with the skirt leading a child by the hand in Minateda; a hunter with his

son at his side perhaps about to start a hunt in one of the most beautiful scenes,
that of the hunt of a mountain goat, in the Remigia cave; the representation of
insects or birds and even, possibly, of plants (Albarracín, Alacón) are, taken all
together, images of a world with a social life already elaborated, which appears
to approach the new atmosphere that the arrival of the Neolithic revolution
supposes.

But, even in this domain, our Levantine painters wanted to leave us a master-
piece of indisputable interpretation. In the cave of Araña in Bicorp appears the
following scene. A man (are we to suppose it is a woman?) has climbed down
some ropes that appear to be supported by poles at the top of the ravine, and
another individual has begun to ascend. The first, carrying a basket in his hand,
has paused before a real cavity in the rock, while from the hole, which is probably
a wild-bee hive, issues a stream of bees that fly about him. There is a curious parallel
between this scene and a photograph of some *Irulas* of India gathering honey from
a wild honeycomb published by Thurston and reproduced by P. Schmidt. The
same practice can be seen among the Vedda, Pygmies, and Bushmen.

XI. RELIGIOUS SCENES

If we accept a magical interpretation of Levantine art, we may include under
this heading the greater part of the scenes in these numerous complexes. But I am
going to point out only those that have an evident ritual or magical character.

Outstanding among these, and unequalled despite the many later discoveries,
is the *Roca del Moros* of Cogul. A masculine figure, showing the sexual organs,
wearing stripes on his leg, is the center; while around him appear approximately
eleven women wearing wide skirts, their hair dressed in various ways. The scene
appears to be a ritual dance. The women appear to be circling, two by two (except one individual), and show signs of having been repainted repeatedly to renew
the efficacy of the rite. On the rocky wall near the paintings are votive inscriptions in Iberian and archaic Latin, dating from the fourth or the fifth century B.C.
at least, and serving to assure us that this rock shelter retained its character as a
sacred place for two or three hundred generations.

There is also a ritual of magical quality in the presence of masked men. The
most typical of them all is the one who appears in the rock shelter of Cingle de la
Mola Remigia in the Ravine of Gasulla (Ares). Near an archer appears a strange
being who, because of the upright position, the general aspect, and the arms, is
probably a man, while instead of a human head is substituted one of a bull, with
an elongated muzzle and strong horns, slightly curved; the tail is somewhat long.
One arrow pierces the lower stomach and another the shoulder. This may be a
hunter masked for ritual reasons or a member of a secret society in the appropriate
disguise. It cannot be doubted that we are confronted with a magical representation.

Many of the scenes described in the previous pages can be interpreted as magical rites for protection, for a favorable chase, or for reproduction. The fallen chief of Saltadora may be a chief whom the people wished to replace; the wounded animals and hunters, the object of rites carried on previous to departure for the hunt; the representations of outstanding personages, a rite of protection invoking the great departed chiefs; the spiders, to obtain the skill for capture possessed by them.

XII. AN ESTIMATE OF POPULATION

We have just seen that the Levantine artist often showed groups of archers as well as women, indicating roughly the size of the groups in which these could live. It is not difficult to count the number of individuals that form these groups and obtain an idea of how many individuals might form the horde, which we assume was the grouping of population in these rock shelters and ravines.

In the combat of the Val del Charco del Agua Amarga, we see eight individuals against seven. An outstanding scene in Alacón has seven individuals, and a group of hunters circling for the hunt has twelve. Twenty-seven archers make up the large group of the cave of Civil. The groups of Gasulla are formed of ten, eighteen, thirteen, five, ten, and five individuals, respectively. At the same site, eleven hunters are grouped in one hunting scene. In the frieze of Les Dogues seventeen individuals battle eleven. Seven archers dance or battle in Morella. Twelve hunters are grouped in Araña, and there are another twelve in a group of Valltorta. Thus we see that the number of warriors varies only a little; and on this basis we could venture to suggest a horde of about a hundred individuals living in each one of these ravines, which would be a favorable environment for life, with easy hunting, water, and refuge.

If we think of the present-day province of Castellón and of the density of known sites, remembering that several hordes of similar size could live in each of the ravines of Ares and Valltorta, we reach the conclusion that, at the time of the apogee of Levantine art, the population probably consisted of two thousand souls in an area of more than six thousand square kilometers, that is, one inhabitant every three square kilometers, approximately. This represents a density sufficient for a hunting population. Considering that there were also zones in Spain less favorably endowed, we may assume the population of the Peninsula during the Mesolithic to have been some 50,000, at a moderate calculation, and some 100,000 as a more liberal figure.

XIII. THE DECADENCE OF THIS WORLD
DURING THE NEOLITHIC

I wish we were able to classify this art as the work of a known ethnic group. When we believed that the Capsian was of Paleolithic age, it was very easy to attribute the Levantine art to African Capsians, as opposed to Magdalenian

Nordics, but this concept has not been accepted for some time. Nowadays solutions are proposed that are no less risky and difficult to prove. One of these is to connect the art of the Levant with the rock paintings of Sicily and Africa. That there is some similarity to the African rock painting is seen very easily. Abbé Breuil has reiterated this position again and again. For him, the rock shelters of Tanganyika, for example, show a synchronic parallel in patina and technique, and he accepts this art as fully Quaternary. But the whole problem of the connection and possible priority as among the two groups, the Spanish and the African, that is, the rock paintings containing human scenes, lies outside our present discussion.

At the present time we are more interested in how to explain the artistic evolution that is assumed for the step from the naturalistic art of the Levantine *sierras* to the increasingly schematic art, dispersed throughout Spain, although denser in the southern regions, and the social and economic change that took place following the transition to the Neolithic. The Levantine paintings of naturalistic style are the work of hunting and gathering groups, while the schematic art is the work of agriculturalists. The magic of the chase is followed by the magic of agriculture, and the masked man of the cave of Letreros (Vélez Blanco), carrying a sickle in each hand, clearly shows the new attitude. Surely a minute study with this hypothesis in mind might arrive at a new point of view unhoped for by a simple evaluation of the schematic rock paintings. But this study also lies outside the present objective. The transition was probably slow, and many aspects of the new times had lingered on from the Paleolithic.

XIV. CONCLUSIONS

From all that has been said, we may conclude that the hunters who lived in the Levantine *sierras* of Spain during the final stage of the Quaternary and the beginning of modern times, continued to cultivate the pictorial art that they had learned from those who invented it during the Upper Paleolithic, at the time of apogee of the hunting of big game. But, little by little, other purposes and other values were mixed with the purely magical intention. Without losing its sacred character, this art acquired a feeling more anecdotal, historical, or memorialistic, thanks to which we can contemplate upon the social and spiritual life of those remote ancestors of ours.

And thus these small hordes who lived in the ravines of our *sierras* can be seen clearly, hunting deer, goats, and boars as their principal means of sustenance, fighting among themselves, and dedicating themselves to the simpler tasks of gathering and to the early techniques that presaged the Neolithic.

This population was transformed shortly afterward by the impact of the Neolithic revolution, which advanced from the eastern shores of the Mediterranean, but fundamentally it had undergone little change, and the population remained essentially the same and is the essential element in the people who live in the eastern provinces of Spain today.

Only on very rare occasions like this have archeologists and prehistorians succeeded in giving us a vision of remote times so interesting from the point of view of primitive social life.

BIBLIOGRAPHY

ALMAGRO, MARTIN
1947: "El Arte prehistórico español." In *Ars Hispaniae*, 1:13–122. Madrid.
1952: *El covacho con pinturas rupestres de Cogul (Lérida)*. Lérida.
1953: *El arte rupestre del Bajo Aragón*. Teruel.
1954: "Las pinturas rupestres levantinas." In *IV Congreso Internacional de Ciencias Prehistóricas y protohistóricas*, Madrid.

BREUIL, HENRI
1912: "L'age des cavernes et roches ornées de France et d'Espagne," *Revue Archéologique*, 19:215.
1920: "Les peintures rupestres de la Peninsule Iberique. XI. Les roches peintes de Minateda (Albacete)," *L'Anthropologie*, 30:150.
1935: *Les peintures schématiques de la Peninsule Iberique*. 4 vols. Lagny.

BREUIL, HENRI, and HUGO OBERMAIER
1912: "Les premiers travaux de l'Institut de Paléontologie Humaine. II. Travaux sur les peintures rupestres d'Espagne. 3. Alpera (Albacete)," *L'Anthropologie*, 23:19–33.

CABRÉ AGUILO, JUAN
1951: *El arte rupestre en España*. Madrid: Comisión de Investigaciones Paleontológicas y Prehistóricas.

HERNANDEZ PACHECO, EDUARDO
1924: *Las pinturas prehistóricas de las cuevas de la Araña (Valencia). Evolución del arte rupestre en España*. Madrid: Comisión de Investigaciones Paleontológicas y Prehistóricas.

JORDA, FRANCISCO, and JOSÉ ALCACER GRAU
1951: "Las pinturas rupestres de Dos Aguas (Valencia)," *Trabajos Varios del Servicio de Investigación Prehistórica de la Diputación Provincial de Valencia*, No. 15. Valencia.

KÜHN, HERBERT
1941–34: "Die Frage des alters ostspanisches Felsbilders," *Ipek*, Vols. 15–16.
1952: *Die Felsbilder Europas*. Stuttgart (trad. esp., Barcelona, 1957).

MARTINEZ SANTA-OLALLA, JULIO
1946: *Esquema paleontológico de la Peninsula hispánica*. 2d ed. Madrid.

OBERMAIER, HUGO
1925: *El Hombre fosil*. 2d ed. Madrid: Comisión de Investigaciones Paleontológicas y Prehistóricas.
1938: "Probleme der Paläolitischen Malerei Ostspaniens," *Quartär*, 1:111–19.

OBERMAIER, HUGO, and HENRI BREUIL
1927: "Las pinturas rupestres de los alrededores de Tormón (Teruel)," *Boletin de la Real Academia de la Historia* (Madrid), 10:511–31.

OBERMAIER, HUGO, and PAUL WERNERT

1919. *Las pinturas rupestres del barranco de la Valltorta.* Madrid: Comisión de Investigaciones Paleontológicas y Prehistóricas.

1929. "La edad cuaternaria de las pinturas rupestres del Levante español," *Memorias de la Real Sociedad Española de Historia Natural,* 15:527–37. Madrid.

PERICOT GARCIA, LUIS

1942. *La cueva del Parpalló.* Madrid.

1950*a*. *La España primitiva.* Barcelona.

1950*b*. *El arte rupestre español.* Barcelona.

1958. "España primitiva y romana." In *Historia de España,* 2d ed., Vol. 1. Barcelona.

PEYRONY, DENIS

1949. "L'art pictural de la grotte de Lascaux et celui dit levantin espagnol," *Bulletin de la Societé Préhistorique Française,* 46:117.

PORCAR, JUAN B.

1953. "Las pinturas rupestres del barranco de Les Dogues," *Archivo de Prehistoria levantina,* 4:75. Valencia.

PORCAR, JUAN B., HUGO OBERMAIER, and HENRI BREUIL

1935. "Excavaciones en la Cueva Remigia (Castellón)," *Memorias de la Junta Superior de Excavaciones y Antigüedades,* No. 136. Madrid.

THE SOCIAL LIFE OF EARLY MAN:
THE EVIDENCE OF SKELETONS

HENRI V. VALLOIS

IN THE present account, the classification will be the following: terms used correspond not so much to strictly defined taxonomical divisions as to morphological stages in which the transformation from prehominid simian forms to recent human forms can be followed. Chronologically, these stages run from the end of the Tertiary to the present era, over a period of at least 700,000 to 1,000,000 years. It should be noted simply that—as in often found in paleontology—this succession is true only in the broadest sense. There is actually some overlapping, each stage continuing for some length of time alongside the stage to which it has just given birth.

Australopithecines

Fossil hominids
$\begin{cases}\textit{Pithecanthropus} \\ \textit{Homo neanderthalensis} \text{ (including the} \\ \quad \text{Pre-Neanderthalians and the various} \\ \quad \text{"Neanderthaloids")} \\ \textit{Homo sapiens} \begin{cases}\text{Presapiens} \\ \text{Upper Paleolithic men} \\ \text{Mesolithic men}\end{cases}\end{cases}$

Finally, there is cause to note that, with respect to the problem at hand, it is really only with the Neanderthal men *sensu stricto* (Classical Neanderthals), that is, from the end of the last Interglacial, from 120,000 to 130,00 years ago, that the fossil human remains become sufficiently numerous to permit conclusions to any great extent. For the preceding periods, whose duration was at least six times as great, the documents are rare, always incomplete, and most often in extremely bad condition. In addition, and even in those from the last Glaciation, many skeletons are nearly always represented only by skulls or fragments of skulls. This makes impossible the study of transformations, like that of the hand, whose social importance is very considerable. All these facts, and some others that will be indicated later, reduce the significance of data resulting from the study of skeletons. Nevertheless, some of these facts can be demonstrated, as will appear from the present report.

CRANIAL CAPACITY

The monkeys and apes live in social groups, as do men today. It may thus be considered as certain that the same was true for fossil men. But the possibilities of a group are the vaster as the intelligence of those who compose it is greater. It is therefore interesting, for the problem that concerns us, to look at the values obtained by determination of the cranial capacity. This is what has been done in Table 1 (Vallois, 1954) in which the cerebral volumes of recent man and the various species of apes have been compared. Since the sex of many of the fossil hominids is impossible to establish with certainty, the figures for the living forms have been given with the two sexes combined in order to facilitate the comparisons.

TABLE 1

COMPARISON OF CEREBRAL VOLUMES OF MEN AND APES

Group	Number Studied	Average Volume (in cu. cm.)	Range of Variation (in cu. cm.)
Hylobates gibbons	86	89.3	87–130
Siamang gibbons	40	124.6	100–152
Chimpanzees	144	393.8	320–480
Orangs	260	411.2	295–575
Gorillas	532	497.8	340–685
Australopithecines	5	576	(450–480–500–700–750)
Pithecanthropes	3	871	(835–880–900)
Sinanthropes	4	1,046	(915–1,015–1,030–1,225)
Ngandong men	6	1,100	1,035–1,255
Pre-Neanderthal men . . .	2	1,175	(1,070–1,280)
Classic Neanderthal men . .	6	1,438	1,300–1,610
Homo sapiens { racial means individual variations*			1,195–1,520 1,010–2,000

* Variations in men of normal development; the capacities from dwarf or giant subjects that exceed the limits indicated here have been omitted.

The figures show that there was progressive enlargement of the brain from the australopithecines to the Neanderthal men. After these, there seems to have been a slight reduction. As far as psychological development may be inferred from the cerebral volume (and it is impossible to obtain other useful criteria of estimation for the fossil remains), the intellectual possibilities of the Australopithecidae-Hominidae together would thus have increased threefold in the Pleistocene by the beginning of the Würm. But it is interesting to observe that the australopithecines were still, in this respect, very close to the apes since three of the five endocranial casts whose capacity could be estimated fall within the limit presented by them. Their psychological development—and likewise their social behavior—

must not yet have been very different, then, from that of the monkeys and apes. It is doubtful that it allowed for the elaboration of traditions such as they exist in human societies and equally doubtful that it permitted the manufacture of tools (Washburn and Avis, 1958). Examination of the table shows further that if one wishes to establish a division point, it is not before the australopithecines that one must place it, but between these and the pithecanthropes. It corresponds to what A. Keith (1948) called the "cerebral Rubicon."

The figures given above might bring forth the objection that what is important above all in such comparisons is the relative capacity, not the absolute capacity. This is a logical objection, and a long time ago anthropologists, in order to prevent it, established several cerebral indices, of which the best known is that of Dubois. But, when fossil fragments are concerned, determination of the relative capacity is naturally impossible, and the anthropologist must be content with what he has. A. Keith (1929), to remedy this gap, attempted to relate the cranial capacity to the surface of the palatal arch. Unfortunately this arch is missing or is too greatly damaged to furnish such a measurement in the very great majority of the earliest forms. An interesting suggestion, on the other hand, is the one recently set forth by S. Washburn (1959) that the australopithecines, judging from the measurements of bones found at Swartkrans (which belong to the variety called *Paranthropus crassidens*), must have weighed from 100 to 140 pounds, which is comparable to the weight of the chimpanzee or of man. Since the cranial capacity of this *Paranthropus* is around 750 cubic centimeters, it may be inferred that the relative growth of the human brain, compared with the relative growth in this australopithecine, was visibly of the same order as the absolute growth.

The slight superiority of the classic Neanderthals in brain volume over recent men may seem incompatible with the double fact of their greater geological age and their cultural development, which is still very primitive. The explanation that is generally accepted is that this greater volume would be related to a large development of the centers associated with the innervation of their powerful musculature. On the other hand, the regions that correspond to the so-called intellectual operations would be less extensive than they are in man. Thus the frontal lobe, seat of a very important psychological center of association (pre-frontal lobe), would represent, in the La Chapelle-aux-Saints and La Quina men), only 35 per cent of the total surface of the hemisphere, as against 43.3 per cent in recent man and 32.2 per cent in the apes (Boule and Anthony, 1911; Anthony, 1913). But this explanation is debatable for several present-day peoples (Australians, Bushmen, etc.), whose way of life requires a very strong musculature, but who, nevertheless, number among those who have the smallest brains.

Perhaps, then, another hypothesis should be brought in, based on the fact, revealed by mammalogists, that when domestic mammals are compared to their wild counterparts, the cerebral weight of the first always proves to be lower. While domestication does not modify the body weight, it lowers the cerebral weight by about 20 per cent, sometimes even by 30 per cent (Herre, 1958).

The phenomenon is universal and has been observed on such diverse species as the dog, cat, lamb, pig, rabbit, rat, and guinea pig. It even holds for the semi-domestic animals that still live more or less at liberty, such as the llama and alpaca. This reduction takes place essentially in the telencephalon, and is related chiefly to the projection centers, while the association centers remain almost the same as in the wild species.

The existence of various morphological characters in recent man analogous to characters that are seen to develop in the domestic animals has been acknowledged for a long time (E. Fischer, 1914). It is thus possible that the reduction of his brain may be attributable to the same cause. Far from indicating a reduction of our psychological potential compared to the Neanderthal's, it would suggest, on the contrary, that with *Homo sapiens*, as compared to the Neanderthals, there was a sudden expansion of culture, with important changes in the way of life that were the indirect cause of modifications in body form. That these transformations strongly affected the social life seems beyond doubt.

THE ANATOMICAL EVIDENCE OF SPEECH

The use of articulate speech has played a fundamental role in the development of human societies. It is therefore of greatest interest to know whether certain skeletal patterns might have been associated with its production; their presence or absence in a human fossil might provide a basis for inferring the existence or nonexistence of speech in the fossil. Three groups of structures have been considered with regard to this point: the general shape of the mandible, the development of the genial tubercles (mental spine), and the special characteristics of the endocranial casts.

1. The lateral branches of the body of the human mandible diverge to a high degree; they leave between them a large space for the tongue. In the monkeys and apes, on the other hand, the two branches are parallel and the space they enclose is narrow; it is further reduced in front by the structure called the "simian shelf." Therefore the area left for the tongue is much more limited.

On the basis of these differences, the early paleontologists believed that the shape of the mandible in man was the only one compatible with speech; it was the only one to allow the development and mobility to the tongue necessary for the execution of speech. From the shape of the mandible—even from the mere degree of separation between the dental arcades—the existence or nonexistence of speech could thus be assumed. Accordingly, Gaudry, in his study on *Dryopithecus* (1890), declares that the narrowness of its mandibular dental arcade shows that this fossil ape, in spite of certain resemblances to man, did not have speech. There is no need to stress the weakness of this argument, which no longer seems to have supporters.

2. Much more widespread is the idea that the superior genial tubercles of

the mandible are directly related to articulate speech. It is, in fact, known that in man there are normally three or four spines (*spina mentalis*) on the posterior surface of the symphysis: those of the lower part, inferior genial tubercles (*spina m. geniohyoidei*), usually united in a vertical crest, provide insertion to the geniohyoid muscles; those of the upper part, superior genial tubercles (*spina m. genioglossi*), give insertion to the genioglossal muscles—two of the muscles essential to speech. But in the apes all these spines are absent and the area of attachment of the genioglossal muscles is a flat surface or, more often, an oval fossa (*fossa genioglossa*). Some anthropologists have concluded from this that the appearance of genial tubercles, especially the upper ones, was related to the development of the corresponding muscles and was a consequence of speech.

Previously suggested in the last century by Schafhausen and de Mortillet, this theory has been more particularly supported by Walkhoff in a series of studies (1911 in particular). The study of plaster casts indicated to this author that, contrary to what several physiologists had said, the genioglossal muscles play an essential part in speech; and radiographic study of human and ape mandibles enabled him to prove the existence, in the former, of a series of cancellous lamellae issuing from the insertion points of these muscles and radiating into the symphysis; these cancelli are absent in the apes. These arguments have influenced many authors. Thus Zaborowski, in a widely distributed manual (1898, p. 61), does not hesitate to write: "As they (the superior genial tubercles) are a consequence in us of great activity of the muscles relating to speech, and resulting from the practice of articulate speech, it may be inferred from this that man of the Neanderthal race possessed only a quite rudimentary articulate speech." And quite recently, E. Hooton wrote (1947, p. 169): "The presence of well-developed genial tubercles is the surest anatomical evidence of articulate speech that the skeleton affords." It must be mentioned, however, that a little further on Hooton states that "a poor development of their bony spines . . . is no evidence at all that the possessor is or was unable to speak."

The question, therefore, deserves careful examination. But, while it is indisputable that the genial tubercles are always absent in the apes, study of various human groups has shown that these tubercles exhibit a variability that is much greater than would be permitted by the essential physiological role that people have wished to attribute to them. A general review made recently by Edgar (1952) has illustrated this point for recent men. It concludes that it is impossible to establish a relationship between the presence or absence of the tubercles and the presence or absence of speech in these men. Whereas the absence of tubercles is observed in the Europeans with a frequency of from 3 to 5 per cent at the most, it reaches 25 per cent in the natives of the Loyalty Islands and 32 per cent in the New Caledonians; it is at least 28 per cent in the Bushmen-Hottentots. And if in the majority of cases the tubercles are replaced by a fossa, in others there is absolutely nothing. What is more, while it is obvious that the individuals so lacking the tubercles had normal speech, the presence of these tubercles has been observed on mandibles of idiots without speech from birth (E. Fischer, 1903).

Examination of human or prehuman groups shows an identical irregularity. Here are the patterns that were observed:

Australopithecus (after Dart, Broom, and Robinson).—The tubercles are absent; there is generally a rather large genioglossal fossa, but this was absent on at least one adult *Plesianthropus*. *Telanthropus* is not distinguishable from *Australopithecus* in this feature.

Sinanthropus (after Weidenreich).—The superior and inferior tubercles are present, although in various forms. Although they are smaller than the ones in recent man, they are just as well differentiated. A fossa has been observed on one young individual.

Neanderthal and Pre-Neanderthal men.—In the primitive forms, Mauer and Ehrings-dorf men, there are no tubercles and there is a well-marked genioglossal fossa. In the "Classic Neanderthals," the tubercles are usually present, although smaller and more irregular in appearance than in recent man; they are very reduced in certain cases. There is sometimes a trace of a genioglossal fossa.

Upper Paleolithic men.—The pattern is the same as in recent men.

These facts, taken together, show that it is difficult to link the development of the *spina mentalis* with the appearance of speech. Indeed, it would have to be admitted that speech existed with *Sinanthropus* when it might have been absent in Mauer man and certain Neanderthals! It seems more logical to suppose that the development of genial tubercles results from the change in the direction of the posterior surface (*facies lingualis*) of the symphysis; oblique at the back and on the lower side in the apes, this surface became more or less vertical in the primitive Hominidae, more oblique at the front and the lower side in the great majority of recent men; the points of attachment of the genial muscles on the mandible thus moved forward little by little, the tubercles developing by progressive ossification of the tendons for muscle insertion. Although there is a certain parallelism, generally speaking, between these modifications of the bone and the appearance of speech, it cannot be said that there is a direct relation. The two phenomena are independent of each other.

3. Finally, it was believed that the discovery on the endocranial casts of fossil hominids of the part of the brain corresponding to the speech center in recent man might imply the existence of articulate speech in these fossils. It is known, from Broca, that the small region of the third frontal convolution (*gyrus frontalis inferior*) lying behind the vertical branch of the Sylvian Fissure (*sulcus sub-centralis anterior*) is generally believed to be the location of this center; it is the "foot" (*pars opercularis*) of this convolution. In the cyto-architectonic area system, as demonstrated by Vogt, Brodman, etc., this region corresponds to the anterior part of the forty-fourth area. But the physiological significance of Broca's center has been disputed. Some consider it to be only a transitional area; others reckon that at least three of the areas, numbering from 45 to 47, situated farther forward on the lateral surface of the frontal lobe, must also come into play to a certain extent in the mechanism of speech.

The first sufficiently accurate study of the disposition of the aforementioned regions in the fossil hominids is the one by Boule and Anthony (1911) on the endocranial cast of Neanderthal Man of La Chapelle-aux-Saints. Having discovered the existence of a *sulcus-subcentralis* occupying the same position as it does in recent man, these authors declare that the "cap" (*pars triangularis*) of the third frontal convolution was well developed, while the foot seemed to them to have been very small. They conclude from this, "if not the probable existence of articulate speech, at least the existence of rudimentary articulate speech." They add that where the *sulcus centralis* might have been farther back than shown on the cast, the foot would then be of normal size, but that "the smooth, simple appearance of the third frontal convolution should still check any modification of the above opinion." R. Anthony, a little later (1913), arrived at the same conclusion from the examination of the cast of the Neanderthal woman of La Quina.

The preceding information would lead us to suppose that in Neanderthal man speech was only at a very primitive stage, an idea that was recently taken up again by Bounak (1958), who based it on the comparison of types of industry. It is, then, curious to state that other authors, also going on the study of the endocranial casts, grant, on the contrary, the existence of well-differentiated speech in forms much earlier than the Neanderthals. It was Elliot Smith and Shellshear (1934) who first identified the speech centers in *Sinanthropus;* and Broom and Schepers (1946), followed with an extensive monograph devoted to the endocranial casts of the australopithecines. These authors, first of all, rediscovered the *sulcus subcentralis*. With this as a basis, together with the shape of the part of the cast that corresponds to the lower *gyrus frontalis*, they inferred the existence "of the areas 44–46 and probably also the area 47." They conclude from this (1946, p. 253) that

they [*Australopithecus*] had the subject matter for articulate speech well under control and . . . [had] developed motoric centres for the appropriate application; they were also capable of communicating the acquired information to their families, friends and neighbors, thus establishing one of the first bonds of Man's complex social life.

Thus research based on the same principle results in conclusions that are obviously mutually incompatible. Therefore, the facts on which they rest must be confronted. Now one primary question dominates the whole discussion: the very great difficulty presented by the interpretation of the endocranial casts. Previously pointed out by various authors, this difficulty has been made particularly apparant by Hirschler (1942), who has shown that many details that may be observed on these casts do not correspond to the actual cerebral structure and that, inversely, a large number of these structures are not registered on these casts. The latter case refers particularly to the central sulcus, which Boule and Anthony themselves admit they could locate only approximately on their casts;

consequently, nothing permitted them to state that the foot of F^3 was really smaller. Further, since most of the present-day physiologists believe that this reduced segment of the cortex is not the only one to be connected with language and that it perhaps plays only a secondary role in its production, it seems hard to accept these conclusions as to the so-called rudimentary speech of the Neanderthals.

Still further evidence of the difficulties in interpretations was offered by Weidenreich, who pointed out the existence of morphological details on the endocranial cast of the orang, which Shellshear had interpreted on *Sinanthropus* as being the speech center.

Wide open to criticism, finally, are Schepers' conclusions. The areas that he believes he has found on the australopithecine casts are in reality characterized only by their microscopic structure, and their boundaries on the brain are independent of the cortical sulci. Even if we had a complete endocranial cast of *Australopithecus*, indicating all the brain sulci—which is far from being the case —no true neurologist would risk tracing the cyto-architectonic areas. Schepers' attempt is untenable.

In fact, the examination of casts by the anthropologists mentioned above seems to show only two things that apply to the problem at hand: (1) the region of the lower frontal gyrus in Neanderthal man appears to differ very little from the same region in man; (2) in the australopithecine, on the other hand, the oblique branch of the fissure of Sylvius does not extend nearly so far forward as it does in us, thus leaving the anterior part of the insula uncovered; the *sulcus subcentralis* is independent of this oblique branch and the tract limiting *pars triangularis* of F^3 at the front is not visible. Thus the whole inferior frontal gyrus region has a structure that recalls the ape structure.

Must it be inferred from this that Neanderthal man, like us, had articulate speech, while the australopithecines, like the apes, did not speak? One must be the more cautious in this matter because, as I have said above, the casts are only an imperfect representation, and sometimes a deformation, of the real brain. Besides, the essential thing in speech is unquestionably not so much a fixed cortical form as the existence of a whole system of psychomotor correlations, which the examination of casts, as complete as they are, will never enable us to reveal.

None of the anatomical forms observable on the fossils, whether it be the general shape of the mandible, the development of certain tubercles on the mandible, or the form of the endocranial casts, may therefore be regarded conclusively as characteristic of the function of articulate speech. The question here, at most, is whether one or two details permit some suggestions, but they have such a degree of uncertainty that there is little cause to linger upon them. It seems to me that the question of the "anatomical evidence" for speech suggests a negative answer.

DURATION OF LIFE

From the stage of eruption of the teeth in the nonadult individuals and the degree of obliteration of the sutures in the adult individuals, one may estimate for modern man the age at death of a skeleton with an approximation of ± 6 months for the first character and ± 5 years for the second. The data obtained in this way retain to a great extent their value for the human remains of the Mesolithic and the Upper Paleolithic, but their application to earlier remains runs up against the difficulty that in the more primitive types of hominids, growth appears to have been more rapid than it is in us; the ages that are calculated thus risk being too high in comparison with modern men (Vallois, 1937). It is likely that the differences for the Neanderthal men are not very considerable. They should be much more considerable for the pithecanthropines (*Sinanthropus*), in which the extreme thickness of the cranial vault in particular must have caused a different, and at the same time a more rapid, progress of synostosis than is found in us (Weidenreich, 1939). It was doubtless the same for the Ngandong men (Weidenreich, 1951).

Using the two criteria of dental eruption and cranial suture closure for all the fossil men known up to that time, I showed, in the work mentioned above, that their age of death had always been much lower than that of recent man; this assumption has been subsequently confirmed by other investigators (above all, Weidenreich, 1939; McCown and Keith, 1939; and Senyürek, 1947). Table 2, which includes all the fossil men discovered to date whose age has been estimated with sufficient certainty (Vallois, 1960), is significant with respect to this point.

The duration of life of fossil men was, then, much shorter than ours; few individuals passed forty years, and it is only quite exceptionally that any passed fifty. Moreover, the ages ascribed here to the Neanderthal men and the Ngandong men, as well as to the sinanthropes, are most likely higher than the true ages for the reasons previously indicated; the figures given for them on the tables thus represent the maxima, somewhat higher than in reality.

Another fact becomes apparent when the two sexes are compared; in the Neanderthals, as in the men of the Upper Paleolithic and the Mesolithic, female mortality was earlier than was male mortality; in the three groups most of the women died before thirty years of age; most men died after thirty years of age, as shown in Table 3. This early female mortality was no doubt the consequence of pregnancy and parturition casualties.

From the statements given above a certain number of suggestions may be made concerning the structure of social groups:

a) A high proportion of children compared to adults. Already apparent on most of the series in the tables, this high proportion must have been still greater in reality. Actually, children's skeletons are fragile and rapidly deteriorate in the soil; many of them in the earlier excavations must have escaped the attention of observers or else have been systematically disregarded. The modern excavations, which are more methodical, underline the large number of children. Thus the Ibero-Maurusian site of Taforalt (Morocco) contained no fewer than 93 children as against 68 adults (Férembach, 1959) and the *Sinanthropus* site of Choukoutien (Weidenreich, 1939) produced 15 children as against 7 adults or adolescents.

b) Absence of old people, in our sense of the term; hence, in the prehistoric societies there was no gerontocracy.

TABLE 2
AGE OF FOSSIL MEN AT DEATH

Name and No. of Fossil Men Studied	Age at Time of Death (in Years)							
	0–14	Per Cent	15–30	Per Cent	40–50	Per Cent	50–60	Per Cent
A. Sinanthropes,* 22	15	68.2	3	13.6	3	13.6	1	4.6

	Age Group at Time of Death							
	Young	Per Cent	Adoles-cent	Per Cent	Adult	Per Cent	Old Adult	Per Cent
Ngandong men,† 11 . .	1	9.1	4	36.1	2	18.2	4	36.4

	Age in Years and Age Group at Time of Death											
	Infants		Juveniles		Adults				Old Adults			
	0–11	Per Cent	12–20	Per Cent	21–30	Per Cent	31–40	Per Cent	41–50	Per Cent	51–60	Per Cent
B. Neanderthals *sensu lato*, 39	15	38.5	4	10.3	6	15.4	10	25.6	3	7.7	1	2.5
Upper Paleolithic Eurasians, 76 . .	29	38.2	12	16.0	15	20.0	11	14.7	7	9.2	2	2.8
North African Ibero-Maurusians, 163 .	101		62%		31	19.0	25	15.3	6	3.7		
Mesolithics, 71	21	29.5	6	8.5	35	49.3	6	8.5	1	1.4	2	2.8

* Weidenreich, 1943.
† *Ibid.*, 1951.

TABLE 3

AGE AT DEATH OF FOSSIL MEN, BY AGE GROUP AND SEX

Fossil Men	Age Group							
	21–30		31–40		41–50		Over 50	
	M	F	M	F	M	F	M	F
Neanderthals	1	5	8	2	2	1	1	—
Upper Paleolithic men . .	5	10	6	5	7	—	2	—
Ibero-Maurusians	14	17	16	9	5	1	—	—
Mesolithic men	15	20	4	2	1	—	2	—

c) Brief time of contact between one generation and the next; if the period from twenty to thirty years of age is considered as the main period of a couple's fecundity, it is evident that when the eldest members of a family reached adult age, usually their mother had already died and their father was not far from his end; it was all the more true for the last-born, whose care and education often had to pass over to the kinsmen.

Spuhler declared in a recent work (1959), with a table of A. H. Schultz as his basis, that in man as compared to the apes, while the duration of growth has visibly doubled (increasing from nine to eleven years in the apes and to twenty years in us), the total length of life has much more than doubled (increasing from thirty to thirty-five years in the apes and to seventy-five years in us); this lengthening might be "a consequence of physiological adaptation to the aquisition of culture" (p. 12). Table 2 shows that this proposal is false; seventy-five years may be the average duration of life in some civilized populations today, and, moreover, in a very small number; but, until the beginning of modern times, the average length of life did not exceed thirty to forty years; that is, it scarcely exceeded that of the apes. While the period of cerebral development, which is the development of intense psychological assimilation, has remarkably increased in us, the period of cultural contacts among adults within a group has, to all intents and purposes, scarcely changed. Prehistoric man, in this respect, was hardly different from the apes.

SEX RATIO

Table 3 has already given an idea of the proportions between the two sexes for the adults. A more complete estimate is achieved through the addition to this of the human remains whose sex, rather than age, could be determined. The results are shown in Table 4, which is based on data from 309 individuals.

With the exception of the Mesolithic men, for whom there is virtual uniformity, just as in the very small Ngandong series, all the other series are seen to agree in exhibiting a greater frequency of the male sex; the sum of all the individuals included in the table is 172 men to 135 women, or a sex ratio of 125, which recalls the ratio of present-day Melanesians. If the Ibero-Maurusians and the Mesolithic men are excluded, we have 73 men and 49 women; the sex ratio rises to 148.

It is hard to say whether this proportion corresponds well to the actual composition of populations of these periods. The determination of sex in the fossil men is not always easy. Besides the fact that it can often be carried out only on skulls or skull fragments, to the exclusion of the rest of the skeleton, it runs up against the fact that, in both sexes, the marks made on the bones by the muscle or tendon insertions are much more pronounced than they are in recent men; thus some female individuals may have been considered as male. But it is hard to believe that such an error may have been made often enough by the anthropologists to produce a sex ratio of 148!

One may also wonder whether all the members of such a group were buried; but, in this case, would it not be the men, exposed to death far from their homes in a hunting expedition, who would be missing, rather than the women, who certainly wandered less from the encampments (unless a certain social selection operated against them, something we evidently cannot know)?

Last, it must be remembered that the series used here were made up from the collection of numerous finds, removed from one another in time and space, the earliest of them and at least a part of the others not even being burials. They are very heterogeneous collections. The only series that would perhaps be able to offer more certainty are the ones that come from restricted groups. Unfortunately, there are not very many of these. Not any is known for the Neanderthals of Europe, where the only site that produced the remains of a large enough number of individuals, the Krapina one, contained skulls so broken that it was with difficulty that the sex could be determined for three or four fragments. And for the neandertaloids from Palestine, the Mount Carmel group comprises

TABLE 4

SEX RATIO IN FOSSIL MAN

	Males	Females
Pithecanthropines		
a) Sinanthropes	10	3
b) Ngandong men	4	6
Neanderthals and Pre-Neanderthals		
a) Eurasia	10	8
b) Palestine Neanderthaloids	8	3
Upper Paleolithic men of Eurasia	41	29
Ibero-Maurusians of North Africa	58	46
Mesolithic men of Europe	41	42

7 men and 3 women, but these remains came from two caves and belonged to several periods. Those are not good conditions. Some series from the Upper Paleolithic are of more use. First of all, the Předmost (Czechoslovakia) one, whose individuals belong to a common cultural type and whose adult and adolescent distribution is 6 male and 8 female. Here the sex ratio is thus reversed. The sex ratio recovers its usual value with the burials at the Grimaldi caves (Italy): 8 men and 4 women. These individuals, it is true, come from four caves and are not all contemporaneous. At Arene Candide (Italy), the proportion of men is still higher: 8 men to 2 women. Finally, in the two large sites of North Africa used in Table 4, which are both of Ibero-Maurusian age, that is, at the dawn of the Mesolithic, the Afalou bon Rhummel site (Algeria) gives the figures 19 men and 17 women, the Taforalt (Morocco) one gives 39 men and 29 women; the greater frequency of males is thus maintained.

It disappears, however, in three of the four Mesolithic series that could be used, series that are interesting because the three first ones, at least, represented small populations (Table 5). Here, rather, there is superiority of the female component, as was pointed out long ago for the kjökkemöddings of Mugem by Paula e Oliveira (1889), who stated that in this site the number of women was twice the number of men, but this statement goes too far. If the sex ratio for all Mesolithic peoples together is, indeed, almost 100, it is related to the fact that in the isolated burials it is chiefly men who are found. If, on the other hand, the individuals from the very strange "burials of heads" of southern Germany are eliminated (Ofnet, Kaufertsberg, Hohlestein, and Bottendorf), the inversion of the sex ratio reappears with only 7 men to 11 women, but perhaps such a burial is related to selection (massacre of the persons left in the encampment?).

In spite of the reservations made above, and recognizing that the statistics on this subject are of value chiefly as an indication, it seems plausible that in the Paleolithic the proportion of males was, in the adults, higher than the proportion of females. This inequality disappears in the Mesolithic. Such a statement should not be surprising. No doubt it was largely related to the fact, noted above, of the earlier death of women in the prehistoric periods. It is very likely, but the documents are not adequate enough to verify this point, that it is only after thirty that the sex ratio clearly rose above 100. Such a fact must not have existed without strongly influencing the type of social organization.

TABLE 5
SEX RATIO IN MESOLITHIC SERIES

	Males	Females
Téviec (Brittany)	6	8
Hoëdic (Brittany)	5	3
Mugem (Portugal)	14	17
Ofnet (Bavaria)	4	10

PALEOLITHIC POPULATIONS

COMPOSITION

It is a well-known fact to prehistorians that what may be called cemeteries, consisting of burial in one restricted area of a number of individuals apparantly more numerous than a single family, are not known to appear until the Mesolithic; moreover, these cemeteries are still very small. The skeletons (or parts of skeletons) from the early periods, when there had been burial, appear either isolated or grouped in one or at the most a few neighboring graves. A study limited to the individuals for whom the principal age category and, most often, also the sex could be determined, including the intentional burials as well as the accidental ones (individuals who were victims of landslides; bodies or bones abandoned and then covered over little by little by the earth) gives results as shown in Table 6.

The isolated graves were thus destined for women as well as for men—although always with an obvious prevalence of men—and further, even in the Neanderthal period (in the case of the children of Teshik-Tash, Staroselje, Engi, and Pech-de-

TABLE 6
(ad. = adult; m. = male; f. = female; i. = infant)

	Isolated Burials	Group Burials
Neanderthals	11 {5 m. / 2 f. / 4 i.	6 {1 ad., 1 i. / 1 m., 1 i. / 1 f., 1 i. / 2 m., 1 i. / 1 m., 1 f., 1 i. / 13 ad., 6–7 i.
Upper Paleolithic men	15 {10 m. / 4 f. / 1 i.	16 {2 m. (3 times) / 1 m., 1 f. (4 times) / 1 f., 1 i. / 2 f., 1 i. / 1 m., 1 f., 1 i. (2 times) / 1 m., 1 f., 2 i. / 1 m., 2 f., 1 i. / 2 m., 1 f., 2 i. / 4 m., 1 f., 2 i. / 6 m., 7 f., 15 i.
Mesolithic men	7 {6 m. / 1 i.	7 {2 m. / 1 m., 1 f. / 1 m., 3 i. / 2 m., 1 f., 1 i. / 4 m., 10 f., 7 i. / 5 m., 5 f., 4 i. / 7 m., 8 f., 8 i.

l'Aze, these last two reduced to the heads), they were destined also for children who were sometimes very young. From this fact it may be inferred that as early as this period the child had a place in the social life. It is seen, on the other hand, that in all the periods the group burials were diversified.

The modalities under which these occur are variable. Some graves have two adults of opposite or of the same sex. Most of them have produced one or two adults and one or several children. Some have a still greater number of individuals. Yet it is often hard in the last case to interpret the find. The Neanderthal cemetery of Krapina (13 adults of both sexes and 6 to 7 children) is generally considered to have resulted from cannibalism. The one at Ofnet of Mesolithic age (4 men, 10 women, and 7 children) likewise appears to have resulted from a massacre. The Upper Paleolithic burials of Předmost, however (6 men, 7 women, 15 children), seem to have come from successive interments by a stable population, extending perhaps over a certain period. It was certainly the same for the Mugen groups (14 men and at least 17 women); but the excavations, made in conditions with inadequate techniques, seem to have overlooked the children; Téviec (7 men, 8 women, 8 children) and Hoëdic (4 men, 5 women, 4 children), but here we are already in the Mesolithic, that is, on the verge of the appearance of the first agricultural civilizations.

The investigations made of modern hunting populations—which have collecting as a supplement that is ultimately necessary—have shown that they are never made up of more than a very small number of families. Davidson (1938) estimates that among the Australians the band includes around 35 individuals. Hallowell (1949) studied the winter hunting groups of two Northern Algonquian groups (Ojibwa) and found that the group in the Grand Lake Victoria region varied from 2 to 17 persons, with an average of 5.6; the group in the Berens River region varied from 4 to 49, with a mean of 14.9. Schapera (1956) gives the figures of from 20 to 30 persons for the Bergdama, and Bleek (1930) notes for the Bushmen that the density of the group scarcely exceeds the number of individuals who can live off the body of an antelope. Similarly, the hunting groups of those Pygmies of the Congo and Cameroons who have retained their primitive way of life do not generally number more than 10 adults, with twice this number of children (Vallois, 1948). As far as may be inferred from the burials of the Neanderthal and Upper Paleolithic men, and except perhaps for unusual cases —such as the Předmost one, where the systematic hunting of the mammoth made necessary larger bands—it is evident that the men of these periods must have been divided into small groups of from 10 to 30 individuals, as the hunters are today.

PROBLEM OF TERRITORIALITY

Such units, found among most of the so-called primitive peoples that we are acquainted with, live in hunting territories with strictly defined limits. The extent of these territories is, nevertheless, very variable and depends chiefly on the ecological conditions: with the Australians, for example, it varies, according to Davidson, from 20 to 5,000 square miles (5,000–1,500,000 hectares); for the Northern Algonquians, Hallowell, who has stressed these variations and their causes for a long time, gives the figures from 64 to 1,716 square miles for the Grand Lake Victoria groups, from 13 to 212 square miles for the Berens River ones. Since the existence of analogous territorial boundaries has been known for several diverse genera of mammals, and in particular for a large number of species of monkeys, it has been concluded that the same must have been true for Paleolithic men.

Such a generalization seems too presumptuous. It must indeed be noted (1) that some hunting peoples of today do not have definite territory (this is the case particularly for most of the Pygmies in the Congo-Cameroon area); (2) that the existence of a seasonal rhythm in Europe during the Würm period, which was accompanied by the annual migration of certain animals (the reindeer in particular), could have brought about similar movements of hunting bands, movements that would hardly be compatible with the presence of defined territories; and (3) that the extreme morphological resemblance undeniably established between certain groups of Neanderthal men (particularly La Ferrassie, La Chapelle-aux-Saints, and Monte Circeo men) or certain Upper Paleolithic men (for example, Cro-Magnon men from the shelter of this name and men from the Grimaldi Caves) leads one to suppose that there were direct relations between these groups in spite of their undeniable geographic separation. All evidence suggests that the Paleolithic bands were not territorial units, that they were capable of large migrations, and that sexual relations must have existed between them.

INTERPRETATION OF LESIONS ON BONE

1. Human paleopathology has provided material for a number of studies, but the study of prehistoric diseases teaches us practically nothing about the social life of the men who were subject to them, unless the assertion set forth some time ago by an imaginative author (Baudouin, 1923) is considered valid. The author, noting the simultaneous existence in the large contemporary mammals of chronic rheumatism (osteoarthritis) and spondylitis, a disease that he considered to be contagious, concluded from this that man was already practicing the domestication of animals during this period! More interesting is the fact of the complete absence of evidence of rickets in the human fossils, young and old, of the Würm age (Vallois, 1934). These men, during their early infancy, thus must have had a diet that was sufficiently rich in vitamins; it may then be believed that, as is true with many primitive people today, the children were breast-fed until their teeth had developed—until either two or two and one-half years of age. Certain psychoanalysts will estimate that from this resulted a special type of mother-child complex, itself capable of influencing the form of social organization.

The assertion that there are well-healed fractures of the limb bones found in

Paleolithic human skeletons has been made several times, but identical healings have been pointed out in present-day wild animals (in the gibbon, for example, by A. H. Schultz, 1944), so there is no cause to interpret them as the result of the beneficial work of "medicine men" skilled in bone surgery. For a long time it was thought that not until the Neolithic might the healing of some especially complicated fractures, or even of certain bone lesions, really suggest that there had been intervention by a healer and, further, that the victim had benefited during his long period of immobility from the effective help of other men, who protected him and nursed him, that the idea of mutual aid therefore already existed (Broca, 1876). The quite recent statement by Dr. Stewart (in Solecki, 1958) that the Mousterian skeleton No. 1 from the Shanidar cave had had its right arm amputated a little below the elbow at a relatively advanced age, and that it had been able to live through the period of healing of this serious operation, shows that this notion was already of importance among the Neanderthals of Iraq, about 45,000 years ago.

2. The existence of initiation rites implies a social organization already complex. Hrdlička (1930) thought that he had found an early trace on the Neanderthal Gibraltar skull: the two upper medial incisors are absent and the resorption of the corresponding part of the alveolar border indicates that these teeth had come out, a long time before death, as the result of a blow. But there is no proof that a ritual injury is involved there and, since no similar mutilation has ever been observed on other Neanderthals or on the numerous skulls known from the European Upper Paleolithic, Hrdlička's hypothesis seems very weak. In fact, it is not until much later, in the Ibero-Maurusian men of North Africa, hence in the neighborhood of the Mesolithic, that such a mutilation of teeth is found again, and this time it appears to be systematic (Boule and Vallois, 1934). Even if the interpretation proposed by Hrdlička is correct, it was no doubt only an isolated case that was observed at Gibraltar.

Certain cave paintings of the Upper Paleolithic caves of France represent hands whose outline has been stenciled and whose fingers usually have only one or two phalanges. Ritual amputations have been inferred from these (Cartailhac and Breuil, 1910; Sollas, 1911, p. 239) similar to the ones that are observed at the present time among many primitive tribes—Australians, various Melanesian tribes, Indus, Bushmen, North and South American Indians, etc.—and that also seem to have existed among the ancient Greeks (Loeb, 1923). But perhaps these so-called mutilations are only apparent ones and might be due to the fact that the hands used as models had their fingers folded under. It should be noted, in addition, that in rare cases in which all or part of the finger skeleton of Paleolithic men is preserved, no injury of the phalanges has ever been pointed out. Now, taking into account the articular connections of the fingers, it seems hard to understand how such amputations could be made without at least some marks on the damaged ends of the phalanges. This does not mean that there were no initiation rites among the fossil men. There is proof of their existence for the

Upper Paleolithic men (Vallois, 1931), but it is not the skeleton that provides evidence of them.

3. On the other hand, the presence of marks of violent injuries or systematic destruction is unquestionable on the skeletal remains of several fossil men, even the earliest; murders have been inferred from these, even customs like decarnization of the dead bodies, cannibalism, or head-hunting, practices by which human societies are totally differentiated from the apes and monkeys.

Before, in the prehuman stage, the fragmented condition in which the australopithecine skulls occur led to the belief that they were voluntarily broken (Dart, 1957), but it is still debatable whether this breaking was done by the australopithecines or by primitive hominids that are as yet unknown, of whom the australopithecines were simply the victims.

Much later, in the *Sinanthropus* skull, identical fragmentation appears for which Weidenreich (1943) did not hesitate to apply the term "head-hunting." The same hypothesis has been made for the Ngandong skulls, which are known to have been separated from the rest of their skeletons, and in some of them, as it appears also for several sinanthropes, the *foramen magnum* had undergone an artificial widening similar to what the Dyak of Borneo were still doing quite recently to extract the brain (Roth, 1896; cf also Wernert, 1936).

Very similar cases turn up in Europe. The Pre-Neanderthal Steinheim skull and the Monte Circeo Neanderthal skull lack the region around the *foramen magnum*, and it is supposed, again, that this was the result of the removal of the brain. A case of another sort is the Tayacian Fontéchevade skullcap (skull No. 2), which exhibits in the occipital region marks of a violent blow that appears to have been made before death; its parietal region had undergone the action of fire (Vallois, 1958). It has been seen above that in Neanderthal man the rock shelter of Krapina is classically considered as having witnessed scenes of cannibalism; skulls, jaws, and limb bones had been broken into such a number of fragments that accidental breakage could not have been involved. The human bones bore marks of cutting, and some were partially burned and mixed in with animal bones that were also burned. The opinion of Gorjanovič-Kramberger (1906) that these are the remains of cannibals' meals is unanimously accepted.

In the absence of marks of cannibalism, there are found, in a number of sites at least, grooves made on the human bones by worked flint for the purpose of removing the flesh; or, again, skulls and long bones are so fragmented that it is impossible not to interpret it as the result of voluntary action. The same holds true when only certain parts of the skeleton are found, the rest being clearly absent. Examples of one or another of these conditions, sometimes of two or even three at once, abound in paleontological literature: Neanderthal remains from Ehringsdorf, Monsempron, La Chaise, La Quina; Upper Paleolithic remains from Isturitz, les Rois, the Pataud shelter, Upper Choukoutien, etc. The same the best known of which is the collective grave of Ofnet, where the skulls, buried with only the first cervical vertebrae (which proves that the head had been cut off the living individual and that secondary burials were not involved), bore the obvious marks of the blows that had caused death (Mollison, 1936). In all these instances, study of the skeleton indicates the existence of funerary rites or practices that are part of an already specialized social structure.

CONCLUSIONS

In spite of the evident insufficiency of the skeletal documents that we have at our disposal—incomplete and often very fragmentary skeletons, scarcity of remains prior to the Würm period, accidental selection of the burials and often in the collection of the fossil documents in the course of the excavations—several observations may be made which inform us on some aspects of the social behavior of early man.

The enormous growth of the brain that is manifest from the time of Pithecanthropus is a fact that is well known and was certainly accompanied by a corresponding development of man's intellectual possibilities. It is worth remembering that the australopithecines are scarcely above the level of the apes in this respect, while recent man is to Neanderthal man as the domestic animals are to their wild counterparts.

No bone structure may be really considered as directly connected with speech; no conclusion one way or another can thus be drawn from the morphological variations of the mandible or the endocranial casts. It can simply be noted with respect to the casts that, contrary to certain assertions, the configurations in the lower frontal region of the australopithecines are more like the ape's than man's. There is nothing to allow the assertion that they had speech.

The duration of life for fossil men was certainly much shorter than ours. This shortness was especially marked in the women, so that the sex ratio, from the thirtieth year, greatly exceeded the value of 100. Thus the social groups did not include old people; as far as can be judged from the often extremely incomplete excavations of prehistorians, they seem, on the contrary, to have included many children, and these must have been nursed over a long period of time. The number of individuals in these groups was certainly very small—from ten to thirty perhaps? Several facts suggest that, unlike the monkeys and several contemporary prehistoric populations, they did not occupy territories with strictly defined boundaries.

From a very early period, at least from *Sinanthropus* times, skeletons are observed with lesions indicating customs such as cannibalism or head-hunting, which are signs of an already complex social structure. The notion of mutual help, on the other hand, seems to be manifest at least from the time of Neanderthal man. The existence of a specifically human mentality in the prehistoric social groups thus seems to have a very great antiquity.

BIBLIOGRAPHY

ANTHONY, R.
1913. L'encéphale de l'homme fossile de La Quina." *Bull. et Mém. de la Soc. d'Anthrop. de Paris*, 6th ser., 4:117–95.

BAUDOUIN, M.
1923. "La préhistoire du rhumatisme chronique: la plus vieille maladie du monde," *La Médecine internationale* (Paris), No. 2, pp. 43–48.

BLEEK, D. F.
1930. *Rock-Paintings in South Africa from Parts of the Eastern Province and Orange Free State.* (Copied by GEORGE WILLIAM STOW.) London: Methuen.

BOULE, M., and R. ANTHONY
1911. "L'encéphale de l'homme fossile de La Chapelle-aux-Saints," *L'Anthropologie*, 22:129–96.

BOULE, M., and H. V. VALLOIS
1934. "Anthropologie." In C. Arambourg, M. Boule, H. V. Vallois, and R. Verneau, *Les grottes paléolithiques des Béni-Segoual, Algérie* ("Arch. de l'Institut de Paléontologie humaine," mém. 13).

BOUNAK, V. V.
1958. "L'origine du langage.' In *Le processus de l'hominisation: Colloques internat. du C.N.R.S., Paris*, pp. 99–110.

BROCA, P.
1876. "Discussion à propos de l'article: Prunières, 'Fouilles du dolmen de l'Aumède sur le causse de Chanac, Lozère,' " *Bull. de la Soc. d'Anthrop. de Paris*, 2d ser., 11:154–56.

BROOM, R., and G. W. H. SCHEPERS
1946. *The South African Fossil Ape-Men: the Australopithecinae* ("Transvaal Museum Memoir," No. 2). Pretoria.

CARTAILHAC, E., and H. BREUIL
1910. "Les peintures et gravures murales des cavernes pyrénéennes," *L'Anthropologie*, 21:129–50.

DART, R.
1957. *The Osteodontokeratic Culture of Australopithecus prometheus* ("Transvaal Museum Memoir," No. 10). Pretoria.

DAVIDSON, D. S.
1938. "An Ethnic Map of Australia," *Proc. Amer. Phil. Soc.*, 79:649–79.

EDGAR, G. W. F.
1952. "A Reconsideration of the Possible Relation between Articulate Speech and the Presence of Genioglossal Spines (*Spinae m. genioglossi*) in Man," *Koninkl. nederl. Akademie van Weternschappen, Proceedings*, s.C., Vol. 55, No. 4, p. 21.

FÉREMBACH, D.
1959. Personal communication.

FISCHER, E.
1903. "Beeinfluszt der M. genioglossus durch seine Funktion beim Sprechen den Bau des Unterkiefers?" *Anat. Anz.*, 23:33–37.

1914. "Die Rassenmerkmale des Menschen als Domestikationserscheinungen," *Zs. f. Morph. und Anthrop.*, 18:179–524.

GAUDRY, A.
1890. "Le Dryopithecus," *C.R. Acad. des Sciences* (Paris), Vol. 110.

GORJANOVIĆ-KRAMBERGER, K.
1906. *Der diluviale Mensch von Krapina in Kroatien: Ein Beitrag zur Paläoanthropologie.* Weisbaden: W. Kreidels.

HALLOWELL, A. I.
1949. "The Size of Algonkian Hunting Territories: A Function of Ecological Adjustment," *Amer. Anthrop.*, 51:37–45.

HERRE, W.
1958. "Einflüsse der Umwelt über das Säugetiergehirn," *Deutsche med. Wochenschrift*, 83:1568–74.

HIRSCHLER, P.
1942. "Anthropoid and Human Endocranial Casts," *Thèse de Médecine* (Amsterdam).

HOOTON, E. A.
1947. *Up from the Ape.* New York: Macmillan Co.

HRDLIČKA, A.
1930. *The Skeletal Remains of Early Man.* ("Smithsonian Miscellaneous Collections," Vol. 83.)

KEITH, A.
1929. "The Antiquity of Man." Vol. 2. London: Williams & Norgate.
1948. *A New Theory of Human Evolution.* London: Watts.

LOEB, E. M.
1923. *The Blood Sacrifice Complex* ("Mem. Amer. Anthrop. Assoc.," No. 30).

McCOWN, T. D., and SIR ARTHUR KEITH
1939. *The Stone Age of Mount Carmel*, Vol. 2. Oxford: Clarendon Press.

MOLLISON, T.
1936. "Zeich en gewaltsamer Verletzungen an den Ofnet-Schädeln," *Anthrop. Anz.*, 13:79–88.

PAULA E OLIVEIRA, F. DE
1889. "Nouvelles fouilles faites dans les kioekkenmoeddings de la vallée du Tage," *Communicaço es da Commissão dos Trabalhos geologicos*, 2:3–27.

ROTH, H. W.
1896. *Natives of Sarawak, British North Borneo*, Vol. 2. London.

SCHAPERA, I.
1956. "Government and Politics in Tribal Societies." London: Watts.

SCHULTZ, A. H.
1944. "A Morphological Study of a Population Sample of a Manlike Ape," *Amer. J. Phys. Anthrop.*, n.s., 2:1–129.

SENYÜREK, M.
1947. "A Note on the Duration of Life of the Ancient Inhabitants of Anatolia," *Amer. J. Phys. Anthrop.*, n.s., 5:55–66.

SHELLSHEAR, J. L., and G. ELLIOT SMITH
1934. "A Comparative Study of the Endocranial Cast of Sinanthropus," *Phil. Trans. R. Soc. London*, s.B, 223: 469–87.

SOLECKI, R. S.
1958. In Rept. Comm. Res. Humanities. *Year Book Amer. Philosoph. Soc.*, 403–7.

SOLLAS, W. J.
1911. *Ancient Hunters and Their Modern Representatives*. London: Macmillan & Co.

SPUHLER, J. N.
1959. "Somatic Paths to Culture," *Human Biology*, 31:1–13.

VALLOIS, H. V.
1931. "Les empreintes de pieds humains des grottes préhistoriques du Midi de la France," *Palaeobiologica*, 4:20.

1934. "Les maladies de l'Homme préhistorique," *Rev. scientifique*, 72:666–78.

1937. "La durée de la vie chez l'homme fossile," *L'Anthropologie*, 47:499–532.

1948. "Chez les Pygmées du Cameroun," *La Nature*, pp. 18–20, 44–47.

1954. "La capacité cranienne chez les primates supérieurs ct lc 'Rubicon cérébral.'" In *C. R. de l'Acad. des Sciences* (Paris), 238:1349–51.

1958. *La grotte de Fontéchevade: IIème partie: Anthropologie*. ("Arch. de l'Institut de Paléontologie humaine," Mem. 29, pp. 7–164.)

1960. "Vital Statistics in Prehistoric Population as Determined from Archaeological Data." In *Wenner-Gren Symposium: The Application of Quantitative Methods in Archaeology*. Chicago: Quadrangle Books.

VALLOIS, H. V., and H. L. Movius
1952. "Catalogue des Hommes fossiles," *XIXe Congrès géologique international*, *Algeria*.

WALKHOFF, O.
1911. "Neue Untersuchungen über die menschliche Kinnbildung," *Deutsche Zahnheilk. in Vorträgen*, 22:1–71.

WASHBURN, S. L.
1959. "Speculations on the Interrelations of the History of Tools and Biological Evolution," *Human Biology*, 31:21–31.

WASHBURN, S. L., and V. AVIS
1958. "Evolution of Human Behavior." In A. ROE and G. G. SIMPSON (eds.), *Behavior and Evolution*, pp. 421–36. New Haven: Yale University Press.

WEIDENREICH, F.
1936. "Observations on the Form and Proportions of the Endocranial Casts of *Sinanthropus pekinensis*, Other Hominids and the Great Apes: A Comparative Study of Brain Size," *Palaeontologia Sinica* (Peiping), s.D., Vol. 7, Chap. 4.

1939. "The Duration of Life of Fossil Man in China and the Pathological Lesions Found in His Skeleton," *Chinese Med. J.*, 55:34–44.

1943. "The Skull of *Sinanthropus pekinensis*: A Comparative Study on a Primitive Hominid Skull," *Palaeontologia Sinica* (Peiping), n.s., No. 10.

1951. *Morphology of Solo Man* ("Anthrop. Papers Amer. Mus. Nat. Hist.," 43:3, 205–90.)

WERNERT, P.
1936. "L'anthropologie rituelle et la chasse aux têtes," *L'Anthropologie*, 46:33–43.

1938. "De quelques mutilations corporelles des Primitifs actuels et paléolithiques," *Revue générale des sciences*, December 15.

ZABOROWSKI, S.
1898(?). *L'Homme préhistorique*. 5th ed. Paris: G. Baillière.

THE PROTOCULTURAL FOUNDATIONS
OF HUMAN ADAPTATION

A. IRVING HALLOWELL

IN A paper contributed to the centennial celebration, in Chicago, of the publication of Darwin's *Origin of Species*,[1] I pointed out that vital evolutionary questions of a sociopsychological order need reconsideration in the light of twentieth-century knowledge. While questions of this kind were among those originally broached in the nineteenth century, along with others essentially biological in nature, evolutionary thinking among psychologists and cultural anthropologists fell into abeyance, as time went on, with the rejection of the recapitulation theory in its classical form and of unilinear theories of cultural evolution. The study of human evolution became more and more restricted to biological problems dealt with by physical anthropologists. But, with the discovery of new types of early hominids (small brained but bipedal in locomotion), the accumulation of observations on the social behavior of nonhominid primates in their natural state, the development of psychoanalytic theories, culture and personality studies, and the conceptualization of the nature of culture provided by twentieth-century cultural anthropologists, we now have a more fruitful point of departure for enlarging the boundaries of evolutionary thinking beyond a morphological frame of reference. What appears to be indicated is a conjunctive approach to problems of hominid evolution in which relevant data from various specialized disciplines can be integrated and major categories of variables defined in the general framework of behavioral evolution (Roe and Simpson, 1951).

Whether we consider hominid evolution in an ecological, a social, a psychological, or a linguistic frame of reference, behavior is the unifying center to which we must constantly return at any adaptive level. As we proceed to new levels, we must consider novel integrations of determinants brought about by potentialities for behavioral adaptations that did not previously exist. In the evolutionary process, differential behavior patterns provide major clues to significant variables. The social behavior characteristic of the mode of cultural

---

1. Hallowell (1960), which should be consulted for more detailed documentation and an extended bibliography, omitted here. An earlier version was circulated among participants in the conference on the "Social Life of Early Man" (June, 1959).

adaptation that eventually became the most distinctive feature of hominid development could not have arisen *de novo*. It must have complex roots in the evolutionary process. It could not have emerged suddenly as a saltatory configuration. Unique as a cultural mode of adjustment appears to be when observed in *Homo sapiens,* there are behavioral continuities as well as discontinuities to be observed when man is considered in the total setting of his primate heritage. In the paper referred to above, as well as in a previous publication (Hallowell, 1956), I suggested that the level of development represented by cultural adaptation can be focused more sharply in evolutionary perspective if we hypothecate a *protocultural* phase in hominid evolution and attempt to define its characteristic features. This earlier stage in development, deductively conceived, should embody some of the necessary, but not all of the sufficient, conditions for a fully developed human level of existence. On the one hand, it must have constituted a behavioral link between early hominids and other primates. On the other hand, it must have provided a preadaptive stage necessary for the later full-blown mode of cultural adaptation with which we are familiar in *Homo sapiens* by direct observation and experience.

What are the earmarks of a protocultural stage, and how may we identify them? We can best proceed, it seems to me, by selecting very broad categories for the purpose of comparing man with other hominids and infrahominid primates that, in addition to being relevant to all species, likewise bring into focus behavorial dimensions in which changes must have occurred in the course of the evolutionary process. What the selective pressures may have been that initiated such changes is not our present concern. The categories chosen here for brief discussion are: (1) social behavior and social structure, (2) ecological relations, (3) modes of communication and their properties, and (4) psychological capacities and organization. Observed behavioral similarities and differences, when considered with reference to the evolutionary process, indicate continuities and discontinuities in such behavioral categories and suggest some of the crucial features that, in combination, distinguish a protocultural phase in hominid evolution from a later and more fully realized level of cultural adaptation.

I. SOCIAL BEHAVIOR AND SOCIAL STRUCTURE

Perhaps the major clue to the basic continuity that links the Hominidae to the other primate groups, and thus makes comparisons of similarities and differences in this category of behavioral evolution significant, is the fact that we are dealing with gregarious animals. Whatever the ultimate determinants of sociality in the primates may be shown to be (Chance, this volume), all forms of cultural adaptation, as we know them in their fully developed stage, are based on some system of social action. But systems of social action are not unique in man. They also occur in infrahuman primates, and, structurally varied as they may be in different species, they constitute, nevertheless, a generic and characteristic mode of adaptation.[2] Consequently, we may infer that social structure long antedated any form of cultural superstructure that, when eventually built into an organized system of social action in the course of hominid evolution, established the foundation of a new level of social living with the inherent potentialities that led to the emergence of various types of socio*cultural* systems. Cultural adaptation, then, is a mode of social existence deeply rooted in the behavioral evolution of the primates, where systems of social action were an ancient and typical feature of primate life. More detailed analysis shows basic similarities, as well as differences, in mating patterns and principles of organization that are meaningful in evolutionary perspective.

Mating patterns, of course, have suggested the closest human analogies. We see these analogies in types of mateship and in the range of their variation. Since lar gibbons, for example, live in groups that consist of one male and one female and their young, we have a close analogy to the "nuclear family" in man, which likewise represents a monogamous type of mateship. Some biological writers have applied the term "family" exclusively to this kind of primate social unit, despite the fact that in anthropological writing the term "family" is never limited to the nuclear family. The gibbon type of mateship, in which the sexual drive of the male appears to be low, would seem to be a limiting case in the total range of social units found among infrahuman primates and without evolutionary implications. In *Homo sapiens* we find two types of polygamous mateships, polygyny and polyandry, and social structures based on these are ordinarily called "families." Relatively rare in man in an institutionalized form, polyandrous mateships appear to be absent in infrahuman primates. On the other hand, polygynous mateships are common in both monkeys and apes. In the chimpanzee and gorilla this type of mateship seems to furnish the basis for independent social groups. In some monkeys, as, for instance, the baboon, "harems" occur as

---

2. Le Gros Clark (pp. 320–21) has emphasized the remarkable fact that the primate order is distinguished from other mammalian orders in "that it includes representatives, still living, which reflect (in a modified form) almost all levels or grades of its evolutionary history from the most primitive to the most advanced; . . . in the Primates each successive grade has developed a new ecological domain, leaving behind representatives of antecedent grades (more or less modified for their local habitat of course) in occupation of the particular arboreal environment for which they had already become adapted. It may be said, indeed, that the trees of African and Asiatic forests still retain in rough outline a stratified population of Primates which represents the successive grades of the evolutionary tree of this order." The "smallest and more primitive types (tree-shrews), by confining their activities mainly to the more attenuated branches of the tree tops, lead a secluded life within the protection of foliage and have thus become effectively segregated from the larger types."

Although Le Gros Clark does not specifically make the point, it seems to me that, in this long-range ecological perspective the hominids, through terrestrial adaptation, may be said to have taken the last step in the series of ecological readaptation that characterize primate evolution. Always retaining a high degree of behavioral plasticity and without extreme specialization, the new ecological domain of the hominids became in turn the theater of cultural adaptation.

subgroups within the larger "troops" or "bands" found in these animals. Monogamous mateships, on the other hand, do not occur in groups of larger size because females in heat mate with more than one male.

Past attempts to establish any regular evolutionary sequence of mateship within *Homo sapiens* have failed, as well as have attempts to link any particular type of mateship in the nonhominid primates with early man. Perhaps it might be better to recognize that, since there are only a limited number of possibilities in mateships, it is not surprising to find them recurring at both the nonhominid and hominid levels of evolutionary development in the primates and in social units of varying size and composition. Whatever form they take, all these mateships serve the same reproductive ends. Their importance lies in this constancy in biological function rather than in any direct relation that can be shown to the evolution of group organization. They all lie close to biologically rooted central tendencies and continuities in behavioral evolution that link *Homo sapiens* to his precursors. For what we find as the common social core of all but the lowest primate groups, despite their variation, is the continuous association of adults of both sexes with their offspring during the portion of the latter's life cycle that covers the period from birth to the threshold of maturity. This core pattern of associated individuals, when considered with reference to their interrelated roles, is linked with the fact that basic functions are involved, that is, the procreation, protection, and nurture of offspring—born singly, relatively helpless at birth, and dependent for a period thereafter. Variations in mateship or size of group may occur without affecting these functions. In addition, the sex needs of adults and the food needs of all members of the group can be taken care of. The role of the female in relation to her young does not seem to vary widely, nor does the behavior of infants and juveniles. The protective role of the male in relation to infants and juveniles is similar in gibbon and howler, even though the young of the group in the latter genus are not all his own offspring, and the actual biological relationship between these two species is remote. Among monkeys and apes the adult males never provide food for juveniles or females. After being weaned, the juveniles always forage for themselves. Whether we call nonhominid primate groups "families," "clans," "troops," or "bands," their basic social composition can be expressed by the same general formula: X males $+ X$ females $+ X$ infants $+ X$ juveniles.

Whatever the mating types or size of early hominid groups may have been, their social composition must have conformed to this fundamental pattern. This generic type of social structure, associated with territorialism, must have persisted throughout the extremely long temporal period during which major morphological changes occurred in the species of the primate order, including those that ultimately differentiated the Hominidae from the Pongidae and later hominids from earlier ones. Underlying it, physiologically, was the type of ovarian cycle characteristic of practically all the primates. In contrast to some mammalian species, in which females have only one oestrus period a year, primate females, along with those of a limited number of other mammalian species, are characterized by successive oestrus cycles in the course of a year. Breeding is not seasonal but continuous.

The evolutionary significance of the social organization of primate groups cannot be fully appreciated, however, without considering behavioral patterns other than those directly connected with reproduction. For the structuralization of infrahuman societies is by no means a simple function of differential roles determined by sex and age. Of central importance in many of the groups so far investigated is the existence of interindividual behavior influences by an order of social ranking in the group, a dominance gradient. Males are, quite generally, dominant over females, and the females associated with them may sometimes outrank other females. While it appears that in different species the "slope" of the dominance gradient varies considerably, some kind of rank order occurs. This factor in the operation of the social structure is important because it reduces aggression between males, determines priorities to mates and food, influences the spatial disposition of individuals within the group, affects the socialization of group habits, and may determine the relations of groups adjacent to one another. Nevertheless, the ranking position of individuals is not fully determined once and for all; an individual's role in the dominance hierarchy may change. There are psychological factors that must be taken into account.

Enough has been said to indicate that in evolutionary perspective a necessary locus and an indispensable condition for a cultural system is an organized system of social action in which social behavior is patterned by role differentiation. Role differentiation in the nonhominid primates, in other gregarious animals, and in man exemplifies a basic principle in the organization of social relations, whether the determinants be innate or learned or a combination of both. A social structure, therefore, can be identified as one of the characteristic features of a protocultural stage in hominid evolution. Once this is recognized, I believe that the emergence of a cultural system is made intelligible if we assume that any adaptive genetic changes that took place inevitably became of vital importance to the social order. The interplay and cumulative effects of changes of all sorts must have been fed back into the system of social action that prevailed and led to modifications in its operation. Cultural adaptation, indeed, may be viewed as the culmination of *social* evolution in the primates. It could not have occurred if there had not been changes in ecological relations, psychological capacities, and codes of communication that directly affected both the behavior of individuals and the social structure. Overemphasis sometimes has been given to the brain as such, in relation to the development of culture. We now know that it was bipedal locomotion rather than brain size that gave initial morphological impetus to the hominid radiation. While no one would wish to minimize the importance of the later expansion of the brain in behavioral evolution, cause-and-effect relations are oversimplified if we do not take into account the continuing social context of behavior, the potentialities for change in the patterns of interindividual relations and, consequently, in the attributes of the social order considered as an evolving system. Whatever new potentialities may be attributed to the acquisition of additional neurones in the brain, and their organization, the resulting behavior must have become functionally manifest in a system of social action already in existence.

II. ECOLOGICAL RELATIONS

A cultural level of adaptation, in addition to requiring a preadaptive base in a system of social action, also required an environmental setting in which ecological relations at a protocultural stage provided the foundation for later developments. Whatever part arboreal adaptation may have played in the earlier evolution of the primates, including the development of distinctive psychological capacities and behavorial patterns, it is difficult, if not impossible, to imagine an arboreal niche as the basic ecological matrix of the hominid line of evolution that eventuated in a cultural mode of adaptation. It was terrestrial living that provided the ecological framework of this development and, when the necessary psychological capacities, experience, and technological traditions had been developed, enabled the hominids to accelerate the behavioral differences between themselves and other primates by exploiting the resources of their environment through knowledge of it and a succession of discoveries and inventions.

Even if capacities for *tool-using* were present in arboreal primates, how could the properties of stone have been discovered, exploited, and developed through shaping techniques into the lithic industries of a *tool-making* tradition by creatures who spent relatively little time on the ground? How could fire have become of importance in the life of primates confined to an arboreal niche? It was terrestrial living that provided the opportunity for the discovery of new food resources and made possible the shift to a carnivorous diet and the cooking of food, which ultimately led, through a scavenging stage perhaps, to the hunting of large mammals. If an upright posture with bipedal locomotion be taken as crucial generic features in hominid structural and behavioral differentiation, the terrestrial adaptation that accompanied them led to radical changes in the ecological relations of evolving hominids as compared with their primate forebears and the arboreally adapted monkeys and pongids. Motor functions already present, like grasping, were freed for new uses, and the discriminatory functions of binocular stereoscopic vision facilitated new developments in tactile skills, in manual dexterity, and probably in visual imagery, which ultimately became increasingly mediated through the more complex level of cortical organization made possible by the expansion of the brain. A new ecological niche provided the opportunity for the exercise, at a new level of behavioral organization, of behavioral potentialities already present, as well as for the development of new behavioral patterns. From an ecological point of view, a terrestrial habitat was a necessary setting for the protocultural stage in hominid adaptation that established the behavioral foundation for subsequent cultural adaptation.

One of the most characteristic features of the adaptation of infrahuman primates is territoriality. The locus of the social structures already discussed is a bounded area defined by the spatial range of the daily activities of members of each group. Ecologically, territoriality is the means by which the dispersal of the total primate population of a given region is spatially ordered and the independence of these breeding and nurturing groups maintained as distinguishable social units. Ordinarily, members of the different groups in a given region do not freely mix, nor do adults of different groups interbreed. The strong avoidance behavior that prevails between different groups is complemented by the factors that promote in-group integration. Territoriality, as observed among living primates is, therefore, a fundamental ecological adaptation that, at the same time, functions as a barrier to social integration of a higher order and to more complex social composition and role differentiation.

If we assume that territoriality persisted among the earliest hominids, some interesting questions arise. What was the size and range of these groups, and at what point in hominid development and under what conditions were groups of a higher order of complexity formed? For in men of the historic period, at least, we always find types of social organization that transcend in composition and role differentiation, if not always in size, what we find at the infrahuman primate level. The later, more evolved, forms of social organization incorporate the nuclear family, as well as other types of family structure, in a larger whole that includes individuals of all ages, as well as both sexes, and three or more generations. At this level, of course, sexual differentiation of roles in the performance of economic tasks has emerged, a phenomenon unknown in the non-hominid primates. We can only assume that, in the course of hominid evolution, factors must have come into play that made possible the functional integration of groups with radically different social composition and role differentiation from those that existed at the earliest stage of hominid development. At the same time it also became possible to transcend, through the development of new patterns of ecological relationships, the older form of ecological adaptation that formerly prevailed. Although social organization and ecological adjustment of the kind just mentioned must have considerable historical depth, for which there is some archeological as well as ethnographical evidence among hunting and gathering peoples, one must associate such developments with euhominids, who already had arrived at a cultural level of adaptation. As Sahlins has said:

Primate territorial relations are altered by the development of culture in the human species. Territoriality among hunters and gatherers is never exclusive, and group membership is apt to shift and change according to the variability of food resources in space and time. Savage society is open, and corresponding to ecological variations, there are degrees of openness" [Sahlins, 1959, p. 58].

At an earlier protocultural stage the size, composition, structure, and behavioral range of social groups was determined by the same basic factors of ecological adaptation generally characteristic of nonhominid primates. At the same time, behavior was limited by psychological factors that made it impossible for systems of social action of a higher order to arise. Washburn and Avis point out:

The acquisition of hunting habits must have been accompanied by a great enlargement of territory, since the source of food was now more erratic and mobile. . . . Whether early man scavenged from the kills of the big carnivores, followed herds looking for a chance to kill, drove game, or followed a wounded animal, his range of operations must have been greatly increased over that of arboreal apes. The world view of the early human carnivore must have been very different from that of his vegetarian cousins. The interests of the latter could be satisfied in a small area, and other animals were of little moment except for the few which threatened attack. But the desire for meat leads animals to know a wider range and to learn the habits of many animals. Human territorial habits and psychology are fundamentally different from those of apes and monkeys . . . this carnivorous psychology was fully formed by the middle Pleistocene and it may have had its beginnings in the depredations of the Australopthecines [Washburn and Avis, 1958, p. 434].

III. MODES OF COMMUNICATION AND THEIR PROPERTIES

The prevailing sensory modes of communication among primates are visual and acoustic. Both appear to be extremely important. Schultz speaks of the intricate "silent vocabulary" of the nonhominid primate.

Crouching down, presenting buttocks, extending hands in pronation, exposing teeth partly or fully, raising eyebrows, protruding lips, shaking branches, pounding chest, dancing in one place, etc., all are actions full of definite meaning. . . . [Although] the long lists of different postures, gestures, and facial movements characteristic of monkeys and apes have not yet been compiled, . . . any careful observer realizes that they represent an intricate "silent vocabulary" of great aid in social intercourse.

In the perfectly adapted arboreal life of monkeys and apes the limited variety of sounds, together with the great variety of meaningful gestures and facial expressions, is fully adequate for all social life within such close contact as permits seeing and hearing these detailed means of communication [Schultz, this volume].

The utterance of sounds, Schultz says, is "the essence of primate life . . . , the simian primates are by far the noisiest of all mammals." In species that have been closely investigated, like the howling monkeys of Panama and the lar gibbon, differentiated vocalizations have been shown to have functional significance in the social co-ordination of the individuals belonging to a group. Schultz says:

The primatologist "regards *language* not as the result of something radically new and exclusively human, but rather as a quantitative perfection of the highly specialized development of man's central nervous control of the anatomical speech apparatus in the larynx, tongue, and lips, the latter being as good in an ape as in man. . . . As soon as the early hominids had ventured into open spaces, had begun to use and even make tools, and had co-operated in hunting, the total variety of all means of expression needed additions, which could come only from an increase in sounds, since the comparatively little changed anatomy had already been fully used for all possible gestures, etc. . . . Gestures have always persisted in human evolution, but they have become overshadowed by an infinitely greater variety of sounds in increasing numbers of combinations [Schultz, this volume].

Oakley and others have suggested that early hominids may have depended primarily on gestures "mainly of mouth and hands, accompanied by cries and grunts to attract attention" and that speech may have been a comparatively late development (Oakley, 1951, p. 75). If so, a nonhominid mode of communication would have persisted in the protocultural phase of hominid evolution. Unfortunately, this interpretation must remain speculative. It is difficult to imagine, however, how a fully developed cultural mode of adaptation could operate without speech. However, if one of the necessary conditions for the functioning of a typically human system of communication is a speech community, an organized social system is as necessary for human language as it is for a cultural mode of adaptation. This condition was present even at the nonhominid level. So what we can discern in primate evolution is a behavioral plateau that provided the necessary context, but, at first, not all the sufficient conditions for either speech or culture.

Hockett has recently pointed out that "part of the problem of differentiating man from the other animals is the problem of describing how human language differs from any kind of communicative behavior carried on by nonhuman or prehuman species. Until we have done this, we cannot know how much it means to assert that only man has the power of speech" (Hockett, 1958, p. 570). He has approached the problem by identifying seven "key properties" of the speech of *Homo sapiens* and comparing them with the available data on non-human systems of communication, discovering that there was considerable overlapping in the properties selected, although they did "not recur, as a whole set, in any known non-human communicative system" (*ibid.*, p. 574). This suggested that the combination of properties that characterize speech, "those design-features . . . which seem to be of crucial importance in making it possible for language to do what it does" (1959, p. 32), did not arise full blown. Hockett argues that this assemblage of properties, considered with reference to man's lineage, "could not have emerged in just any temporal sequence. Some of them either unquestionably or with high likelihood imply the prior existence of some of the others" (1958, p. 581). Consequently, he is led to suggest a tentative evolutionary reconstruction. Since one of the key properties of a human system of communication is "cultural transmission," a property absent in the communication systems of primates and other animals, this factor becomes highly significant chronologically and, I think, has wider implications than those developed by Hockett, who suggests, in effect, that, although learning and the social transmission of habits, or what he calls "culture of a rather thin sort," may have existed at a very early stage in the development of the higher primates, the associated system of communication that prevailed may have operated without "cultural transmission."[3] The significance of the fact that these earlier codes of communication did not function through learning and social transmission lies in the limitations this imposed upon the systems of social action developed in nonhominid and, perhaps, the earliest hominid groups. At the same time, these codes of communication, operating through the same sensory modes that appear at a later level may be considered prerequisite for the evolutionary development of a communication system characterized by the total assemblage of properties discussed by Hockett.

This kind of evolutionary inquiry is, of course, a far cry from earlier approaches, particularly those that began by concentrating on the problem of "primitive" languages spoken by *Homo sapiens*. Hockett's approach does permit us to have a fresh look at speech in greater evolutionary depth. And by direct observation we know that, whereas some of the great apes have been able to acquire a "thin sort" of human culture when closely associated with members of our species, they do not have the capacity to acquire and use our distinctive form of symbolic communication, even when systematically motivated (C. Hayes, 1951, Chap. 8). There seems little reason to doubt that in the course of behavioral evolution psychological capacities of crucial importance lay back of the ultimate emergence among the hominids of a characteristic system of linguistic communication. While this system shared some "design features" with that of nonhominid primates, capacities that transcended those of the other primates permitted the development and integration of novel features. These, in turn, resulted in the functional potentialities of speech as we know it in *Homo sapiens*.

IV. PSYCHOLOGICAL CAPACITIES AND ORGANIZATION

Far down the evolutionary scale we have evidence that indicates that some activities of animals may originate, or be changed, through experience and affect subsequent behavior. When such responses cannot be reduced to innate determinants, or maturational processes, they are ordinarily referred to as "learned," although the conceptualization is loose. Harlow maintains that "there is no evidence that any sharp break ever appeared in the evolutionary development of the learning process" while, at the same time, "it is quite clear that evolution has resulted in the development of animals of progressively greater potentialities for learning and for solving problems of increasing complexity" (Harlow, 1958, pp. 288, 289). My principal concern here is with the relevance of learning to the question of a protocultural platform in hominid evolution.

---

3. Hockett (1959, p. 36), says: "A behavior pattern is transmitted culturally if it is not only learned but *taught*, and if the teaching behavior, whatever it may be, is also learned rather than genetically determined." Cf. 1958, pp. 578–80. Teaching and learned teaching behavior, of course, require a level of psychological organization far higher than that observed in any nonhominid primate.

While, as Nissen once said, "experience will not make a man out of a monkey," nevertheless, the extent to which learning is an integral part of the systems of social action, ecological relations, and modes of communication in monkeys and apes is relevant for an understanding of hominid evolution in an inclusive evolutionary perspective. What needs particular emphasis is what is learned and what is not, and the fact that what is individually learned by one animal may directly influence the behavior of other animals. It is not learning as such that requires consideration as a diagnostic characteristic of a protocultural stage. What is significant is that the part that learning plays in the life history and social relations of the nonhominid primates closely parallels, at so many points, the part that it plays in human sociocultural systems.

Beach, for example, says: "Descriptions of mother-infant relations in monkeys and chimpanzee leave no doubt as to the importance of learning in the filial responses of immature primates. The infant learns to obey gestures and vocal communications given by the mother and derives considerable advantage from her tuition and guidance" (Beach, 1951, p. 426). Socialization of the young, moreover, is an important factor in the formation and maintenance of infra-human primate groups, as Carpenter pointed out long ago (Carpenter, 1942, pp. 256–57). And Collias, considering socialization in the wider perspective of behavioral evolution, points out: "In both insect and vertebrate societies, maintenance of cooperative relations depends to a large extent on socialization of the young. Among vertebrates, this trend reaches its climax in the primates" (Collias, 1950, p. 1087). The formation of dominance gradients likewise involves learning, even in lower mammals (Scott, 1956, p. 217) and the phenomenon of territoriality in the primates also requires learning (Carpenter, 1958, p. 241).[4] It seems reasonable to assume, therefore, that the intimate relations between learning, social structure, and ecological adaptation, so fundamental in the functioning of culture, were well established in the nonhominid primates prior to the anatomical changes that led to both erect posture and the expansion of the brain.

Even more important, perhaps, is that fact that, at this same stage in both monkeys and apes, learned habits might not only be acquired by individuals of various ages but also could be transmitted through social interaction to other individuals in the group. The most striking cases have been reported by observers who have been studying *Macaca fuscata* at the Japanese Monkey Center (Imanishi, 1957; Frisch, 1959). These primates have been lured from their forest habitat into open feeding places, where, among other things, they have been offered new foods. Systematic observation has shown that newly acquired food habits, such as eating candies, become quite readily socialized. Imanishi points out, moreover, that young macaques acquire the candy-eating habit more quickly than do the adults and that some mothers learned to eat candies from

4. Carpenter notes Harrows' belief that "arboreal trails are learned by African monkeys."

their offspring, rather than the other way round. It has likewise been observed that the spread of a new food habit may be directly related to the dominance gradient that is a central feature of their social structure. Adult females of high rank were observed to imitate the wheat-eating of a dominant male very quickly, and the habit was passed on to their offspring. Females of lower rank, in a more peripheral position in the group, only later acquired the habit from their offspring, who, in turn, had picked it up through association with their play-mates. The rate of transmission was extremely rapid in this case, the entire process occurring within two days. In another instance, a young female initiated the habit of washing sweet potatoes before eating them. This habit, having been transmitted to her playmates, as well as to her mother, was slowly transmitted to a number of groups during the next three years. The same class of pheno-menon in the anthropoid apes is illustrated by nest-building in chimpanzee and the transmission of the technique of working the drinking fountain at Orange Park, which champanzees learned from each other.

In the past, the social transmission of acquired behavior patterns has some-times been stressed as one of the distinctive characteristics of culture. But in the light of our present knowledge of primate behavior it is better to consider it as one of the conditions necessary for cultural adaptation rather than as the dis-tinguishing feature of it. Social transmission of acquired behavior patterns is, rather, a prerequisite of culture and an earmark of an earlier protocultural behavior plateau. The fact that even some animals other than primates may learn from one another or that some chimpanzees in social interaction with members of our species have acquired "culture traits," is no indication that a full-fledged level of cultural adaptation has been reached in these species. It only confounds the conceptualization and the investigation of hominid evolu-tion if the term "culture" is applied, without qualification, to the phenomena of social transmission of simple habits in infrahuman species. J. P. Scott, for example, writes:

The more the capacities for learning and for variable organization of behavior are present, the more it is possible for an animal to learn from its parents and pass the information along to the next generation. As we accumulate greater knowledge of natural animal behavior, we find more and more evidence that many animals possess the rudiments of this new ability, which we can call cultural inheritance. The migration trails of mountain sheep and the learned fears of wild birds are two of many examples. . . . At the present time all our evidence indicates that cultural inheritance exists only in quite simple form in animals other than man, but future research may show that it is more common and complex than we now suspect [Scott, 1958, p. 237].

While it is true that a variety of gregarious animals possess the *rudiments* of an ability to be influenced by the behavior of other individuals of their species, the part this ability plays in their total life history and social relations is what needs precise analysis. In phylogenetic perspective it is only in the primates that capacities and conditions arose which led to the transcendence of a rudimentary stage. And at this stage the primates are distinguished from other animals by a higher capacity for observational learning. Munn concludes that: "it is only in monkeys and apes that anything clearly approximating such observational learning can be demonstrated and even at this level the problems solved by imitation are relatively simple" (Munn, 1955)[5] If we use the term culture to refer to different levels of behavioral evolution, our vocabulary fails to discriminate the quantitative and qualitative differences between cultural adaptation in man and the very rudimentary "cultural" manifestations found in infrahuman animals, to say nothing of possible differences between primates and nonprimates. Dobzhansky, in a brief discussion of the "Rudiments of Cultural Transmission among Animals," has pointed out one essential difference between a protocultural and a cultural level of behavior, although he does not analyze specific cases in detail and his chief citations refer to birds[6] rather than to primates. He says:

In animals the individuals of one generation transmit to those of the next what they themselves learned from their parents—not more and not less. Every generation learns the same thing which its parents have learned. In only very few instances the evidence is conclusive that the learned behavior can be modified or added to and that the modifications and additions are transmitted to subsequent generations [Dobzhansky, 1955, pp. 340–41].

Simple conditioning and possibly observational learning account for these facts. The greater capacity for observational learning in primates also accounts for the socialization of nest-building habits in chimpanzee and the spread of the habit of washing sweet potatoes observed in the macaque group already referred to. But, so long as social transmission was dependent on capacities for observational learning, this fact limited the kind of acquired habits or innovations that could become significant in the adaptation of the group. Intervening factors were required before quantitative and qualitative differences in the kind of innovations possible at this level could be modified or changed and become effective through other mechanisms of socialization. It is difficult, for example, to imagine how the manufacture of tools, and the development of tool-making traditions could have arisen at a protocultural stage at which the mechanism of social transmission was exclusively observational learning and at which communication was mediated through signs rather than through any form of symbolic representation. Washburn and Avis, moreover, have expressed the opinion that tool-using may require

much less brain than does speech and might have started as soon as the hands were freed from locomotor functions. Oral traditions essential for complicated human society probably were not possible with less than 700 or 800 cc. of brain [as contrasted

5. See Munn (1958, pp. 129–30) for references to the experimental data on observational learning. Cf. Hayes and Hayes (1952) on a home-raised chimpanzee. Instances of spontaneous imitation on the part of Viki were: operating a spray gun, prying off the lids of cans with a screwdriver, etc.
6. For a discussion of "tradition" in birds see Hochbaum (1955).

with a range of about 450 to 600 cc. in the Australopthecines], and there is no likelihood that elaborate traditions of tool making are possible at lesser capacities, although simple pebble tools might well be [Washburn and Avis, 1958, p. 432].

Among other things, too, tool-making must have involved a whole series of discoveries and the accumulation of information necessary in a discriminating search for and selection of lithic materials with particular properties, in addition to the development and application of skilled methods of chipping. Even if we assume that there must have been successive stages in the development of tool-making traditions, these cannot be envisaged in a social and psychological vacuum, so that questions about a capacity for temporal orientation toward the future, the existence of property rights, as well as the kind of communication system to be assumed are relevant to the problem. It has often been said, for example, that a fully developed tool-making tradition is difficult to conceive in the absence of speech. It becomes all the more significant, then, that, despite the part that learning plays in the life of living primates at a protocultural level, they can be negatively characterized by the fact that no code of communication exists with the assemblage of properties appearing in speech and that whatever sublinguistic codes prevail appear to be transmitted genetically rather than through learning. We also know that chimpanzees cannot be taught to speak, despite the fact that, when closely associated with members of our species, it is possible for them to acquire many human habits through learning. Whatever inferences we make about the transition from a protocultural stage to a level of cultural adaptation, we must consider what habits were socially transmitted and what were not. And, quite aside from the properties of any code of communication, the question of its social transmittal must be taken into account.

Thus, while we may say that in the course of hominid evolution all the characteristic features of a protocultural stage were incorporated at a subsequent level of cultural adaptation, at the same time we must account for the differences observed. Here, organic changes, considered as intervening factors, must be taken into account. At the protocultural stage the psychological capacities of the actors determined the limiting framework of social and ecological adaptation. Although we cannot now observe the behavioral characteristics of the proto-hominids themselves, subsequent hominid developments in social structure, ecological relations, and modes of communication can hardly be dissociated from the known organic changes in the central nervous system after prior morpho-logical changes in posture and locomotion have distinguished the hominid radiation. Account must be taken also of the sociopsychological effects produced by biological factors that prolonged dependency of the young, delayed repro-duction, and increased the life span in an already well-advanced hominid whose psychological functioning was, at the same time, being greatly enhanced and restructured. All the distinctive features of a protocultural stage were being raised to a new level of sociopsychological integration through the increasing part that cortical processes came to play. In time, this new level of psychological organization affected every aspect of the earlier mode of protocultural adaptation. It led to the transformation of provincial social structures, through a change in their underlying dynamics, into the more inclusive, complex, and diversified socio*cultural* systems of the euhominids. At this more evolved stage a normative orientation became an inherent and distinctive feature of these systems of social action. Psychological factors became paramount in the functioning of these systems because the socially sanctioned values that characterized them were linked with the cognitive processes, motivations, and need satisfactions of individuals through the formation of a new and distinctive type of personality organization molded in the socialization process. What was learned in this process, beginning in infancy, not only included habits, roles, and adjustment to a physical environment, but also speech and a sense of values that pervaded every phase of personal adjustment and behavior. Conduct was evaluated in relation to socially sanctioned ethical standards. Food and material objects were not merely possessed; possession was regulated by a system of property rights. Skills and techniques used in the manufacture of material objects were also appraised in relation to recognized standards. Knowledge and beliefs were judged true or false, and art forms and linguistic expression were brought within the sphere of a normative orientation. All sociocultural systems became infused with appraisals that involved cognitive, appreciative, and moral values.[7] If the total ramifications of the normative orientation of human societies are taken into account, we have a major clue to the kind of radical psychological transformation that must have occurred in hominid evolution and a measure of its depth and significance for an understanding of the dynamics of a cultural mode of adaptation as compared with what we find at a protocultural level.

Psychologically, a normatively oriented social order requires a capacity for self-objectification on the part of the individual actors. This makes possible self-identification over time, and an appraisal of ones' own personal conduct and that of others in a common framework of socially transmitted and sanctioned values (Hallowell, 1955, Chap. 4). Without the capacity for a psychological level of organization that permits the exercise of these and other functions, the social system could not function at the level of normative orientation nor could moral responsibility for conduct exist. Learning remains important, of course, but it operates at a higher level of sociopsychological integration than

7. See Edward C. Tolman, "Value Standards, Pattern Variables, Social Roles, Personality" (pp. 344–46), and Clyde Kluckhohn, "Values and Value-Orientations in the Theory of Action" (pp. 388–433) in Parsons and Shils (1951). Kroeber and Kluckhohn in their discussion of "General Features of Culture" (1952, pp. 172–73) emphasize the fact that human values must be considered "part of nature, not outside it. They are the products of men, of men having bodies and living in societies, and are the structural essence of the culture of these societies of men. . . . Values are important in that they provide foci for patterns of organization for the material of cultures. They give significance to our understanding of cultures. In fact, values provide the only basis for the fully intelligible comprehension of culture, because the actual organization of all cultures is primarily in terms of their values."

was possible at a protocultural level. The relations between needs, motivation, socially recognized goals, and learning are more complex because cortical processes have become increasingly important. It is impossible to attribute an equivalent level of psychological functioning to the earliest hominids.

What occurred in the psychological dimension of hominid evolution was the development of a human personality structure in which the capacity for self-awareness, based on ego functions, became of central importance. The functioning of ego processes contributed new qualities to the psychological adjustment of individuals in the socialization process. Ego functions became integral factors in determining responses to the outer world in the interests of inner needs, particularly when delay or postponement of action is required. They became intimately connected with such cognitive processes as attention, perception, thinking, and judgment. Considered in evolutionary perspective, ego may be said to be the major "psychological organ" that structurally differentiates the most highly evolved members of the Hominidae from infrahuman primates. At the same time, there is some evidence that suggests that rudimentary ego functions may be present in some of the higher apes, so it is possible that equivalent functions may have been present in the early hominids.

In ontogenetic development, as observed in *Homo sapiens,* ego processes can be identified in the first half-year of life, but a fully developed sense of self-awareness represents a psychological level of functional integration that is only manifest later. The initial development of the ego process does not appear to be dependent upon the prior existence of speech or culture, whereas self-awareness, on the other hand, requires socialization, a normative orientation, and the manipulation of what I have called extrinsic forms of symbolization. In other words, self-awareness is an integral psychological factor in cultural adaptation itself. It is rooted not only in ego functions but also in an already existent psychological capacity to abstract significant bits from the flow of experience and to represent their content in a meaningful form of expression extrinsic to the experience itself. This capacity to *project and objectify* significant aspects of experience may be contrasted with the evidence for *intrinsic* symbolic processes that occur in nonhominid primates and even lower mammals, that is, central processes that function as substitutes for, or representatives of, sensory cues or events that are not present in the immediate perceptual field. In the evolved hominid, processes of this kind can become socially significant by objectification in a variety of extrinsic symbolic forms. In nonhominid primates, on the other hand, only outward behavior in its concrete forms can become meaningful through perception. And the response, as has been indicated, may be observational learning. But what is privately sensed, imaged, "conceptualized," or "thought" cannot be responded to without an overt sign that represents it, but is, at the same time, extrinsic to the experience itself. In the evolved hominid, extrinsic symbolic forms, functioning through vocal, graphic, plastic, or gestural media, make it possible for groups of human beings to participate in a common world of meanings and values that is no longer confined to the perception of outward behavior alone or to concrete objects or events immediately given in perception. Both art and speech exploit this novel capacity for extrinsic symbolization. The artists of the Upper Paleolithic were capable of invoking intrinsic symbolic processes (memory images of animals), abstracting significant features, and representing these animals in a graphic form. In principal, the same capacity, expressed in arbitrary sound clusters that have no iconic relation to the objects and events represented, is one of the characteristics that distinguishes speech from infrahuman forms of communication in which signs, without symbolic value, are found.

The capacity for individual and social adaptation through the integral functioning of intrinsic symbolic processes and extrinsic symbolic forms enabled an evolving hominid to enlarge and transform his world and to become, at the same time, an object to himself. Means now became available whereby inwardly as well as outwardly directed references to an individual's own experience and that of others, and to objects and events in his world other than self, could find common ground through symbolic mediation. The immediate, local, and time-and-space-bound world of other primates who could not deal effectively with objects and events outside the field of direct perception was transcended. Speech, through the use of kinship terms, made it possible, among other things, for an individual to symbolize, and thus objectify himself, in systems of social action. And, as Professor Grace A. De Laguna has pointed out, becoming an object to one's self "carries with it the awareness of other persons not only as *objects*, but as *fellow-subjects*. An 'other' person is not only 'him' *of* whom I speak, but you *to* whom I speak and in turn an 'I' who speaks to me" (De Laguna, MS). As a consequence of self-objectification, sociocultural systems could function through the commonly shared value orientations of *persons*, self-conscious individuals in contrast to the societies of nonhominid and early hominid primates, where ego-centered processes, even though they existed in a rudimentary form, had not yet become salient at the psychological level of self-awareness. In fact, when viewed from the standpoint of this peculiarity of man, culture may be said to be an elaborated and socially transmitted system of meanings and values that, in an animal capable of self-awareness, implemented a type of adaptation that made the roles of the human being intelligible to himself, with reference both to an articulated universe and to his fellow men.

In anthropological writing prior to the culture and personality movement, the connection between learning and culture remained vague because it had not been carefully analyzed in relation to the development of personality structure, cognitive orientation, motivation, etc. The fact had been overlooked that the only way in which a sociocultural system can be perpetuated is through the characteristic psychological structuralization of individuals in an organized system of social action. In the perspective of hominid evolution it is significant that the foundation for this later development was laid at the protocultural level, where learning was also intimately linked with the functioning of social structures, dominance gradients, and with the social transmission of habits. But at this protocultural stage what was learned was greatly restricted by the psychological capacities of the nonhominids. In *Homo sapiens*, on the other hand, we see the quantitative maximization of learning that, because of expanded psychological capacities, has led to qualitatively distinctive consequences. Among other things, we find cognitive processes raised to a higher level of functioning by means of symbolic forms, which can be manipulated creatively through reflective thought and experience. Cultural modes of adaptation, or certain aspects of them, learned and transmitted as they may be, can be objectified, thought about, analyzed, judged, and even remodeled. Man has never been completely enslaved by this traditional cultural heritage. The great novelty, then, in the behavioral evolution of the primates was not simply the development of a cultural mode of adaptation as such. It was, rather, the psychological restructuralization that, occurring in a primate where a system of organized social action already was present, not only made possible a more advanced level of social existence but laid the foundation for subsequent cultural readjustment and change. The psychological basis of culture does not lie only in a capacity for highly complex forms of learning and personality organization. What should not be overlooked is the potentiality that exists for transcending what is learned a capacity for innovation, creativity, reorganization, and change in sociocultural systems themselves.

BIBLIOGRAPHY

BEACH, FRANK A.
   1951. "Instinctive Behavior: Reproductive Activities." In S. S. STEVENS (ed.), *Handbook of Experimental Psychology*. New York: Wiley.

CARPENTER, C. R.
   1942. "Characteristics of Social Behavior in Non-human Primates," *Trans. New York Acad. Sci.*, ser. 2.
   1958. "Territoriality: A Review of Concepts and Problems." In ANNE ROE and G. G. SIMPSON (eds.), *Behavior and Evolution*. New Haven: Yale University Press.

CHANCE, M. R. A.
   1959. "The Nature and Special Features of the Instinctive Bond of Primates." This volume.

COLLIAS, N. E.
   1950. "Social Life and the Individual among Vertebrate Animals," *Annals, N.Y. Acad. Sci.*, Vol. 50.

DE LAGUNA, GRACE A.
   MS. "The *Lebenswelt* and the Cultural World" (unpublished MS).

DOBZHANSKY, T.
1955. *Evolution, Genetics and Man.* New York: Wiley.

FRISCH, JOHN E.
1959. "Research on Primate Behavior in Japan," *Amer. Anthrop.*, Vol. 61.

HALLOWELL, A. IRVING
1955. *Culture and Experience.* Philadelphia: University of Pennsylvania Press.

1956. "The Structural and Functional Dimensions of a Human Existence," *Inart. Rev. Biol.*, Vol. 31.

1960. "Self, Society and Culture in Phylogenetic Perspective." In SOL TAX (ed.), *Evolution after Darwin*, Vol. 2. Chicago: University of Chicago Press.

HARLOW, HARRY F.
1958. "The Evolution of Learning." In ANNE ROE and G. G. SIMPSON (eds.), *Behavior and Evolution.* New Haven: Yale University Press.

HAYES, CATHY
1951. *The Ape in Our House.* New York: Harper.

HAYES, K. J., and C. HAYES
1952. "Imitation in a Home-raised Chimpanzee," *J. Comp. Physiol. Psychol.*, 45: 450–59.

HOCHBAUM, H. ALBERT
1955. *Travels and Traditions of Waterfowl.* Minneapolis: University of Minnesota Press.

HOCKETT, CHARLES F.
1958. *A Course in Modern Linguistics.* New York: Macmillan.

1959. "Animal 'Languages' and Human Language." In J. N. SPUHLER (ed.), *The Evolution of Man's Capacity for Culture.* Detroit: Wayne State University Press.

IMANISHI, KINJI
1957. "Social Behavior in Japanese Monkeys, *Macaca fuscata*," *Psychologia*, Vol. 1.

KROEBER, A. L., and CLYDE KLUCKHOHN
1952. *Culture: A Critical Review of Concepts and Definitions.* ("Papers of the Peabody Museum of American Archaeology and Ethnology, Harvard University," Vol. 47, No. 1.)

LE GROS CLARK, W. E.
1960. *The Antecedents of Man.* Chicago: Quadrangle Books.

MUNN, NORMAN L.
1955. *The Evolution and Growth of Human Behavior.* Boston: Houghton Mifflin Co.

OAKLEY, KENNETH P.
1951. "A Definition of Man," *Science News*, No. 20 (Penguin Books).

PARSONS, TALCOTT, and EDWARD A. SHILS (eds.)
1951. *Toward a General Theory of Action.* Cambridge: Harvard University Press.

ROE, ANNE, and GEORGE GAYLORD SIMPSON (eds.)
1958. *Behavior and Evolution.* New Haven: Yale University Press.

SAHLINS, MARSHALL D.
1959. "The Social Life of Monkeys, Apes and Primitive Man." In J. N. SPUHLER (ed.), *The Evolution of Man's Capacity for Culture.* Detroit: Wayne State University Press.

SCHULTZ, A. H.
  1959. "Social Behavior of Baboons and Early Man." This volume.
SCOTT, JOHN PAUL
  1956. "The Analysis of Social Organization in Animals," *Ecology*, Vol. 37.
  1958. *Animal Behavior*. Chicago: University of Chicago Press.
WASHBURN, S. L., and VIRGINIA AVIS
  1958. "Evolution of Human Behavior." In ANNE ROE and G. G. SIMPSON (eds.), *Behavior and Evolution*.

SEDENTARY AND MOBILE BENTS
IN EARLY SOCIETIES

CARL O. SAUER

GLOSSES ON THE GENERAL THEME

MY ORIGINAL title, "Farther Roots of Agricultural Society," is here rephrased for better accord with the general theme as it was developed in the discussions. The conference put major emphasis on primate biology for reconstructing the social life of early man. Man as an animal was compared anatomically with his various kindred, in particular as to size and topography of the brain. Behavior of monkeys, baboons, and the great apes was considered at length, especially as to their sexual conduct. Thus there were implicit assumptions and explicit inferences that the social life of early man involves a group of behavioral patterns exhibited in simian individuals and communities. My interests as historical geographer lie far afield from such mechanistic biologic thinking and turn to questions of how man explored his habitable world, learned skills and communicated them to others of his kind, and diversified his ways of living, in short became maker of culture.

A serious difficulty with the simian model is that the males are dominant (also there is an order of dominance within each group), that they are promiscuous, are food-snatching instead of sharing, and are indifferent to their offspring. The most that can be said for them seems to be that they will rally round for defense and attack. How then has the psychologic and cultural gap between the simian groups and the most primitive human society been bridged? The biological version of "humanization" retains the dominant male, but places him and his subordinated horde in a new environment that requires a change in food habits from "frugivorous" to "carnivorous." This may be explained by migration—leaving a forest home to occupy "open savanna" habitat—or by climatic change—desiccation shrinking the cover of vegetation. In either case the male is thought of as turning to hunting game, which he brings home to share with his womenfolk and children. The type of the alpha ape is transformed into paterfamilias, who recognized his dependents and accepted the responsibility of caring for them. I do not see that such a reversal in primate behavior is explained either by migration into a new environment or by climatic change. The dominant simian male I should judge to be the wrong exemplar for the forming of human society.

The lineage of man has been developing for a very long time and so has that of the apes. The length of divergent evolution limits the propriety of drawing inferences from living pongids to primordial man. On the other hand we are acquiring new knowledge of hominid evolution. Dr. Hürzeler was invited by his sponsor, our host foundation, to show the remarkably preserved *Oreopithecus* remains he has been collecting from central Italy, probably of Upper Miocene age. If these are hominid, they will mean another advance, morphologically and also geographically, toward the knowledge of human origins. Also we were briefed at some length on the current status of australopithecine studies, again a subject in which the foundation has been interested. Their hominid filiation, as has been advocated previously by J. T. Robinson and Le Gros Clark, had favorable attention. The rudiments of culture found with *Australopithecus* open up new vistas of the threshold of humanity. South Africa and now also East Africa are at present the centers of greatest interest for human origins. South Africa is, however, at a farthest end of the Old World land mass. In such a cul-de-sac location archaic forms are more likely to survive or to undergo terminal variation than are new and successful lines of evolution likely to originate. This remote land's end is, rather, an area in which relict hominid groups survived beyond their time. It will be interesting to see whether their origin may be traced to lands farther north and more favorably situated for evolution and dispersal.

The larger question is, I think, of cultural origins and growth beyond the reach of biologic determinations. Phylogeny, mental capacity, ideas, and culture are not in a single series. The Lower Pleistocene has yielded primitive human remains and artifacts, both showing slow progression toward more advanced forms, the osteologic materials being the more scanty, discontinuous, and less consistent. But may we say that there ever was one Rubicon of evolution, as marked by the acquisition of brains of a certain size and conformation, at which we can aver that humanity began?

ENVIRONMENT IN THE ICE AGE

Conventionally and conveniently the Ice Age is considered as the "Age of Man." There is sufficient evidence in both Europe and North America that the so-called First Glaciation (Güns, Nebraskan) was preceded by at least one widespread glaciation, which was followed by a deglaciation. This agrees with paleontological inclinations to place the Villafranchian (Blancan of North America?) as of Quaternary rather than Pliocene age. The Sicilian marine high terrace (of interest to early archeology) thus would record the first interglacial stage. It also seems most probable that we are still living in the Ice Age and are experiencing an earlier phase of an interglacial stage. At a rough estimate the earth has been undergoing extreme climatic changes and displacements of climatic regions for the past million years. The known history of mankind falls into a geologic time of maximal climatic instability and contrast.

Glaciers formed and continued to grow only so long as more snow fell in winter than was melted in summer. Glaciation depended on high relative humidity, extending pretty much throughout the annual cycle, in other words on reduced winter cold and summer heat. There was less sun and more cloudiness over high and middle latitudes and especially over continental interiors. Equatorward from the ice margins pluvial zones extended far inland. Desert areas were at their minima. Least is known of tropical conditions during glacial stages, though there is evidence of somewhat lowered temperatures. Ewing and Donn lately have advanced interesting arguments that the Arctic Ocean was open during glacial stages; this would have fed more snow to the northern margins of the ice caps and tempered greatly the winters of the Far North.

Present weather may be considered characteristic of interglacial conditions, with polar and tropical air masses strongly developed and circulating vigorously. Areal climatic contrasts are now accentuated as to seasonal heat and cold and also as to extremes of aridity and humidity. It should also be noted that the Arctic Ocean is wholly frozen over in winter and helps to refrigerate the high latitudes.

It is therefore not proper to speak in too general terms of cold glacial and warm interglacial phases. A good deal is being learned of what happened in and at the end of the last glacial stage, provisionally summed up thus: The last interglacial stage (Riss/Würm, Sangamon) seems to have merged slowly into the "Fourth" glacial stage as a lengthy time of moderated weather in intermediate and higher latitudes. The spread of the continental ice caps proceeded gradually to a culmination, followed by recessions and gradually diminishing readvances. Somewhat more than ten thousand years ago a sharp swing took place into the great deglaciation that we call postglacial time and that is construed as marking the establishment of the contemporary pattern of atmospheric circulation. Early Würm time saw the yielding of Mousterian to Upper Paleolithic cultures in Europe and the replacement then of Neanderthal man by modern forms. It is, however, gross oversimplification to read this change in terms of the rigors of glacial cold.

The Pleistocene climate swings were accompanied by large alterations in flora and fauna. A good deal has been inferred, though little is actually known, about the thermal tolerances and water requirements of specific animals and plants of importance to man. Growth and decrease of ice caps and of deserts alternately spread and shrank available ranges. Undemanding and mobile forms had the best of it; ecologically the times favored pioneers. Some plants increased or decreased; animals came or went, but only in some cases may the change be attributed to temperature change or to rainfall. Some plants are disseminated quickly; some germinate freely on mineral soil; some fail to reproduce under increased shade. The conditions involved in plant successions have made ecology a complex and interesting study, more and more cautious about climatic effects. The climatic explanation of grasslands has failed in case upon case, be they tropical savannas or mid-latitude prairies or steppes. The identification of Pleistocene herbivores with particular climatic conditions and vegetation is similarly dubious. Of the three living species of bison, which are interfertile and perhaps only geographic races, the European Wisent and the American woodland bison lived in woodlands and largely on browse, and only our plains buffalo was mainly grass-consuming. Few herbivores can be claimed as necessarily dependent on grass rather than browse; palatability and availability were main determinants of their feeding habits. The frequence, presence, or absence of specific plants or animals depends on so many biotic, edaphic, and climatic elements that inference of a single cause, such as climatic change, is rarely valid.

Sea levels the world over fell with each glaciation and rose during each deglaciation. These glacial eustatic changes are estimated to have had an amplitude well in excess of a hundred meters. Since the last glacial recession began, about 10,500 years ago by radiocarbon determination, sea level appears to have risen by more than thirty meters, and it is fairly certain that most of this occurred in the first half of the time elapsed. This rise is thought to be about one-third of the total since the maximum of the Fourth Glaciation. The sea coasts of the world as we know them are very young, developed within Recent geologic time. Those on which Paleolithic man lived and also much of their adjacent lowlands lie well submerged. Only the landward remnants of the highest sea stages reached in interglacial times are exposed to our view.

The eustatic fluctuations of sea level have also had world-wide effects on lowland rivers flowing into the sea. As sea level rises, either the entering stream course is drowned or it builds its bed higher, aggrading the valley floor laterally and especially upstream. The great lowland flood plains of today, too, have been fashioned by the last deglaciation. When sea levels were lowered, the valley floors were trenched. The glacial succession of cutting and filling was first and fully documented for the Mississippi River and tributaries from the Gulf of Mexico to above the junction of the Ohio River; how far it applies to the upper valley has not been worked out. At interglacial times the valley floors were subjected to flooding, deposition of alluvium, and the forming of swamps. In glacial stages drainage was accelerated and coast plains were eroded into ridges and valleys. The Arctic Coast plains of eastern Siberia and Alaska, both of which remained unglaciated, then were well drained, with less or even without tundra and permafrost. Was such the time when woodlands of aspen and birch and conifers prevailed in the Yukon and the New Siberian Islands and there were mammoths and bison? And an open Arctic Ocean moderated conditions for hyperborean living?

BIOLOGY AND THE FAMILY

If the simian horde and its dominant male are in part irrelevant and in part incompetent to serve as models for primordial human society, we need to consider the human female as to our beginnings. She has always lived, of necessity, closer to the daily biologic realities and responsibilities than has the male. Why should she be cast in a subordinate and passive role as to our social origins?

The human infant is born prematurely as compared with the other higher mammals. It has been proposed that this prematurity was progressive in human evolution, the female pelvis not continuing to enlarge along with the increase in size of the foetus and its head. Care of the progeny least developed at birth falls upon the human mother; the time during which the infant remains wholly dependent is longest in humans and may have grown longer as evolution went on.

The period of suckling among primitive peoples is usually at least two years. It may determine the spacing of pregnancy in part; when the next child is born, the elder one, though probably weaned, still must have its food prepared and provided. The cluster of dependent children grows, and dependence is lessened only gradually as the brood increases. There is no break until after puberty is attained, and then it is only partial. The mother continues to watch over, feed, and instruct her young through childhood, the male parent in time taking on the training of the boys. However much or little he may participate, she is the center and creator of family life. Family ties are lasting; no primitives lack recognition of kinship, which may take forms much more elaborate than those in civilized societies. The enduring family is a major human innovation; it is due to the role of the mother and has a singular biologic base. It involves awareness of the past and anticipation of a future and is expressed in a sense of history.

It was the woman's daily task to forage for food for her offspring. These reduced her mobility and shortened the radius over which she could range at collecting. If she covered less ground, she learned to know its food potentials more intimately. Also she trained the young ones with her how to recognize what was to be taken or avoided and how to go about collecting.

How the putative father was attached to the family circle is more uncertain. He ranged at will, with other male companions probably more often than alone, and it is not probable that he set out on such excursions, originally, with any idea of bringing back food to share with others. When he came back hungry, his woman may have saved something for him and gradually conveyed the idea to him that if he wished to be assured of bed and board he had better help to provide.

As the male came to accept association with a particular woman and her offspring and thus his part in parenthood, the bilateral biological family came into being. The mother always had her family in mind; the father had to be brought into it, overcoming his reluctance toward domestication. Altruism, prime requisite for social advance, begins with the mother in the care and affection for her own, extends to the kindred, and becomes interfamilial aid. The trend, encouraged by the woman, is toward monogamy. Regard for others beyond and above the call of glands is the postulate of humanity.

The figure of the hunter, male of course, has been overstressed for both primordial and primitive man. Humans were not choosy as to what they ate or how they got their food so long as it agreed with them; food specialization came with cultural specialization. Man is omnivorous, with a dietary range approached by very few creatures. This quality, original or acquired, has had much to do with his success. The bones of larger mammals found in some early archeologic sites are not enough to prove hunting economy or skills; we do not know whether part of them was secured by scavenging or represents disabled and infirm aged or young individuals. The club may be conceded to earliest man; the wooden spear already required considerable skill in the making and use. Modern primitive societies, although all of them have some specialized hunting skills, continued to depend primarily on collecting in many parts of the world. For the majority of tribes of Upper and Lower California the food procured by hunting game was minor and hardly of critical importance.

An extension of the theme that early man was a carnivore and ruthless killer is the attribution to him of cannibalism, the illustrations cited being australopithecine and Peking man. The imputation is one of serious abnormality; beasts do not prey on their own kind. Cannibalism is not a trait of primitive peoples or of hunting tribes, nor is it a matter of food economy anywhere so far as I know. It has existed perhaps only in certain agricultural societies, where it has a sacrificial ceremonial character. The adduced evidence for early man is to be taken with reserve; there are other interpretations, such as funerary cult for Peking man (see the article by Bergounioux).

WOMAN AND FIRE

Although we are dealing with man of the Old and Middle Stone Age, it was less the stones he shaped than the fire he employed that provided the greater range to his artifices and stimulus to cultural diversity. With the use of fire he entered on the promethean road that has led to the technology of today. It is, however, with Vesta rather than Prometheus that I am concerned, with woman as the keeper of the fire.

The capture of fire brought with it the duty of keeping it "alive," as we still say. Ages may have elapsed before the art of making fire was discovered, and then the making of new fire was not easy. Continuous possession of fire is a theme of ancient religions as sacred or eternal fire, in the care of female attendants.

Keeping the fire is the duty and privilege of the woman. Her sessile inclinations, rooted in the care of her family, were strengthened by adding the care of the fire. Hearth and home are synonymous. The hearth fire gave security against the great predators, especially at night. It invited evening gathering for social activity and leisurely discourse. The social hours, firelit after sunset, were best suited for exercising the faculty of thought and the fashioning of speech. As woman learned to cook, new food potentials were developed. Animal foods may be eaten raw, though their taste is varied and improved by cooking, which also makes foods keep better. Man's ability to digest raw starch and the seed proteins is slow and therefore limited. Women were the original food chemists and botanists. They experimented with roots, stems, and fruits at the hearth and learned to identify in the field which ones could or could not be made palatable. Proper application of heat made available plants that were bitter and poisonous. Where heat alone did not suffice, soaking and washing in water was learned (we do not know when). Before there were carrying containers, collecting perhaps concentrated on large units, such as the digging of underground starchy stems, tubers, bulbs, and corms. However, natural containers were often available, such as carapaces, the shells of large mollusks, and the large and tough leaves of some plants. We should also consider the utility of stone tools in cutting starchy stems of aroids (Alocasia), Musas (ensete), palms (sago), etc., all requiring preparation by cooking. We may be confident that recognition and experimentation went on and that a new success at the hearth was reported out from woman to woman and group to group; also that, the more successful the cook, the firmer her position in the society.[1]

AGE AND ORIGIN OF FIRE-USING

Choukoutien has been called the earliest center of fire use, but how old is it? As in other early Paleolithic sites in eastern and southern Asia, there is very large uncertainty as to age. Their current interpretations incline toward Middle rather than Lower Pleistocene age, not perhaps on the basis of better evidence. There is still the question of the "eoliths" (Red Crag) of the Ipswich area of East Anglia, which are acceptable geologically and satisfy some competent archeologists but not others. These are acknowledged as bearing proof of fire, though fire has hardly been considered in the controversy, since it has been assumed that natural fires could have swept the site.

The inference of natural fires should not be accepted as casually as has been done here and elsewhere in archeology. About fires from volcanic action there is of course no doubt. The easy assumption of lightning fires in sites that are under scrutiny as to human occupation is not proper. Where thunderstorms are rain storms, and such is the case for very much of the world where early man lived, the chances of natural fire are extremely slight. (We must eliminate the conductors and dry fuels that have been provided by modern man.) Mountainous

---

1. Perhaps in time there may be enough known of early hearths to tell something of what went on, such as whether there were raised hearths or cooking pits—the latter indicative of steam cooking.

areas in arid and semiarid lands do set up dry-season turbulence with lightning discharges into inflammable plant matter. Such fires occur under conditions of low humidity and are accompanied by little or no rain. These, however, are exceptional regions, hardly involved in the early archeologic problem. It would be of importance to know whether or where charcoal is known from any of the great body of Pleistocene and Pliocene alluvial deposits beyond the time of human presence. The occurrence of charcoal, burned earth, and fire-crazed or fire-broken stone needs to be considered with care as circumstantial evidence of the presence of man.

The capture of fire by man raises psychological (it has been suggested psychiatric) questions. Dr. Galdston called the attention of the meeting to the orgasmic quality of pyromania. How did fear of fire become fascination and excitation, how did fire worship come, and how was the sacred fire linked to fire of domestic utility?

The capture of fire may well have come about as a discovery in food-collecting following after a natural fire. As the source of such a fire I should prefer vulcanism. Italy and the eastern Mediterranean, the East African Rift, and especially the Sunda volcanic arc all are in such favorable position with regard to early man. The first premise is a natural fire that swept across part of a collecting range, killing and roasting animals trapped in its path. The next is the entry of humans into the burned area, the collection of carcasses, the enjoyment of their improved taste, and the recognition that this was an easy way to get a lot of better food. The third is that someone picked up a brand and started another fire. (The original version is by Charles Lamb as *A Dissertation on Roast Pig.*) Then fire was brought to the living place and given to the care of woman. Whatever that first use of fire, if there was a decisive moment to the course of human events, this was probably it. We need to know the various myths of the getting of fire, the fire cults and divinities, and the cremation customs in order to add insight to old, very old aspects of culture.

DIVERSITY OF HABITAT AND HABIT

Physiology supports the guess that mankind may have originated in some temperate land, without extremes of heat and cold or of aridity and humidity. An inland origin is assumed. Those who would have primordial man leave the forest and stray out into the open savanna rely both on the hunter image and on the postulate of wide grasslands at that time.

It may be proposed that, wherever man came from, the discovery of the tidal sea was a major event. The seashores must have had the strongest attraction for primitive and artless folk. Here was abundant and diverse food, waiting to be picked up or dug twice daily, and less subject to seasonal fluctuation than were land supplies. Fish and sea mammals were stranded occasionally. In season there were the eggs and young of sea fowl to be got at rookeries. There was edible seaweed and salt for seasoning. Driftwood supplied ever-replenished fuel and good stuff for tools, being seasoned in salt water instead of decaying on land. Headlands and coves provided tough, wave-selected, and wave-shaped cobbles, better than those fashioned by stream corrosion. May not man have been helped to learn the kinds and shapes of stones most useful to his lithic industries by living along the sea?

Primitive man could hardly find a better prospect than in beachcombing, which also was conducive to social grouping and to reduced mobility. In arid lands coastal sites are more likely to provide drinkable water than are interior ones, for various reasons of physical geography. In cold lands a harvest of food may still be possible at the edge of salt water when the land is locked by frost and snow. The dispersal of settlement along arid coasts and into high latitudes was invited by moving farther along shores provided with familiar foods and materials. The wider exploration and occupation of the world must have been helped greatly by following the coast lines. In later days we find the strandloopers as backward peoples, possibly because they lacked the challenge necessary to progress. In the infancy of humanity, however, such habitat meant better opportunity for food and other raw materials and more chance for social living. It does not matter that there is slight archeologic evidence of the early habitation of coast lines; all but the higher sea margins of the interglacial levels are now submerged as are, of course, the marine lowlands of the glacial stages.

There can be hardly any doubt that man sought out the shelter of a natural roof wherever he could. Under an overhang of rock he might be out of the wet and wind, with a dry floor to sleep and sit on, and with less nightly chilling of the air than in the open. Such shelters provided the preferred, perhaps the first, home in any clime and became virtually a necessity when fire was kept. Mankind found rather than built its early homes. Suitable shelter niches are provided where differential weathering and erosion produce longish shallow recesses. Sedimentary or volcanic beds, flat lying and differing in resistance to weathering, form such rock shelters, in particular when they are undercut by stream or wave. Where the sea meets the land, unless the latter is very low, one need rarely seek far to find such shelters, including some that have been notched by storm waves. Inland, as in uplands formed of limestone and shale or of sandstone or interbedded lava and ash, recesses are fashioned by the downcutting and lateral erosion of streams. In all cases these are ephemeral geologic features, being made, crumbling away, and being replaced. We know them mainly as used by Upper Paleolithic or later folk, but it is improper to infer, as has been done, that men turned late to inhabiting them. I refer, of course, to rock-shelter habitation, not to ceremonial use of deep and dark caves. The sequential geomorphologic processes have erased older abodes as they have ancient kitchen middens.

The primordial habitation patterns were determined by abundance, diversity, ease of securing food and water, and availability of shelter, and also, I suspect, very early by a good supply of fuel. These conditions were provided by seashores and in some valleys. If these are the right trails, they take us into areas of accentuated relief, both coastal and interior, of varied, abundant, and useful flora and fauna, either marine or terrestrial localities of superior advantage for population increase, social grouping, sedentary trends, and cultural variation.

As occupation spread into arid lands, or when aridity spread, increased mobility was exacted. Of such necessities the men became the principal providers of food, the scouts and trail-makers, and the leaders of the group on the march from camp to camp. Thus emerged protohunting groups and, one may infer, primacy of the male. The high latitudes perhaps were accessible only to hunting societies. Boreal and subboreal vegetation is rather poor in plants edible by man and also in the lower and smaller animal life that can be had by simple means of collecting. Such areas would await the development of hunting skills.

Our knowledge, our terminology, and in some measure our interpretation of Paleolithic man is still predominantly European, except for the current African discoveries. It is only from the Upper Paleolithic that hunting cultures are clearly known. The Middle Paleolithic has uncertain indications of such specialization, as in the Mousterian points. The long Lower Paleolithic has yielded only artifacts of kinds that may have served for many uses, such as the so-called scrapers, choppers, and bi-faces or "hand-axes." Hand-axes are serviceable for cutting and splitting, for taking bark and bast, and for adzing, digging, and pounding, but they are not very suitable for killing game or for combat. It has been suggested that the makers of "core" tools were woodland-dwelling collectors and that those of "flake" industries were ancestral to hunting societies and their militant offshoots. Despite evident oversimplification, there may be something to the contrast.

The ancient users of hand-axes and choppers are known especially from the great passageway of mankind that runs between the western shores of Europe through the Mediterranean and the Near East across India (Soan culture) and Burma (Anyathian) to the South China Sea. It is from somewhere in these attractive lands that the derivation of later agricultural villagers are to be sought. The Mousterian of Middle Paleolithic, borne by the Neanderthal race, mainly, it would seem, an endemic growth in the shelter of the European peninsula, will hardly serve as an antecedent. It was inundated and swept away by incursions of the great hunters of the Upper Paleolithic. The last of these, the reindeer hunters of Ahrensburg, have now been dated as contemporaries of the first town of Jericho, the earliest known agricultural date. The conventional sequence of Paleolithic, Mesolithic, and Neolithic may still fit Europe and its borders as sequences, not as developmental stages. The hunters came from elsewhere. The cultivation of plants and the keeping of domestic animals were brought to Europe from the outside, apparently also borne by new peoples. Since the arrival of the first Aurignacian elements, Europe has been invaded many times by new cultures and new peoples, perennially a colonial land, especially for the East.

The hunters radiating from inner and northern Asia brought masculine societies. The roots of agricultural living are to be sought elsewhere, as in southern Asia, by the diversification of skills proceeding from collecting, with the forming of larger and more sedentary local groups.

As it is inferred that the mother had the major role in the making of earliest human culture, so her influence continued to find in genial climes new means of expressing itself in household and vicinal skills. Culture growth takes a long time to gain momentum; the simplicity, persistence, and slow diversification of the artifacts of the greater part of Paleolithic time illustrate the slow accretion of learning.

As familiar and mistress of the hearth, woman continued to learn most about plants and their uses. The lore of curing was hers, especially as to simples. Plants that could not be made edible by cooking alone might be made so by first leaching them. Soaking and pounding opened the way to extracting and felting plant fibers and gave the start of textile skills, which have remained chiefly in woman's domain. It was discovered that certain plants macerated in water would stupefy fish, which then were easily collected and cooked without ill effects. Comparative ethnology indicated this as a primitive and perhaps earliest mode of fishing; there seems to be no sex limitation in this manner of taking fish, which otherwise is men's work. Fresh-water fish communities, as I have tried to show elsewhere,[2] gave the best conditions for beginning agricultural life.

These matters take us far beyond the half light of what we know of archeology, but their linkage is through a progressive collecting economy in which the women were free to develop their bent toward sedentary living, the arts and goods of the household, and pacific community life. The great and decisive advance by steps leading to agricultural life were made by securely sedentary communities, living with sufficient leisure in certain amply rewarding situations and enjoying the stimulation of communication between settled groups.

2. Carl O. Sauer, "Environment and Culture during the Last Deglaciation." In *Proc. Amer. Phil. Soc.*, 92:65-77.

SOME GENETIC IMPLICATIONS
OF HUMAN EVOLUTION

ERNST W. CASPARI

I SHOULD like to speak about a few thoughts that have come to me during the course of this symposum. They are based on some facts that have been brought up repeatedly and in several contexts. They concern observations on the variability of apes and early man, which to an evolutionist seem very interesting. Professor Schultz has emphasized that there is a large amount of interindividual variability among the great apes. In particular, he mentioned the gibbon and the gorilla, but it may be added that in recent man interindividual variability appears to be relatively large as compared with a number of other species. On the other hand, it has been pointed out by Professor Vallois and Professor Blanc that it was different with Neanderthal man; all the Neanderthal men who have been found are remarkably similar to one another even over relatively great distances. Since variability in populations is of crucial importance in studies of evolution, I should like to start my discussion with a consideration of the possible meaning of this difference in variability between different groups.

As is well known, it was a hundred years ago that Darwin pointed out that the variability between individuals forms the basis of evolution. Darwin did not get much further in the analysis of variability because his ideas about the transmission of variability from generation to generation were unclear, and he did not have real knowledge about the biological basis of variability. The answer to this problem has been supplied by modern genetics, and therefore it has been in the twentieth century, particularly through the efforts of Sir Ronald Fisher, Sewall Wright, J. B. S. Haldane, and others, that a new theory of evolution has evolved, a theory of evolution that is based completely on Darwin insofar as it considers variability and selection in a variable population as the main basis of the evolutionary process. In addition, it has built into the theory the knowledge that had in the meantime been acquired concerning genes. We have now fairly definite ideas about the physical and chemical nature of genes, but I do not have to go into that at this point. The only thing that has to be considered here is the fact that the genes constitute the only bridge between generations. In other words, that which is transmitted from the parents to the offspring are only the genes. Therefore, it might be interesting at this point to recall some of the characteristics of genes that are known, so that we can keep them in mind.

Every individual, human or animal, carries in every one of its cells a certain number of genes. The exact number is not known but may be estimated to be of the order of 5,000–10,000 pairs of genes. Out of every pair of genes, only one gene is retained in the germ cells, so the new individual obtains one complete set of genes from his father and one set of genes from his mother. These genes have the ability to duplicate themselves, and they also have the ability to influence the development of the individual in certain specific ways. The modern theory of evolution is based on some thought experiments that have been carried out in the following way: mathematical models have been constructed that describe a population in terms of the genes that are present in the population; this means that, as a first approach, the individuals that constitute the population are neglected, and it is described only in terms of its genes. This is, of course, an oversimplification. But it ought to be pointed out that the construction of a consciously oversimplified model of a process is a rather powerful way of thinking about it. This type of thinking has been used with great success by the physicists, and it appears to be a legitimate way of proceeding in the study of evolution. After the simplest possible model has been built, one complication after the other may be introduced in order to see how it will influence the behavior of the model. In this way one can get, step by step, closer to the actual situation.

If a random-breeding population is regarded as a gene pool, that is, as a collection of genes in which the genes are distributed, so to speak, to the different individuals, then these genes will be shuffled around in the population at random, so that in one generation a chance distribution will be reached that will remain unaltered from generation to generation, in the absence of mutation, selection, and drift.

Selection may be defined as the differential probability with which two genes in a gene pool are transmitted from one generation to the next. The classical way of describing selection is "survival of the fittest" individual. But, since genes are the only structures that are actually transmitted in sexual reproduction, selection is best interpreted as an effect on genes and can be defined best as the preferential transmission of one gene over its partner in a population. If one gene is transmitted more frequently, even though the advantage may be small, then in the long run of generations the whole population, the whole gene pool, will change in one direction, that is, to the elimination of the more unfavorable one of the pairs of genes. This means, then, that anything—an environmental factor or other genes—that influences the probability of a gene's being transmitted to the next generation will have a selective effect on this pair of genes. The mechanism by which the selective advantage of one gene may be accomplished is its influence on the phenotype of the individuals carrying it. It may endow them with a superior ability to survive to reproductive age, either through survival of the action of predators or, as Professor Blanc has pointed out, through resistance to disease. An additional component of the adaptive value of a gene consists in the fertility and fecundity it gives to its carriers. If a certain gene endows its carriers with higher fertility, it may be of selective advantage, even though the survival of these individuals may be somewhat reduced. The adaptive value is the final result of all the effects of a gene.

We have, then, a certain number of genes in a population that are being transmitted from generation to generation and that are being recombined in different ways in every generation. It should be pointed out that the number of combinations that may be obtained from 5,000 or 10,000 genes, even if only two alleles for each gene are present in the population, is very large—is so large, in fact, that in a particular population all of them can never be realized. Therefore, every individual in a population has a specific genetic makeup different from that of every other, and every one of these genetic combinations will be tested by selection. The genes in any particular combination will have a characteristic selective advantage or selective disadvantage. We can then introduce into the model mutations and migrations, that is, changes in the relative number of genes in the population. It is found, then, that a changed gene pool may be obtained. But as long as the population is subjected to the same selective pressures as the original gene pool was, it will, in the long run, tend to return to a state similar to the original genetic state. The most interesting feature is the way in which selection will work on the gene pool. In order to clarify the action of selection, a few concepts concerning the action of genes in the individual and in development must be introduced.

Genes are present in the nucleus of every cell of an organism. They are regarded as specific macromolecules, and it is generally agreed that deoxyribose-nucleic acid (DNA) is the genetic material. It is not known with certainty what the primary activity of DNA in the cell is, but it is usually believed now that it is concerned, directly or indirectly, with the synthesis of specific proteins. This is the reason why enzymes, which are specific proteins, are so frequently influenced by gene substitutions. It is not known whether the control of protein structure is the *only* primary activity of genes, and this question is not important from our present point of view. It is important, however, to realize that under the influence of an altered protein in a cell or in an organism secondary consequences may occur. The whole metabolism of the cells and, secondarily, of the organism may be changed (Caspari, 1952). The connection of these changes to the primary action of the gene may in some cases be obvious, but in others it is not so obvious. We give to these secondary effects of genes the name "pleiotropic effects." Pleiotropic gene action means that a gene does influence not merely one character. It is, of course, difficult to exclude the possibility that a gene may have more than one primary action. But for simplicity's sake it is usually assumed that the pleiotropic action pattern of a gene

is based on the secondary metabolic and developmental consequences of the
primary gene effect, the control of the structure of one specific type of protein.
The general occurrence of pleiotropic gene effects is not really astonishing.
A cell or an organism constitutes an integrated system, and it is therefore not
to be expected that an important constituent of the system can be altered without having secondary influences of some kind on other characteristics.

A simple example of pleiotropic gene effects, taken from man, is the gene
causing phenylketonuric idiocy. This condition is due to a single recessive gene
and is characterized by the fact that certain unusual chemicals, notably phenylpyruvic acid, are excreted in the urine. The primary effect of the gene has been
shown, in this case, to be absence or alteration of an enzyme that is concerned
with the oxidation of the amino acid phenylalanin to tyrosin. As a result,
phenylalanin is stored or converted to other substances that are excreted in the
urine. In addition, these abnormal substances effect the central nervous system
in such a way that its activity becomes impaired. This is the secondary effect
that we call idiocy. Assuming that the first step in the action of this gene is the
inhibition of the oxidation of phenylalanin to tyrosin, two ways in which this
chemical effect might influence intelligence could be imagined. One way would
be that one of the products of phenylalanin is necessary for a normal functioning
of intelligence; the other hypothesis would be that one of the abnormal substances, which arise because of the fact that the normal breakdown of phenylalanin is blocked, might be poisonous for intelligence. These two hypotheses
can be tested. Under the first assumption, if an organism carrying the gene
for phenylketonuria is given the substances by injection or by mouth, these
missing substances should be able to produce normal intelligence. If the second
hypothesis were correct, the condition should be improved if the person eats
a diet from which phenylalanin is excluded, since less of these secondary substances would be formed in this way (Bickel *et al.*, 1955; Jervis, 1954).

It turns out that the latter is the case. This is an example of how a certain
defect in cellular metabolism may affect the metabolism of the organism in
such a way that a developmental process, and consequently intelligence, is
altered. Examples of this kind from animals and plants are quite frequent. We
may therefore state that every gene, besides its primary activity, may have a
number of secondary pleiotropic effects, and it is the whole pattern of these
effects, not only the morphologically most obvious characteristics, that will
determine the selective value of a particular gene. If, then, a gene causes a certain
physiological change, which may in itself be advantageous or disadvantageous
or neutral, and, at the same time, conveys to the individuals carrying it a greater
resistance against a certain disease, or a high probability of mating or greater
fertility, the adaptive value of the gene will be the balance of all these effects.

Furthermore, genes have an important effect on developmental rates. The
mechanism of the genic control of developmental rates is not quite clear, but
there is evidence that this control of developmental rates is a secondary aspect

of primary enzyme activity. It is clear that normal development depends really on the close synchronization of a number of processes that are going on side by side, more or less independently. If one of them is altered, a disorganized system will result and frequently an abnormality or lethal effects will be obtained. This means that selection will act in such a way as to synchronize these processes so that a normal development will be assured.

Finally, it should be pointed out that a gene does not always determine the appearance of a character in 100 per cent of the cases. The idea that certain genes determine the appearance of a particular phenotypic character unalterably is very widespread. This impression has been created by geneticists because they prefer to work with genes that show 100 per cent expression in certain important types of experiments. These experiments are concerned with problems of the arrangement of genes in chromosomes and, more recently, with the nature of the genic material. In these experiments, genes with variable expression may also be used, but in this case the work becomes technically more difficult and laborious. Therefore, genes with variable expression have, in the past, frequently been called "bad genes" and discarded. Those who are not aware of this procedure may gain the impression that specific genes invariably control a specific set of characters. Actually, genes that produce a particular character only in a certain percentage of the carriers are quite frequent.

As an example, harelip and cleft palate in the mouse may be mentioned (Reed, 1936). The abnormality is dependent on the presence of a recessive gene *h*. The severity of the condition is very variable in *hh* animals. Also, in a certain percentage of the homozygotes, no abnormality is found. The percentage of normal "overlap" depends on a number of environmental conditions, for instance, the age of the mother, indicating that there exist conditions in the uterine environment that favor or suppress the expression of the gene *h* in homozygotes. In addition, harelip and cleft palate can be induced in embryos from normal strains not containing the gene *h* by injections of cortisone into the uterus at a certain sensitive period. The success of this experiment depends to a certain degree on the strain of mice used, that is, it is dependent on the genotype (Fraser *et al.*, 1954). In other words, it cannot be said that the appearance of the phenotype harelip depends on genes only; it does not depend on environmental influences alone either, but on an interaction between genes and the environment. A similar determination of harelip seems to be present in humans (Mather and Philip, 1940). In this case, the genic determination seems to be somewhat more complex, apparently involving several genes, and sex seems to be important in the expression of the genotype, harelip occurring more frequently and in more severe form in males than in females.

This type of interaction between genes and environment has frequently been expressed by stating that genes control the norm of reaction of the organism to the environment; a gene or a complex of genes does not necessarily control the development of a specific character, but it determines how a specific individual is going to react in a particular environment. This not only applies to morphological characters, such as harelip, but is apparently also important for behavioral characters. The ability or inability to learn certain behavior patterns may be assumed to be determined genetically. The concrete content of the learned behavior is, on the other hand, determined by environmental factors.

From these interactions between genes and environment in development another type of environmental influence on the genotype must be distinguished: the adaptive values of genes are dependent on the environment. The same allele will have different adaptive values, compared to its allele, in different environments. If we think of a population whose gene pool is being kept in a certain equilibrium by selective forces, then a change in the environment will induce changes in the adaptive values of the genes constituting the gene pool, and their transmission to the next generation will proceed with altered frequencies. There will occur a more or less gradual shift in the relative frequencies of these genes in the population. This mechanism provides an effective means for adaptation of the population to changes in its environment.

A spectacular example of this type of adaptation has been witnessed recently with the introduction of DDT and the consequent changes that have occurred in insect populations. There must have been present, in these populations, a certain small number of genes that were able to convey to their carriers a certain degree of resistance to DDT. Before man started to use DDT, these genes must have been kept in the population for reasons different from their effect on DDT resistance. But, with the invention of DDT by man, these genes gave to their carriers a strong advantage, which led to an accumulation of genes favoring DDT resistance in the population. This has led in some instances to a shift in the gene pool that was strong enough to give complete DDT resistance to the population (King, 1955; Oshima, 1958). Warburton (1958) has expressed situations of this kind by stating that selection is the mechanism by which information is transmitted from the environment to the gene pool. The composition of the gene pool is always in such a state that it can easily become changed and reorganized. This reorganization proceeds under the influence of the environment, because the environment determines the adaptive values of the genes and combinations of genes that constitute the gene pool.

As stated in the beginning, the phenotypic variability of man and the great apes is relatively high. The question of the meaning of phenotypic variability with respect to the constitution of the gene pool may therefore be asked. This question of the evolutionary meaning of phenotypic polymorphism has been raised by Mayr (1959). In very general terms, differences in phenotypic variability in populations can be accounted for in either one of two ways. High phenotypic variability might mean that the genetic variability is high, or it might mean that genic substitutions lead to a greater amount of phenotypic change than a similar degree of genic polymorphism would induce in a more stable organism. This second interpretation assumes that in a phenotypically more variable species developmental homeostasis is less effective. While the mechanisms of developmental homeostasis are not fully understood, the facts known about normal development demonstrate its existence beyond doubt. In the progress of normal development, there will frequently occur slight variations as a result of genetic or environmental influences. Either these variations may be compensated in the further course of development—regulation after injury in embryonic stages has been frequently observed—or development may proceed in an abnormal way, the slight primary aberration affecting other developing characters secondarily, so that in the further course of development increasingly abnormal patterns of pleiotropic gene effects are produced. Grüneberg (1947) has analyzed a number of striking examples from the development of the mouse and the rat.

I am inclined to believe that in many instances of high phenotypic variability a lower level of developmental homeostasis may be involved. The reason for this suggestion is that, in species that appear relatively stable phenotypically, a large amount of phenotypically unexpressed genetic variability has been demonstrated. No need exists, then, to assume that a relatively variable species, such as man or the gibbon, must possess a greater amount of genetic polymorphism than does a more stable species.

Development, then, may be said to proceed under a certain margin of safety. If variations remain below this margin of safety, regulation will take place and development will go on normally. If this margin of safety becomes relatively low, even slight variations in development will lead to phenotypic alterations. It would be expected that, at the same time, abnormalities of a pathological character would be found relatively frequently in the population. This may well be the case with apes, since, as Professor Schultz pointed out, the frequency of abortions that may, at least in part, be due to lethal genes and of abnormalities such as polydactylism and syndactylism is high in wild populations of apes.

It is well known that the margin of safety for specific developmental processes is under genic control and that it is possible to select for a lowering of the margins of safety (Waddington, 1953). In a population in which developmental homeostasis is relatively low, there will therefore exist a certain amount of selective pressure tending to re-establish it, since in such a population organisms with low developmental homeostasis would be expected to die preferentially or at least to exhibit lower viability and fertility. On the other hand, conditions may exist in which a large amount of phenotypic variability would be of selective advantage for the population as a whole. Two types of selective pressure, then, would exist, affecting the margin of safety of development, acting against each other. This consideration may contain a key for understanding the morphological homogeneity of Neanderthal man, as contrasted with other human populations and apes. If it is assumed that in Neanderthal man the developmental margin of safety has become wider, a population would be expected that is relatively stable phenotypically. In such a population evolution with respect to morphological characters may be assumed to be slow and to a certain degree limited.

In the evolution of the main stem of the human line no evidence for such a lowering of phenotypic variability can be found. Furthermore, the morphological changes occurring in human evolution have apparently progressed exceedingly fast compared to the usual evolutionary rates. The increase in the cranial size of man seems to have gone on for hundreds of thousands of years, or perhaps some millions of years, but certainly did not extend over tens of millions of years. Human evolution must have proceeded under the influence of selective pressures, and, besides the low degree of developmental homeostasis that made relatively fast morphological changes possible, strong selective pressures must have been present in human evolution. Speculating on the nature of these selective pressures appears to be an interesting problem.

We have stated earlier that the adaptive values of genes are determined by the environment of the organism. One of the characteristics of man is that his environment is to a large degree determined by cultural and social conditions, that is, by the activities of man himself. It has sometimes been maintained that in the evolution of man adaptation by cultural means has taken the place of adaptation by genetic means. This implies that the morphological and biological evolution of man took place first and that cultural evolution has taken over afterward. Our present knowledge seems to contradict this assumption, since it is known that human ancestors already possessed a certain degree of culture, as evidenced by tool-making, before they had reached all the morphological characteristics of modern man, particularly modern brain size. Our present considerations show that the process must have been more complicated. As soon as cultural activities had started, they must have had a feedback on the biological activities of man, since the existence of culture would change the adaptive value of genes considerably.

As an example, I should like to discuss the gene for sickle-cell anemia, since it is the best-known case both from a molecular and from an evolutionary point of view. The gene for sickle-cell anemia, s, determines the formation of an abnormal hemoglobin and leads, therefore, to the death at an early age of the homozygotes. The heterozygotes contain in their red blood cells 60 per cent normal hemoglobin and 40 per cent sickle-cell hemoglobin, and they are perfectly viable. It has been shown, particularly through the investigations of Allison (1954a) that heterozygotes for sickle-cell anemia may be favored by selection under conditions in which tropical malaria is prevalent. In countries in which tropical malaria occurs, particularly the children are strongly affected and frequently die from the disease, usually below the age of five years. Heterozygotes for sickle-cell anemia are to a certain degree protected from the disease. Under conditions in which malaria is present, the heterozygotes will be at a selective advantage, but, since heterozygotes do not breed pure, both the alleles for normal hemoglobin and for sickle-cell hemoglobin will be kept in the population indefinitely. It has been found, in accordance with this expectation, that in East African tribes the frequency of the gene s is correlated with the incidence of malaria (Allison, 1954b).

The situation appears to be more complex in western Africa. Livingstone (1958) observed a pattern of occurrence of the gene for sickle-cell anemia that is difficult to explain in terms of migrations or of the relations of the tribes to one another and that shows no clear correlation with the incidence of malaria. Livingstone comes to the conclusion that the selective advantage of the heterozygotes has developed relatively late in history, so that no equilibrium has as yet become established. He points out that in hunting populations, as shown by the Pygmies, malaria does not seem to play a very large role, since the breeding opportunities for mosquitoes in the forest do not permit them to reach a high population density. When agriculture becomes established, the forest is cut down and the crops are irrigated, mosquitoes find much better breeding opportunities, and malaria will become an important selective factor. Livingstone assumes that agriculture started late in western Africa, probably after A.D. 900, since it is not based on the culture of cereals, which form the basis of agriculture in other areas, but on the cultivation of yams, which were apparently domesticated in Africa.

There may be other similar instances of cultural conditioning of selective pressures in man, but they are not so well understood genetically. The closely inhabited cities of antiquity and of the Middle Ages presented favorable conditions for the spread of air-borne and water-borne epidemics and may therefore have led to a selective advantage for genes' increasing immunity against those diseases. With the control of epidemics by public health measures in the late nineteenth century and by antibiotics in the middle of the twentieth century, the adaptive value of genes' conveying immunity to infection may be presumed to have decreased. It has been pointed out by Dobzhansky (1958) that the adaptive values of genes and gene complexes are determined by environmental conditions at any particular time, not by the conditions present in the Paleolithic or even in the Middle Ages. Since the environmental conditions of man are changing constantly, under the influence of his cultural activities, the selective pressures and adaptive values of genes may be assumed to change accordingly. As a result, we would expect relatively fast changes of the human gene pool. It is exceedingly difficult, however, to specify the nature of the selective pressures at any time in history.

It has been stated in some of our earlier discussions that human evolution has gone on at an increasingly accelerated rate. This is certainly true for the progress of culture. The Lower and Middle Paleolithic has been of long duration, and human culture and physical appearance seem to have been quite homogeneous during that period. Starting with the Upper Paleolithic, a faster development of culture seems to have occurred, accompanied by greater physical heterogeneity. These changes can be visualized by the model of an interaction of genic and cultural evolution, if it is assumed that selective pressures have tended toward the selection of genes favoring social and cultural activities. The increase of brain size in the course of human evolution may indicate that this has actually taken place, since Rensch (1956) has shown that between related species brain size is correlated with intellectual capacity. We may assume that man started out with a rather static population and a genotype that determined a certain amount of cultural possibilities. When these are realized, cultural changes occur that change the environment and the strength and quality of selective pressures, leading to a change in the gene pool. If it is assumed that this altered gene pool possesses different social and cultural capacities, environment will be changed in turn, and again different selective pressures will develop. Thus a second step will be obtained, which will again feed back on the genotype of the population, producing a situation that may be compared to an avalanche. At first the process proceeds quite slowly, but, as the capacity for cultural changes increases, the feedback on the genotype will become accelerated, until a rate of change, biologically and culturally, is obtained as it has been observed in more recent human evolution. The limit for acceleration of this process would be given by the human rate of reproduction. As has been shown in the example of DDT resistance in insects, fast-breeding organisms can adapt genetically very efficiently to sudden environmental changes brought about by cultural accomplishments of man. But this mechanism implies a fast rate of reproduction, and for a slowly reproducing species like man a limit for genetic adaptation may be expected.

BIBLIOGRAPHY

ALLISON, A. C.
1954a. "Protection Afforded by Sickle-Cell Trait against Subtertian Malarial Infection," *Brit. Med. Jour.*, 1:290–94.
1954b. "The Distribution of the Sickle-Cell Trait in East Africa and Elsewhere, and Its Apparent Relationship to the Incidence of Subtertian Malaria," *Trans. R. Soc. Trop. Med. & Hyg.*, 48:312–18.

BICKEL, H., R. J. BOSCOTT, and J. GERRARD
1955. "Observations on the Biochemical Error in Phenylketonuria and Its Dietary Control." In H. WAELSCH (ed.), *Biochemistry of the Developing Nervous System*, pp. 417–43. New York: Academic Press.

CASPARI, E.
1952. "Pleiotropic Gene Action," *Evolution*, 6:1–18.

DOBZHANSKY, T.
1955. "A Review of Some Fundamental Concepts and Problems of Population Genetics," *Cold Spring Harbor Symp. Quant. Biol.*, 20:1–15.
1958. "Genetics and the Destiny of Man," *Proc. Xth Internat. Congr. Genetics, Montreal*, 1:468–74.

FISHER, R. A.
1930. *The Genetical Theory of Natural Selection*. Oxford: Clarendon Press.

FRASER, F. C., H. KALTER, B. E. WALKER, and T. D. FAINSTAT
1954. "The Experimental Production of Cleft Palate with Cortisone and Other Hormones," *J. Cell. & Comp. Physiol.*, 43 (Suppl. 1): 237–59.

GRÜNEBERG, H.
1947. *Animal Genetics and Medicine*. New York and London: Hoeber.

HALDANE, J. B. S.
1932. *The Causes of Evolution.* London: Longmans, Green.

JERVIS, G. A.
1954. "Phenylpyruvic Oligophrenia (Phenylketonuria)." In *Genetics and the Inheritance of Integrated Neurological and Psychiatric Patterns: Proc. Assoc. Nerv. Ment. Dis.*, 33:259–82.

KING, J. C.
1955. "Evidence for the Integration of the Gene Pool from Studies of DDT Resistance in Drosophila," *Cold Spring Harbor Symp. Quant. Biol.*, 20:311–17.

LIVINGSTONE, F. B.
1958. "Anthropological Implications of Sickle Cell Gene Distribution in West Africa," *Amer. Anthrop.*, 60:533–62.

MATHER, K., and U. PHILIP
1940. "The Inheritance of Hare Lip and Cleft Palate in man," *Ann. Eugenics*, 10:403–16.

MAYR, E.
1959. "Where Are We?" *Cold Spring Harbor Symp. Quant. Biol.*, 24:1–14.

OSHIMA, C.
1958. "The Resistance of Strains of *Drosophila melanogaster* to DDT and Dieldrin," *Proc. Xth Internat. Congr. Genetics, Montreal*, 2:210.

REED, S. C.
1956. "Harelip in the House Mouse, I: Effects of the External and Internal Environments; II: Mendelian Units Concerned with Harelip and Application of the Data to the Human Harelip Problem," *Genetics*, 21:339–74.

RENSCH, B.
1956. "Increase of Learning Capability with Increase of Brain Size," *Amer. Naturalist*, 90:81–95.

WADDINGTON, C. H.
1953. "Genetic Assimilation of an Acquired Character," *Evolution*, 7:118–26.

WARBURTON, F. E.
1958. "Natural Selection as the Accumulation of Information from the Environment," *Proc. Xth Internat. Congr. Genetics, Montreal*, 2:308.

WRIGHT, SEWALL
1931. "Evolution in Mendelian Populations," *Genetics*, 16:97–159.

THE RELEVANCE OF RECENT EVOLUTIONARY

CHANGES TO HUMAN STRESS BIOLOGY[1]

DAVID A. HAMBURG

IN THIS conference a good deal has been said about various relics left by early man, inferences that can be made from those relics, and questions raised by them. The questions I wish to raise are derived from research on another relic of early man, namely, modern man. What we find in modern man may raise rather pointed questions about the conditions of life over the long course of human evolution. It is particularly important to piece together clues regarding selective pressures among early men; these pressures must have shaped *Homo sapiens*, even though some of them may no longer be operating. Such material may give us valuable leads to discovery of basic characteristics of the contemporary human species.

It is exceedingly important to emphasize the time perspective of evolution. The biological equipment of the human organism has evolved over a very long period of time. Even if we leave our remote ancestry aside, we have to face the fact—well established from the fossil record—that primates have been in existence for many millions of years, probably upward of 50 million. Moreover, distinctly human forms (australopithecine) were living at least a half-million years ago, quite likely as far back as a million years. *Homo sapiens* has been dated by newer techniques to an age of 30,000–50,000 years (Washburn and Howell, 1960). Agriculture came into use from 8,000 to 10,000 years ago, and the industrial revolution occurred, in this context, only yesterday.

Since cultural change can occur very much more rapidly than genetic change, it is highly probable that most of our biological equipment evolved as it did because it had selective advantage over an exceedingly long period of time under environmental conditions very different in some respects from our own. It may be that the very rapid cultural changes of modern times have made our environment so radically different from those in which we evolved that some of our biological equipment is obsolete and perhaps even maladaptive. This is an intriguing

1. The ideas presented here have developed over a good many years, in the course of which a variety of people have been helpful. I want especially to thank a few with whom I have had the opportunity for recurrent, stimulating discussions: Roy Grinker, Rachmiel Levine, John Mason, David Rioch, and Sherwood Washburn.

question that, on careful analysis, might lead to important new observations and experiments.

Pittendrigh, in a stimulating paper on adaptation, natural selection, and behavior, makes several points that are relevant here.

. . . The study of adaptation is not an optional preoccupation with fascinating fragments of natural history; it is the core of biological study. . . .

The nature of natural selection as differential reproductive success between contemporary genetic alternatives merits continual re-emphasis because of the light it sheds on problems of adaptation. . . . Mammalian organization evolved not because its constituent features were a unique and indispensable solution to the problems of land life but because in a historical succession of environmental opportunities mammalian features rendered organisms that possessed them the more efficient reproducers among the alternatives which the then current genetic alternatives realized.

. . . since the environment is itself continually evolving we are surely confronted in many contemporary forms with organization that is, as it were, an adaptive anachronism; much of the organism must have evolved as adaptation to conditions— and in terms of genetic potentialities—long since past.

Adaptive organization [is] a patchwork of makeshifts pieced together, as it were, from what was available when opportunity knocked, and accepted in the hindsight, not the foresight, of natural selection [Pittendrigh, 1958].

We may well inquire whether changes of environmental conditions within recent times have drastically modified behavior patterns that had selective advantage through a very long evolutionary course. An instance of such change may perhaps be found in the matter of muscular exertion. It is quite probable that the necessity for muscular exertion has run through the entire course of mammalian, primate, and human evolution until very recent times—and even yet in some parts of the human world. This would sometimes involve short periods of intensive activity, in other cases long periods of sustained activity— and there may be important differences between the two. Descriptions of contemporary mammals under natural conditions (Bourlière, 1954), including recent field observation of nonhuman primates (Washburn and Devore, 1961), document the concept that muscular exertion is required for survival in a variety of contexts: coping with predators, obtaining food and water supply, coping with climatic changes, and reproductive behavior. Similarly, observation of preindustrial human groups suggests that frequent exertion is required, though there is considerable variation with environmental conditions (Goldschmidt, 1959). Moreover, close analysis of hunting-and-gathering societies (which cover the great bulk of the human evolutionary time span) in the context of newer evidence from the prehistoric archeological record points to the same conclusion. Consider, for example, the following statement by Desmond Clark, based on his research in southern Africa on human evolution.

As hunter-gatherers are entirely dependent on the natural resources of their environment their survival depends on there always being available to them an adequate food supply. They cannot, therefore, establish any permanent homes but must be continually on the move. During the rains they spread out to gather the many wild fruits and other veldkos to be found at that season, and during the dry season, when the vegetable foods are scarce, they concentrate more on the permanent water (and, one may suggest, on a meat diet). Thus the band moves continually round its hunting preserves. Much has been said about the carnivorous habits of early man but it is certain that vegetable foods must have formed as important a source of supply for his needs and to begin with were probably by far the more important. A hunting band would probably cover an area of several hundred square miles in the course of a year, moving from place to place, feeding off wild fruits and roots as they became ripe or in season. In order to secure a meat supply the band also followed the game which, in particular the gregarious, herbivorous animals, spreads out far from the permanent water during the rains and as the temporary supplies dry up retreats upon the rivers and other permanent water during the dry season. This seasonal movement is a rule of life that is in fact rigidly followed by all lower groups of hunter-gatherers and is even not dissimilar to the practices of the higher mammals [Clark, 1959].

To recognize the necessity for muscular exertion permitting intensive activity of the whole organism in mammalian evolution calls attention to the bodily processes that support such action and make it possible. I would now like to quote a few excerpts from the classic work of Walter Cannon in this field—a remarkable combination of experimental analysis and conceptual integration. Cannon described a set of physiologic changes that facilitate vigorous effort, indicated that they occur not only during exercise but prior to it, and finally that these same changes occur in association with a variety of intense emotional experiences, whether or not they are accompanied by exercise.

. . . the adrenin secreted in times of stress has all the effects in the body that are produced by injected adrenin. It cooperates with sympathetic nerve impulses in calling forth stored carbohydrate from the liver, thus flooding the blood with sugar; it helps in distributing the blood to the heart, lungs, central nervous system and limbs, while taking it away from the inhibited organs of the abdomen; it quickly abolishes the effects of muscular fatigue; and it renders the blood more rapidly coagulable. These remarkable facts are, furthermore, associated with some of the most primitive experiences in the life of higher organisms, experiences common to all, both man and beast—the elemental experiences of pain and fear and rage that come suddenly in critical emergencies. What is the significance of these profound bodily alterations? What are the emergency functions of the sympathico-adrenal system?

The facts at once have significance if considered in relation to the struggle for existence. For ages past this struggle has disciplined and relentlessly selected the most efficient. If fear always paralyzed it would result only in danger of destruction. But fear and aggressive feeling, as *anticipatory* responses to critical situations, make *ready for action* and thereby they have had great survival values. And the remarkable system of internal adjustments which attend these emotions and which mobilize the forces of the body are such as to have had great survival values. Thus the bodily changes may reasonably be interpreted. When a more reasonable theory is offered it will be welcomed [Cannon, 1929]. [Italics mine.]

The broad outlines of the picture drawn by Cannon have held up well in the intervening years. A great variety of research with newer methods has filled in important details, amplified most of his points, and modified some of them. One of the important extensions of his work has to do with the co-ordinated functions of nervous and endocrine systems in meeting changes in environmental conditions. Cannon's work centered on the sympathetic portion of the autonomic nervous system, its extension in the adrenal medulla and one hormone of that gland, epinephrine (adrenalin, adrenin). Research in recent years has explored a wider range of nervous and endocrine functions.

Increasingly, we have come to realize that the autonomic nervous system is not autonomous, as its name suggests, but rather that it is substantially under central nervous control (Patton, 1960). Moreover, the CNS regulatory effects on cardiovascular, endocrine, and other physiologic systems operate not only through the hypothalamus (which has been most extensively studied) but also through higher centers, including the cerebral cortex (Mason, 1959). Much valuable work in recent years has centered on the limbic system, the oldest cerebral cortex (Nauta, 1960). In the course of evolution this structure has largely shifted from its earlier olfactory functions to more complex functions involving integration of emotional and visceral processes. Indeed, one of the major trends in contemporary physiology is the growing recognition of the pervasive influence of the brain in regulation of physiologic processes, the evidence perhaps being most impressive in relation to endocrine and cardio vascular functions (Eichna and McQuarrie, 1960; Reiser *et al.*, 1954; Mason, 1959). Recent work suggests that endocrine changes of the type described by Cannon are not limited to emergency conditions, though they are most striking under these conditions. Some similar changes, on a smaller scale, have been observed in connection with the less extreme stresses of ordinary living, but these are difficult to detect in laboratory "stress" experiments, which frequently involve events of trivial significance for the subject (Handlon *et al.*, 1961).

Stress research increasingly suggests that the anticipation of personal difficulty, whether it be physical or psychosocial in nature, may lead to important changes, not only in thought, feeling, and action, but also in endocrine and autonomic processes, and hence in a wide variety of visceral functions. In recent years, much interest has been centered on the adrenal *cortex* in relation to psychological stress. Stimulation of certain brain areas produces major changes in circulating concentration of hydrocortisone, one of the principal adrenocortical hormones. Stimulation of the infundibular portion of the hypothalamus in *Rhesus macaque* produces marked elevation of plasma hydrocortisone levels, whereas control stimulation in the putamen or anterior thalamus does not. Functional relationships between two limbic-system structures and the pituitary-adrenocortical system have been described. First, it was observed that stimulation of the amygdaloid nucleus produced a maximal increase in pituitary-adrenocortical activity; in addition, the hippocampus-fornix system appears to be capable of exerting an unusual, prolonged suppressive action on the pituitary-adrenocortical system (Mason, 1958). With respect to behavior, certain stressful experimental procedures have produced sharp increases in plasma hydrocortisone. Both a conditioned fear situation and a conditioned avoidance situation were associated with similar marked increases in plasma hydrocortisone levels in the *Rhesus macaque;* these elevations were as great as those observed following injection of a large dose of adrenocorticotrophic hormone.

Since the introduction of a precise, reliable biochemical method for measuring hydrocortisone by Nelson and Samuels (1952), several laboratories have undertaken major studies of plasma hydrocortisone concentrations under naturally occurring stressful conditions in man. In aggregate, 269 individuals have been studied in several laboratories under conditions of fairly intense distress. These groups consistently show mean plasma hydrocortisone levels around 20 mg/100 ml in early morning (between 8:00 and 9:00 A.M.). Extensive control studies in the same laboratories of healthy individuals experiencing little or no distress have shown mean plasma hydrocortisone levels of 12–13 mg/100 ml at the same time of day. The differences between these levels and those of the distress groups are highly significant statistically.

The measurement of urinary corticosteroid excretion under psychological stress has also been a matter of considerable interest. Several groups have investigated this problem under naturally occurring stressful conditions. Data are available on 87 individuals under conditions of personal threat, sustained tension, and in some cases fairly intense distress. These individuals were studied in nine different groups at five institutions. Each of these studies shows higher twenty-four hour urinary excretion of corticosteroids under stress conditions than under nonstress conditions (Hamburg, 1961).

Modern methods of measurement have been applied most extensively to hydrocortisone under conditions of psychological stress. However, there is a growing and intriguing body of work with newer methods on three other adrenal hormones: epinephrine, norepinephrine, and aldosterone. There is now considerable evidence to indicate increased urinary excretion of these three hormones under conditions of fairly intense emotional arousal and distress (Elmadjian *et al.*, 1958; Euler *et al.*, 1959; Curtis *et al.*, 1960; Venning *et al.*, 1957).

The evidence very briefly summarized here indicates that emotional disturbance in man is associated with elevated blood levels and urinary excretion of adrenal hormones. The most reasonable interpretation of these elevations is that they reflect increased secretion of its four principal hormones by the adrenal gland, involving both the cortex and the medulla. The increase in adrenocortical activity, and quite likely the increase in adrenomedullary activity too, is associated with a wide variety of stressful conditions and emotional responses. These studies indicate that increased adrenal activity may be associated not only with stresses that directly threaten the physical survival of the subject but also with stresses that threaten his self-respect or crucial human relationships.

It is difficult to understand why the adrenal secretes such large amounts of these hormones in emotionally distressing circumstances. What is the biological function of this endocrine response? In attempting to clarify this question, it may be useful to consider the more recent evidence on the actions of these hormones; however, it is possible here to discuss only one major set of actions. With respect to hydrocortisone, J. Russell in a recent review emphasizes the conversion of protein to carbohydrate. She says: "The idea that the adrenalectomized animal suffers mainly from a defect in the rate of withdrawal of body protein for catabolism is supported by a variety of observations" (Russell, 1960). Furthermore, the oxygenated adrenal steroids upon injection have a catabolic effect on protein metabolism, and a very high rate of gluconeogenesis has been observed in animals given large doses of cortisone.

Research of the past few years has shown that the adrenal not only facilitates mobilization of carbohydrate but *mobilization of fat* as well. Thus, adrenal secretions tend to pull the body's principal fuels out of their storage depots into the circulation, broken down into short-chain molecules ready for burning.

Epinephrine and hydrocortisone act co-operatively in accomplishing fat mobilization (Wool *et al.*, 1954; Wool and Goldstein, 1953). The well established effect of epinephrine in raising circulating concentrations of plasma lipids (notably cholesterol, free fatty acids, and phospholipids) is dependent upon an intact adrenal cortex. The effect of injected epinephrine can be experimentally abolished by adrenalectomy and restored by injection of hydrocortisone (Shafrir and Steinberg, 1960). Moreover, chronic low-grade injection of epinephrine to normal dogs produces relatively chronic elevation of cholesterol and phospholipids; administration of cortisone to normal dogs further accentuates the plasma lipid response to injected epinephrine (*ibid.*). These latter experiments are particularly interesting, since they suggest a parallel with psychological stress situations in man.

Is there any direct evidence in men under stress of such fuel mobilization? A recent report is pertinent here (Bogdonoff *et al.*, 1960). Twenty students were studied before, during, and after a brief but important and difficult academic examination. The investigators found sharp, consistent increases in free fatty acids during the examination, along with elevation of plasma glucose concentration. Moreover, urinary excretion of epinephrine rose in all twenty subjects. They conclude that lipolysis and glycogenolysis are part of the organism's response to arousal.

Several research groups have found elevated serum cholesterol levels in men under stress (Friedman *et al.*, 1958; Thomas and Murphy, 1958; Wertlake *et al.*, 1958). Similarly, there are now several reports of substantial free fatty acid elevations in acute fear situations (Cardon and Gordon, 1959; Bogdonoff *et al.*, 1959).

Altogether, it now seems reasonable to conclude that the increased secretion of adrenal hormones under psychological stress facilitates energy mobilization involving increased availability of carbohydrate and fat for burning. This makes sense if it is viewed as serving a preparatory function for the oxidative processes required in muscular exertion.

In the long run of mammalian evolution, in the course of dealing with all sorts of harsh environmental contingencies, such a capacity for *anticipatory mobilization* may well have had selective advantage. Indeed, the trend toward increasing anticipatory powers, including the anticipatory regulation of physiologic processes, may be one of the crucial features of primate evolution. The great development of the forebrain in man may in large measure be viewed as an anticipatory network that permits some of the cardinal features of human adaptation.

But with man's increasing mastery over his environment, these anticipatory mobilizations have less and less often been followed by vigorous activity. With the development of efficient food production, mastery over predators, machines for transportation, communication, and heavy work—all the fantastic developments of the continuing industrial revolution—the need for intensive physical activity has greatly diminished. Moreover, even the possibility for intensive activity is sharply restricted by many circumstances of modern living, for example, industrial and professional settings in which personal tensions cannot readily be relieved by taking action.

The net effect seems to be that the contemporary human organism frequently gets mobilized for exertion but ends up doing little or nothing—preparation for action, without action.

What difference, if any, does this make? There are many facets to this problem that cannot be explored here. For the present, I want only to draw attention to the possibility that these stress responses may be less useful than they once were, and in some circumstances may actually be harmful. To illustrate how this evolutionary shift might work, let me briefly call attention to one clinically important problem area: atherosclerosis. The secretion of adrenal hormones under psychological stress may, in the context of many contemporary circumstances, produce a mobilization of fat without subsequent utilization. Perhaps some of the fat that used to be burned in the process of exertion now gets deposited in the intimal lining of the arteries—at least in predisposed individuals.

In this view, the susceptibility to development of atherosclerotic pathology would be increased by: (*a*) frequent and/or prolonged stress responses and (*b*) circumstances or life styles that inhibit muscular exercise. These conditions would favor a high level of fat mobilization with a low level of fat utilization. Such a formulation helps to integrate two sets of observations pertinent to incidence of atherosclerotic heart disease: both chronic psychologic stress and a sedentary way of life seem to be predisposing factors. In research and clinical discussions, these factors are often set in opposition to each other. Perhaps these are two sides of the same coin that can be viewed whole in light of human evolution.

This discussion is necessarily speculative and one-sided. Many factors are relevant in pathogenesis of atherosclerosis, and most of the crucial questions are much in need of further evidence. These suggestions are offered in the hope that they may have a stimulating effect on future research. It is interesting to note that, as evidence accumulates, investigators are increasingly in agreement on the finding of cholesterol elevation in atherosclerotic disease (Dock, 1959). While a variety of factors may elevate cholesterol levels—with diet apparently being quite significant—one of these factors is psychological stress, very likely medicated by adrenal activity as sketched above. Year in, year out, preparation-for-action-without-action may contribute to chronic elevation of cholesterol (and perhaps other lipids) that play a part in pathogenesis of atherosclerosis.

Even if these speculations on atherosclerosis should prove to be entirely wide of the mark, the more general point deserves serious consideration by investigators in the broad field of human biology: some of the old adaptations of the human species may have been rendered less adequate or even obsolete by the radical changes in environmental conditions brought about in very recent times by man himself. One way in which students of human evolution can greatly contribute to the clarification of such problems is by delineating the selection pressures that operated on early man. Much work is needed on the shaping of specifically human characteristics during the evolutionary period of rapidly increasing brain size (and probably brain complexity as well). The relatively rapid evolution of the small-brained australopithecine into large-brained modern man must have involved heavy selection pressures favoring certain behavioral characteristics. Greater understanding of the life of early man can lead to recognition of crucial behavior patterns that must have been highly adaptive in those times. A significant part of contemporary man's heritage, both genetic and cultural, may lie in a readiness to learn such behavior patterns, and some of them may no longer be appropriate to the problems we face.

Julian Huxley, in concluding his work of synthesis on evolutionary research, raises a question of this sort:

> . . . After most of the major progressive steps taken by life in the past, the progressive stock has found itself handicapped by characteristics developed in earlier phases, and has been forced to modify or abandon these to realize the full possibilities of the new phase. . . . This evolutionary fact is perhaps most obvious in relation to the vertebrates' emergence from water on to land. But it applies in other cases too. The homothermy of mammals demanded the scrapping of scales and the substitution of hair; man's erect posture brought with it a number of anatomical inconveniences. But man's step to conscious thought is perhaps more radical in this respect than any other.
>
> By means of this new gift, man has discovered how to grow food instead of hunting it, and to substitute extraneous sources of power for that derived from his own muscles. . . .
>
> The problem immediately poses itself whether man's muscular power and urges to hunting prowess may not often be a handicap to his new modes of control over

his environment, and whether some of his inherited impulses and his simpler irrational satisfactions may not stand in the way of higher values and fuller enjoyment [Huxley, 1943].

Research in human evolution is a basic science for the whole of human biology. Much of what man *is* may best be understood in terms of *how he came to be that way*. Indeed, understanding of his evolutionary development may well tell us where to look for important features of his contemporary function that might otherwise be overlooked. An appreciation of the nature and magnitude of the recent change in human environmental conditions may help the biological and behavioral sciences to understand the dislocations and difficulties of today's troubled human species.

BIBLIOGRAPHY

BOGDONOFF, M., H. ESTES, W. HARLAN, D. TROUT, and N. KIRSHNER
1960. "Metabolic and Cardiovascular Changes during a State of Acute Central Nervous System Arousal," *J. Clin. Endoc. & Metab.*, 20:1333–40.

BOGDONOFF, M., H. ESTES, and D. TROUT
1959. "Acute Effect of Psychological Stimuli upon Plasma Non-esterified Fatty Acid Level," *Proc. Soc. Exptl. Biol.*, 100:503.

BOURLIÈRE, F.
1954. *The Natural History of Mammals*. New York: Knopf.

CANNON, W. B.
1929. *Bodily Changes in Pain, Hunger, Fear, and Rage*. 2d ed. New York: Appleton.

CARDON, P., and R. GORDON
1959. "Rapid Increase of Plasma Unesterified Fatty Acids in Man during Fear," *J. Psychosom. Res.*, 4:5–9.

CLARK, J. D.
1959. *The Prehistory of Southern Africa*. Penguin Books.

CURTIS, G., R. CLEGHORN, and T. SOURKES
1960. "The Relationship between Affect and the Excretion of Adrenaline, Nor-adrenaline, and 17-Hydroxycorticosteroids," *J. Psychosom. Res.*, 4:176–84.

DOCK, W.
1959. "Cardiovascular Diseases (Atherosclerosis)," *Ann. Rev. Med.*, 10:77–92.

EICHNA, L. W., and D. G. McQUARRIE (eds.)
1960. "Central Nervous System Control of Circulation," *Physiol. Rev.* (Suppl. 4), 40:311.

ELMADJIAN, F., J. HOPE, and E. LAMSON
1958. "Excretion of Epinephrine and Norepinephrine under Stress," *Rec. Prog. Hormone Res.*, 14:513–53.

EULER, U., C. GEMZELL, L. LEIR, and G. STROM
1959. "Cortical and Medullary Adrenal Activity in Emotional Stress," *Acta Endocrinol.*, 30:567–73.

FRIEDMAN, M., R. ROSENMAN, and V. CARROLL
1958. "Changes in the Serum Cholesterol and Blood Clotting Time in Men Subjected to Cyclic Variation of Occupational Stress," *Circulation*, 17:852.

GOLDSCHMIDT, W.
1959. *Man's Way*. Cleveland: World.

HAMBURG, D. A.
1961. "Plasma and Urinary Hydrocortisone in Naturally Occurring Psychological Stresses." In S. KOREY (ed.), *Ultrastructure and Metabolism of the Nervous System.* Baltimore: Williams & Wilkins.

HANDLON, J., J. FISHMAN, E. SACHAR, D. HAMBURG, and J. MASON
1961. "Mild Stress and Adrenocortical Function: Psychological Factors in Lowering Plasma Hydrocortisone Concentrations." (Paper presented to Amer. Psychosom. Soc., April, 1961.)

HUXLEY, J.
1943. *Evolution: The Modern Synthesis*. New York: Harper & Bros.

MacLEAN, P. D.
1960. "Psychosomatics." In H. MAGOUN (ed.), *Handbook of Physiology-Neurophysiology*, 3:1723–44.

MASON, J. W.
1958. "The Central Nervous System Regulation of ACTH Secretion." In *Reticular Formation of the Brain*, pp. 645–62. Boston: Little, Brown.
1959. "Visceral Functions of the Nervous System," *Ann. Rev. Physiol.*, 21:353–80.

NAUTA, W. J.
1960. "Limbic System and Hypothalmus: Anatomical Aspects," *Physiol. Revs.* (Suppl. 4), 40:102–4.

NELSON, D., and L. SAMUELS
1952. "A Method for the Determination of 17-Hydroxycorticosteroids in Blood: 17-Hydroxycorticosterone in the Peripheral Circulation," *J. Clin. Endoc.*, 12:519.

PATTON, H. D.
1960. "Higher Control of Autonomic Outflows: The Hypothalamus." In T. RUCH, and J. FULTON (eds.), *Medical Physiology and Biophysics*, pp. 234–48. Philadelphia: Saunders.

PITTENDRIGH, C. S.
1958. "Adaptation, Natural Selection, and Behavior." In A. ROE and G. G. SIMPSON (eds.), *Behavior and Evolution*, pp. 390–416. New Haven: Yale University Press.

REISER, M. F., E. B. FERRIS, and M. LEVINE
1954. "Cardiovascular Disorders, Heart Disease, and Hypertension." In E. WITTKOWER and R. CLEGHORN (eds.), *Recent Developments in Psychosomatic Medicine*, pp. 300–325. Philadelphia: Lippincott.

RUSSELL, J. A.
1960. "The Adrenal Cortex." In T. RUCH and J. FULTON (eds.), *Medical Physiology and Biophysics*, pp. 1082–1100. Philadelphia: Saunders.

SHAFRIR, E., and D. STEINBERG
1960. "The Essential Role of the Adrenal Cortex in the Response of Plasma Free Fatty Acids, Cholesterol, and Phospholipids to Epinephrine Injection," *J. Clin. Invest.*, 39:310–19.

THOMAS, C., and E. MURPHY
    1958. "Further Studies on Cholesterol Levels in the Johns Hopkins Medical Students: The Effect of Stress at Examinations," *J. Chron. Dis.*, 8:661.

VENNING, E., I. DYRENFURTH, and J. BECK
    1957. "Effect of Anxiety on Aldosterone Excretion in Man," *J. Clin. Endoc. & Metab.*, 17:1005–7.

WASHBURN, S. L., and I. DEVORE
    1961. "Social Behavior of Baboons and Early Man." In this volume.

WASHBURN, S. L., and F. C. HOWELL
    1960. "Human Evolution and Culture." In S. TAX (ed.), *The Evolution of Man*, pp. 33–56. Chicago: University of Chicago Press.

WERTLAKE, P., A. WILCOX, M. HALEY, and J. PETERSON
    1958. "Relationship of Mental and Emotional Stress to Serum Cholesterol Levels," *Proc. Soc. Exptl. Biol.*, 97:163.

WOOL, I., and M. GOLDSTEIN
    1953. "Role of Neurohumors in the Action of the Adrenal Cortical Steroids: Mobilization of Fat," *Amer. J. Physiol.*, 175:303–6.

WOOL, I., M. GOLDSTEIN, E. RAMEY, and R. LEVINE
    1954. "Role of Epinephrine in the Physiology of Fat Mobilization," *Amer. J. Physiol.*, 178:427.

COMMENTS

IAGO GALDSTON

I SHARE with many of my professional confreres the conviction that between medicine and anthropology there exists a native and profound affinity. Each is avowedly "a science of man," yet they do differ in certain respects. Anthropology is the more embracive discipline, concerned as it is with man's being, over the span of as-yet-undetermined hundreds of thousands of years. Medicine, in contrast, is bound to the contemporary scene. Medicine is a science of man subserving the functions of service—those of preventing and treating disease and also of safeguarding health. The conjunction between medicine and anthropology is effected by the need to know man as a historically evolving creature, unique in that, in addition to his somatic and physiological evolution, man has also acquired and developed culture.

This need to comprehend man's complex developmental history is now felt most acutely in psychiatry. The anatomists were the first to sense this need. In recent decades, however, it is the psychiatrists, confronted as they are more frequently and more intensively with the cultural components of man's being and operations, who have turned in greater numbers to anthropology, hopefully expecting to find therein some illumination of the problems that they are called on to understand and to help resolve.

This expectation has been fulfilled, *to some extent*. That the fulfillment has not been greater is due, I believe, to certain communication difficulties arising from a difference in the orientation of the psychiatrists and of the anthropologists.

I should like to define this difference in orientation and perforce must do so in subjective terms. The anthropologist seeks to reconstruct man's history from "before to the present"; the psychiatrist wants to understand the present in the perspective of the before.

My approach begins not with the hominoids but with modern man. I am hopeful and expectant that in your expert labors you will uncover evidence bearing on the phylogenetic derivations of the sequential ontogenic stages exhibited in the biosocial development of contemporary man. I am, naïvely perhaps, projecting upon anthropological experience the schemata of embryology, expecting and assuming that biosociological ontogeny must likewise have its phylogenetic roots and a discernible evolutionary history.

I have mentioned our interest in the phylogenetic derivations of man's bio-social ontogenic stages of development; let me then briefly describe them. They are four in number: the biologic, the social, the aesthetic, and the moral. They are spoken of as "stages" and are said to be "sequential." In a general sense they are, but not in a segmented sense. They are not related as links in a chain. They are more like shingles, which overlap. They are distinguished as "stages" by the dominance of their qualities and their distinctive preoccupations. Thus, achieving biological growth and development *within* the unique constitution of the individual is the dominant preoccupation of the child. The child, however, is not entirely exempt from "socialization." On the contrary, he is subjected to socializing discipline almost from the first week of his life. The cue term in this affirmation is "subjected." The child during his early years does not intentially contribute to his own socialization. He becomes actively contributory at a somewhat later age, at puberty, when the gonadic thrust is experienced. At this juncture the "biologic stage" does not terminate and yield to the social, but it does recede, yielding predominance to the social. It is worth noting that linear growth (stature) slows down, and the epiphyseal cartilages are absorbed as gonadic function develops.

Reverting to the "echelons of ontogenic" development, I would point out that "the biologic" we share with all living creatures, and the social (minus the cultural) with many. The aesthetic and the moral, on the other hand, are uniquely human. By "the moral" we intend the ability to define, and to be partisan of, an ethos, and not any specific set of moralisms.

The aesthetic represents, in the ontogenic pattern, the high level of individuation. The aesthetic is the conscious tribute of man to himself—to himself as a unique individual emancipated from the compulsions of biologic and group necessities. In aesthetic creativity man is for a time and in some dimensions a free agent, and, where bound, it is by a free-chosen union with the transcending, the moral. The moral is essentially bound up with man's effort to project meaning upon, or to extract it from (most often both), his living experience.

These echelons of ontogenic development are presented as a schematization of observed processes and not as objective entities. They are useful in the comprehension of social behavior as well as in the visualization of psychopathological dynamics. They are, of course, not entirely arbitrary, nor are they fanciful. Behind the scheme there are the processes, and behind the processes, some physical and historical realities. May we not look to anthropology to test out the validity of these hypothecated, ontogenic stages, to see whether there is any phylogenetic evidence to support, to correct, or to deny them?

I am not so naïve as to believe that on these scores anthropological data can provide us with direct, large blocks of evidence. Our questions can be tested out and answered only by indirection, through derivative intelligence of an inferential nature. But for that there is need of bold imagination in formulating questions and in seeking out the meaningfulness of data. We need to scan widely the varieties of reasonable combinations that can be made of the anthropological data possessed, being ever mindful that even the sound assumptions upon which we structure our reasoning seldom if ever exhaust the reasonably possible alternatives.

I shall end by venturing an example of what I mean by the "need to scan widely the varieties of reasonable combinations." During this conference we have heard frequent reference to the "cerebral Rubicon." Implied in this crucial concept is that "hominization" is a function of cerebral mass, in other words, that the humanness of man was made possible not only through but *because* of the increment in his brain bulk. There seems to be little doubt that certain dimensions of brain mass are critical requisites for a number of the higher functions of human cerebration and for consequent, derivative, behavior. However, this does not establish the primacy of brain as *the* humanizing organ. I can think of the endocrine system as the more likely "organ." And to give earnestness to my speculation I can reflect on the profile changes that distinguish *Homo sapiens* from the anthropoids, and in that relation make note of the skeletal-somatic changes occurring in acromegalic disease. It has been noted that in the domesticated animal the pituitary is generally smaller than it is in its wild homologue. Similarly, the skull contours of animals are said to foreshorten under domestication.

More suggestive than this is the recognition that, elementarily, socialization is an emotive rather than a rational process. It is inspired by emotion, not by reason. It is later defined by reason, but only as an act of rationalization or as a process in the verbal communication of an emotion. The brain stem (hypothalamus) and the endocrine system are functionally intimately related to emotions and emotive behavior.

I do not know where such a scanning, or speculation if you will, might lead. Possibly it could yield new configurations of what is known and suggest new ways to new knowledge. It would, I believe, facilitate communication between medicine—notably psychiatry—and anthropology. I know it would profit psychiatry, and I suspect it would benefit anthropology. It would postulate meaning for datum, without which datum is elementary and static.

INDEX